RELATIVISTIC ELECTRON THEORY

. . . The theory of electrons already forms so vast a subject that it will be impossible for me to treat it completely.

H. A. Lorentz, THE THEORY OF ELECTRONS

RELATIVISTIC ELECTRON THEORY

M. E. ROSE
Chief Physicist
Oak Ridge National Laboratory

NEW YORK · LONDON, JOHN WILEY & SONS, INC.

Library of Congress Catalog Card Number: 61–5667

Printed in the United States of America

This book is devotedly dedicated to

A. M. R.

B. S. R.

and

J. S. R.

who provide the frame of reference

Preface

The preface of a book is traditionally a device enabling the author to divulge his intentions and hopes as well as his motivations. At the same time it provides the reader of the book with a preview of things to come. In that sense this Preface is in accord with tradition.

It is not the purpose of these prefatory remarks to describe the contents of this book in any detailed manner. A study of the table of contents should provide an adequate guide to the material covered here, as to the scope of the discussion as well as, possibly, to the level of sophistication which has been assumed on the part of the reader. Lest there be any ambiguity with reference to the latter, it is assumed that the reader has become acquainted with the general principles and methods of quantum mechanics. In view of recent trends in the graduate curriculum, most first-year and virtually all second-year graduate students should find themselves adequately prepared, and presumably equipped to undertake the study of relativistic electron theory. In this connection it is of interest to note that this book has been designed for use as a reference as well as a text.

It is important to recognize the place in the scheme of things which this part of physics occupies. To begin with, we are here concerned with the theory of all spin one-half particles (fermions) which are lighter than a nucleon. Therefore the word "electron" in the title stands for mu meson, neutrino, and their antiparticles as well. In making this remark we recognize that, in light of recent developments, the neutrino, in particular, may well require special discussion but this, properly speaking, is an off-shoot of the more general electron theory and is taken up in the last chapter of the book.

The second point of importance is to recognize that we deal here with what is sometimes called the "*c*-number theory." The fields with which we are concerned are not quantized. This means that certain effects, radiative corrections to electromagnetic processes for example, are, strictly speaking, beyond the scope of the present treatment. This does not, of course, preclude a discussion of radiative processes: bremsstrahlung, Compton scattering, and the like. The contents of this book may properly be referred to as the single particle Dirac theory. This theory is the extension of quantum mechanics to include the effects of special relativity. As such, it may be thought of as forming a link between the simpler form of the quantum theory and the more advanced version wherein all the fields are treated as quantized entities. It will be quite evident, however, that the Dirac theory occupies a more important position in the development of modern physics than this ancillary role would imply. As will be seen, it has a wide range of applicability. To the extent that it does not give complete answers to all conceivable problems, in the realm of electron theory, it partakes of the nature of all other physical theories which are useful, powerful, even elegant, but not final.

This book is intended, then, as a comprehensive treatment of the single particle description of relativistic quantum mechanics. Explicitly we are concerned with spin one-half particles which are not subject to strong couplings (for instance, the pi meson field); it is well known, however, that in at least a formal way parallel considerations may be made for spin zero particles with mass. This would then exhaust the non-field theoretic descriptions of known particles in the quantum theory.

In the past it has been customary, in books expounding the principles of quantum mechanics, to conclude with an all too brief chapter on the relativistic single particle theory. That this kind of discussion, abbreviated as it must usually be, inevitably leaves the student with an inadequate understanding of this important extension of quantum mechanics is presumably very well appreciated by all the authors who have been forced into this position for obvious practical reasons. Several years ago, when an appreciable fraction of graduate students were not expected to acquire a knowledge of quantum mechanics beyond the treatment of the standard textbooks, this curtailed treatment of the relativistic theory or, more pertinently, the absence of a book dealing with the subject in a detailed and extensive manner was not so serious a drawback. It is clear, however, that this is no longer the case. At present, courses dealing with the present subject have become rather common in most graduate curricula.

Obviously, the degree of emphasis which each topic has received is a matter of personal taste and judgment. The motivation in making such decisions has been to give as much prominence as possible to the conceptual basis of the theory. Secondly, particular attention has been given to the presentation of techniques which would enable the user of the book not only to "follow the literature" but also to use the theory on his own. Applications of the theory appear throughout but are most frequently found in later chapters. A number of ingenious solutions of the Dirac equations have not been included because it appears that their main interest is mathematical rather than physical.

About a hundred problems appear in the book. These are to be found at the end of each chapter. They present a wide range of content and a broad spectrum so far as degree of difficulty is concerned. With the exception of a few general references listed at the end of the book, the literature cited in the text is referenced at the end of the appropriate chapter. I offer my apologies to the many contributors whose excellent papers have not been cited. No attempt has been made to provide a complete bibliography. Instead, the references cited constitute recognition of the important early papers and the most recent developments in the case of each topic discussed. In any event, these references should furnish an adequate starting point for the reader interested in pursuing any particular topic in greater detail.

It is a pleasure to record my thanks to Dr. Roland H. Good, Jr., of Iowa State University for his kindness in reading the manuscript. Needless to say, the responsibility for all that follows rests entirely with me. This applies especially to whatever errors of omission and/or commission may exist herein.

M. E. Rose

Oak Ridge, Tennessee
November, 1960

Contents

I.

Non-relativistic spin theory

1. INTRODUCTION

The relativistic theory of the electron, as distinct from relativistic particle theories in general, is a theory of a particle with spin $\frac{1}{2}\hbar$. By spin we shall mean the *intrinsic* angular momentum associated with the particle. In contrast, the total angular momentum is the resultant of the spin and the orbital angular momentum which the particle possesses by virtue of its motion. Thus the spin is the total angular momentum in the rest system. This property of intrinsic angular momentum is, of course, a quantum effect since it cannot appear in a classical theory, that is, the limiting form of the theory as $\hbar \to 0$. By way of contrast, the orbital angular momentum $l\hbar$ does have a classical limit since the quantum number l is not bounded in this limit.

Needless to say, the relativistic theory which forms the subject of our discussion is, in a sense, more than a description of the spin. It is immediately obvious that such a theory must be consistent with the invariance requirements of the special theory of relativity. Indeed, when this requirement is imposed, a number of theories appear as possible candidates. Moreover, each of these theories contains the result that the particle under discussion does, in fact, exhibit a spin $s\hbar$, where $2s$ is any non-negative integer. The particular form of the theory, unique for a particle with non-vanishing mass, which corresponds to $s = \frac{1}{2}$ is the well-known Dirac theory with which we shall be almost exclusively occupied in this exposition. Consequently, it is proper to say that, in detail, the spin properties of an electron are a natural consequence of the requirements of relativistic invariance. The validity of this statement is explicitly demonstrated in the sequel.

Historically, the concept of electron spin arose in a phenomenological way.[1]† The first formal theory[2] of spin was not a relativistic theory, and, in view of the basic principle that simpler things come first, this historical order was a most natural one. This theory, the Pauli theory, is the limiting form of the rigorously correct theory in the limit in which the velocity of light (c) tends toward infinity.‡ Consequently, all the quantitative results of the non-relativistic theory can be obtained as limiting values of corresponding results as given by the Dirac theory. In fact, it is a curious circumstance that in some cases the exact theory yields these results in a simpler and more straightforward manner. Accordingly, it might appear logical to dispense with a discussion of the approximate theory and obtain all the results of the Pauli theory as limiting forms of the more rigorous treatment. Nevertheless, it is advantageous to approach the study of the relativistic theory from the standpoint of the Pauli theory, since the latter provides a unique insight into the structure of the former.

2. EMPIRICAL BASIS OF THE SPIN THEORY

The concept of a spinning electron was first suggested by Compton[3] in 1921 in connection, appropriately enough, with the origin of the natural unit of magnetism. The idea became firmly established in physics when in 1925 Uhlenbeck and Goudsmit[1] proposed the electron as a point magnet with intrinsic spin in order to clarify the anomalous Zeeman effect. The main results of the argument were:

(a) The electron must have an intrinsic spin $\frac{1}{2}\hbar$. Hence single electron atomic levels must be characterized by half-integer angular momentum.

(b) The electron magnetic moment arising from the spin must have a magnitude equal to the Bohr magneton:

$$|\mu| = e\hbar/2mc \equiv \mu_0 \tag{1.1}$$

where m is the rest mass of the electron and $-e < 0$ is its charge. Moreover, in terms of a vector model, $\boldsymbol{\mu}$ and $\mathbf{s}$ (the angular momentum in units of $\hbar$) must be oppositely directed. Therefore a vector equation

$$\boldsymbol{\mu} = -(e/mc)\hbar\mathbf{s} \tag{1.2}$$

can be written. It will appear that this equation is valid as an *operator* equation. The magnetic moment (μ) as a measured quantity is then the average (expectation) value of μ_z for the state in which s_z has the constant

† References are found at the end of the chapter.

‡ More precisely, the non-relativistic spin theory can be correct only to order v/c, where v is the velocity of the electron. In the case of bound states, $v/c \sim \alpha Z$, where $\alpha = e^2/\hbar c \approx 1/137$ is the fine structure constant and Z is the atomic number.

value $\frac{1}{2}$. The connection between the spin and the associated magnetism implies that the spin must be a relativistic phenomenon.

The gyromagnetic ratio is

$$g_s = \mu/\mu_0 s = 2 \tag{1.3}$$

in contrast to the result for the orbital angular momentum, where the corresponding ratio is

$$g_l = \mu_l/\mu_0 l = 1 \tag{1.4}$$

and μ_l is the magnetic moment due to the orbital motion. It is possible to make a classical argument,[4] based on relativistic invariance, which leads to the value $g_s = 2$. However, it is much simpler to obtain this result from the complete quantum mechanical treatment of spin given in later chapters. For the moment it is of interest to mention that, if $g_s = 1$ is assumed, the Zeeman effect with spin leads to the "normal" Zeeman triplet, contrary to experimental evidence. Obviously, the conclusion that $g_s = 2$ precisely is obtained from neither the empirical evidence nor as a consequence of the approximate spin theory. In this theory it must be taken as a postulate.

The postulated magnetic dipole to be associated with the electron immediately leads to a spin-orbit coupling since, in the frame of reference of the electron, the rest of the atom provides a magnetic field which is coupled with the electron magnetic dipole moment. In these terms the doublet structure of the spectra of the alkali atoms and other multiplet structure observed in optical spectra could be understood. However, a quantitative accounting for the measured doublet separations depends on a more detailed analysis of relativistic effects (section 7) than this simple discussion would seem to entail.

3. FORMAL THEORY OF ANGULAR MOMENTUM†

Definition of Angular Momentum

Since we are concerned with a particle with angular momentum, intrinsic and possibly orbital angular momentum as well, it is very useful to establish in a formal way just what is meant by these terms. If we are given a wave function ψ which represents the state of a particle, there is a procedure, as indicated below, by means of which we can determine what

† Here and henceforth the unit of angular momentum is $\hbar$. Hence the term "angular momentum" will refer to a dimensionless quantity which, as a matter of fact, is integer or half-integer. The contents of this section appear in several other places; for example, see reference A in the General References at the end of the book. In the text, references in this general list will be denoted by an upper-case Roman letter.

angular momentum, if any, characterizes this state. Since we do not in general start with a given wave function, it is more to the point to establish some properties which the requisite function must exhibit in order that it properly describe the given angular momentum associated with the state.

In the last analysis a definition of angular momentum must be based on a measurement or set of measurements. However, the logical chain may be reversed: angular momentum may be defined in terms of a formal operation, and from this definition a connection will eventually be established between the angular momentum thus defined and a measured quantity—a cross section, shape of an angular distribution, or the number of lines in a spectrum of some type of radiation emitted by an atom or by a corresponding physical system.

The concept of angular momentum is intimately connected with three-dimensional rotations. This is clear in classical as well as in non-relativistic quantum mechanics where, as is to be expected, only orbital angular momentum is involved. Nevertheless, the connection with rotations is a general one. For instance, the statement that a physical system is rotationally invariant implies, in both classical and quantum theory, that the Hamiltonian describing it commutes with the operator representing the rotation. It will become evident that in the general case this leads to the result that the total angular momentum is a constant of the motion.

Starting with a wave function ψ which depends on spatial coordinates and possibly other coordinates as well, we consider a rotation R described by three parameters. These can be taken to be the three Euler angles or the two angles specifying the orientation of a unit vector $\hat{\mathbf{n}}$, the rotation axis, and an angle θ, the rotation angle around $\hat{\mathbf{n}}$. Under the rotation ψ is transformed to ψ' and

$$\psi' = R(\hat{\mathbf{n}}, \theta)\psi \tag{1.5}$$

Since R must be unitary, it can be written

$$R(\hat{\mathbf{n}}, \theta) = \exp\left[-iS(\hat{\mathbf{n}}, \theta)\right] \tag{1.6}$$

where S is hermitian and $S(\hat{\mathbf{n}}, 0) = 0$. Considering infinitesimal rotations around the x-, y-, and z-axes respectively, we write, in each case

$$\delta\psi = R\psi - \psi = -i\theta\left(\frac{\partial S}{\partial \theta}\right)_{\theta=0}\psi \tag{1.7}$$

where $(\partial S/\partial\theta)_{\theta=0}$ depends on the axis of rotation. Since a rotation is a continuous transformation, the function S must have corresponding properties and, for instance, the derivatives of S with respect to θ must exist at any value of θ.

The angular momentum operator, actually three operators, J_x, J_y, J_z, are defined by choosing $\hat{\mathbf{n}}$ along the x-, y-, and z-axes. Since infinitesimal rotations commute, we can define the J_i operators in terms of

$$\left(\frac{\partial S}{\partial \theta}\right)_{\theta=0} = \hat{\mathbf{n}}\cdot\mathbf{J} = \hat{n}_x J_x + \hat{n}_y J_y + \hat{n}_z J_z \tag{1.8}$$

Clearly J_x, J_y, and J_z are all hermitian. In (1.8) a convention has been made with respect to a choice of sign, and, in detail, this choice is fixed in terms of the manner in which a positive rotation, for example, is specified. From (1.7),

$$R(\hat{\mathbf{n}}, \theta) = \exp(-i\theta\hat{\mathbf{n}}\cdot\mathbf{J}) \tag{1.9}$$

which has the property that two rotations around the same axis commute:

$$R(\hat{\mathbf{n}}, \theta_1)\, R(\hat{\mathbf{n}}, \theta_2) = R(\hat{\mathbf{n}}, \theta_1 + \theta_2)$$

as is necessary.

Since finite rotations do not commute, it is clear that the components of $\mathbf{J}$ will not commute. In fact, if a rotation around the y-axis through an angle θ_y is followed by one around the x-axis through θ_x, the result is not the same if the rotations are carried out in reverse order. For simplicity assume that both rotations are infinitesimal and consider terms of second order in θ_x, θ_y. Then the difference between the first pair of rotations and the second pair (first pair in reverse order) produces the same displacement as an infinitesimal rotation around the z-axis through an angle $\theta_x\theta_y$. Hence, with an obvious notation,

$$R(\hat{\mathbf{x}}, \theta_x)\, R(\hat{\mathbf{y}}, \theta_y) - R(\hat{\mathbf{y}}, \theta_y)\, R(\hat{\mathbf{x}}, \theta_x) = -\theta_x\theta_y(J_x, J_y) \tag{1.10}$$

where we have introduced the commutator; that is,

$$(A, B) = AB - BA$$

From the statement made above, the quantity on either side of (1.10) is $-i\theta_x\theta_y J_z$. Hence

$$(J_x, J_y) = iJ_z$$

It follows that two similar equations obtained by cyclic permutation of the indices x, y, z are also valid. These three equations are summarized by

$$\mathbf{J} \times \mathbf{J} = i\mathbf{J} \tag{1.11}$$

These are the commutation rules of the angular momentum operators. It is evident that, if $\mathbf{J}$ and $\mathbf{J}'$ form two sets of operators conforming with (1.11) and if each component of $\mathbf{J}$ commutes with each component of $\mathbf{J}'$, then the sum $\mathbf{J} + \mathbf{J}' = \mathbf{J}''$ also satisfies (1.11). Each component of $\mathbf{J}''$ is an angular momentum operator, while $\mathbf{J}''$ itself is referred to as a *vector* angular momentum operator. The measured quantity generally referred to as the angular momentum of a physical system cannot be a vector because this would imply that each component of that vector is a constant of the motion, and that, in view of (1.11), is impossible. Clearly the angular momentum must be the eigenvalue of a rotationally invariant operator and hence must be related to

$$\mathbf{J}^2 \equiv J_x^2 + J_y^2 + J_z^2$$

From (1.11) it follows that $\mathbf{J}^2$ commutes with each of J_x, J_y, and J_z and hence with the rotation operator R. Consequently we can make $\mathbf{J}^2$ a constant of the motion, and the eigenvalues of this operator will not depend on the orientation of the coordinate axes.

Eigenvalues and Eigenfunctions of the Angular Momentum Operators

Consider a physical system described by a Hamiltonian H which is rotationally invariant. This means that H commutes with each component of $\mathbf{J}$ and

$$(H, R) = 0$$

Of course, it follows that

$$(H, \mathbf{J}^2) = 0$$

so that $\mathbf{J}^2$ is a constant of the motion. In addition, one component of $\mathbf{J}$, say J_z, can be made a constant of the motion. The angular momentum representation in which $\mathbf{J}^2$ and J_z are simultaneously diagonal with H is given in terms of a set of eigenfunctions ψ_j^m for which

$$\begin{aligned} \mathbf{J}^2\psi_j^m &= \eta_j\psi_j^m \\ J_z\psi_j^m &= m\psi_j^m \end{aligned} \tag{1.12}$$

In the first of (1.12) the notation implies that the eigenvalues η_j of $\mathbf{J}^2$ depend on a number j to be determined. Because $\mathbf{J}^2$ and J_z are hermitian, η_j is real and non-negative, m is real, and the eigenvalue of $\mathbf{J}^2 - J_z^2 = J_x^2 + J_y^2$ is

$$\eta_j - m^2 \geqslant 0 \tag{1.13}$$

Introducing the operators

$$J_\pm = J_x \pm iJ_y \tag{1.14}$$

and the function

$$\phi_\pm = J_\pm\psi_j^m \tag{1.15}$$

we see that

$$\mathbf{J}^2\phi_\pm = \eta_j\phi_\pm$$

because $(\mathbf{J}^2, J_\pm) = 0$ and

$$J_z\phi_\pm = [J_\pm J_z + (J_z, J_\pm)]\psi_j^m = J_\pm(J_z \pm 1)\psi_j^m$$
$$= (m \pm 1)\phi_\pm$$

Therefore $\phi_\pm$ is an eigenfunction of $\mathbf{J}^2$ with the same eigenvalue as ψ_j^m and is also an eigenfunction of J_z with eigenvalue $m \pm 1$. Thus

$$\phi_\pm = \Gamma_\pm \psi_j^{m\pm 1}$$

where $\Gamma_\pm$ is a constant the value of which is determined below.

Since application of J_+ to ψ_j^m raises the value of m, for given j, it follows from (1.13) that for some m, say m_2, the resulting function ϕ_+ must vanish; that is,

$$J_+\psi_j^{m_2} = 0 \tag{1.16a}$$

Then $m \leqslant m_2 \leqslant \eta_j$. In a similar way we deduce that there exists a value of m (say m_1) for which

$$J_-\psi_j^{m_1} = 0 \tag{1.16b}$$

and $m \geqslant m_1 \geqslant -\eta_j$. Operating on (1.16a) with J_- and on (1.16b) with J_+ gives

$$J_\mp J_\pm \psi_j^{m_i} = [\mathbf{J}^2 - J_z(J_z \pm 1)]\psi_j^{m_i}$$
$$= [\eta_j - m_i(m_i \pm 1)]\psi_j^{m_i} = 0 \tag{1.17}$$

and $i = 1, 2$ for lower and upper signs respectively. Since $\psi_j^{m_i}$ are bona fide members of the set, it follows that the square bracket in (1.17) must vanish. Eliminating η_j from the two equations obtained in this way, we find the result

$$(m_2 + m_1)(m_2 - m_1 + 1) = 0$$

Since $m_2 \geqslant m_1$ it follows that $m_2 - m_1 + 1$ cannot vanish and so $m_1 = -m_2$. Also, consecutive m-values differ by unity. Hence $m_2 - m_1$ is a non-negative integer which we denote by $2j$; that is,

$$j = 0, \tfrac{1}{2}, 1, \tfrac{3}{2}, 2, \ldots$$

It follows then that

$$m_2 = j, \qquad m_1 = -j \tag{1.18}$$

and, from (1.15),

$$\eta_j = j(j + 1) \tag{1.19}$$

Classically, $j \to \infty$ and the eigenvalue of $\mathbf{J}^2 \to j^2$. Therefore it is to be expected that the number j is the angular momentum (in units of $\hbar$). The linear term in j is a result of the uncertainty principle as expressed by the commutation rules (1.11). This is apparent in (1.17). From (1.16) the projection quantum number m is restricted by

$$-j \leqslant m \leqslant j \tag{1.18'}$$

so that there are $2j + 1$ eigenfunctions for given j.

The next problem is that of determining the matrix elements of the angular momentum operators in the angular momentum representation. These will be denoted by

$$(jm|J_k|j'm')$$

for each of the operators J_k. In writing these matrices in explicit form, the first row refers to $m = j$ and the first column to $m' = j$. The nth row and column refer to $m, m' = j - n + 1$. Clearly,

$$(jm|J_z|j'm') = m\delta_{jj'}\delta_{mm'} \tag{1.20}$$

Also

$$(jm|\mathbf{J}^2|j'm') = j(j+1)\delta_{jj'}\delta_{mm'} \tag{1.20'}$$

corresponding to the diagonalization of these operators. For the other components we observe that

$$|\Gamma_\pm|^2 = (J_\pm\psi_j^m, J_\pm\psi_j^m)$$

(The detailed prescription for forming the scalar product will be discussed below.) The ψ_j^m are taken to form an orthonormal set. Thus, using $J_\pm^* = J_\mp$, where * means hermitian conjugate,

$$|\Gamma_\pm|^2 = (\psi_j^m, J_\mp J_\pm\psi_j^m) = (\psi_j^m, [\mathbf{J}^2 - J_z(J_z \pm 1)]\psi_j^m)$$
$$= j(j+1) - m(m \pm 1) = (j \mp m)(j \pm m + 1)$$

The phase is chosen so that $\Gamma_\pm \geqslant 0$:

$$\Gamma_\pm = [(j \mp m)(j \pm m + 1)]^{1/2} \tag{1.20''}$$

From (1.15) it follows that

$$(jm|J_\pm|j'm') = \Gamma_\pm\delta_{jj'}\delta_{m,m'\pm 1} \tag{1.20'''}$$

These matrices therefore have non-vanishing elements only in the diagonals adjacent to the principal diagonal.

4. APPLICATION TO SPIN ONE-HALF

Each of the matrices derived in the preceding section has $2j + 1$ rows and columns. For $j = \frac{1}{2}$ we obtain the angular momentum matrices for the intrinsic spin of an electron. Using $\mathbf{s}$ for $\mathbf{J}$ in this case we write

$$\mathbf{s} \equiv \tfrac{1}{2}\boldsymbol{\sigma} \tag{1.21}$$

and from (1.20‴) it follows that

$$\sigma_x = \begin{pmatrix} 0 & 1 \\ 1 & 0 \end{pmatrix}, \qquad \sigma_y = \begin{pmatrix} 0 & -i \\ i & 0 \end{pmatrix}, \qquad \sigma_z = \begin{pmatrix} 1 & 0 \\ 0 & -1 \end{pmatrix} \tag{1.22}$$

in the representation where s_z or σ_z is diagonal. These $\boldsymbol{\sigma}$-matrices are the well-known Pauli matrices. Together with the 2 by 2 unit matrix I_2 they form a complete set in the sense that any 2 by 2 matrix can be written in terms of them. To see this we observe, first, that I_2 and the three Pauli matrices are evidently linearly independent. Thus

$$a_0 I_2 + \mathbf{a}\cdot\boldsymbol{\sigma} = 0$$

if and only if $a_0 = 0$ and $\mathbf{a} = 0$. Second, the trace of each $\boldsymbol{\sigma}$-matrix is zero, whereas $\mathrm{Tr}\, I_2 = 2$. Hence, for any 2 by 2 matrix M,

$$M = \tfrac{1}{2}[\mathrm{Tr}\, M + (\mathrm{Tr}\, M\boldsymbol{\sigma})\cdot\boldsymbol{\sigma}] \tag{1.23}$$

In view of (1.11) we can write immediately

$$\mathbf{s} \times \mathbf{s} = i\mathbf{s} \tag{1.24}$$

or

$$\boldsymbol{\sigma} \times \boldsymbol{\sigma} = 2i\boldsymbol{\sigma} \tag{1.24'}$$

In addition, the Pauli matrices have the following properties:

$$\begin{aligned} \sigma_x\sigma_y &= -\sigma_y\sigma_x = i\sigma_z \\ \sigma_y\sigma_z &= -\sigma_z\sigma_y = i\sigma_x \end{aligned} \tag{1.24''}$$

$$\begin{aligned} \sigma_z\sigma_x &= -\sigma_x\sigma_z = i\sigma_y \\ \sigma_x^2 &= \sigma_y^2 = \sigma_z^2 = 1 \end{aligned} \tag{1.24'''}$$

In addition to being hermitian, each of the Pauli matrices is unitary: $\sigma_x^* = \sigma_x^{-1}$. The existence of the inverse matrices follows, since $\det \sigma_k \neq 0$. For integer spins, for instance, the matrices are singular, as is clear since one value of m which always occurs is $m = 0$. The anticommuting property of the $\boldsymbol{\sigma}$-matrices is peculiar to spin $\frac{1}{2}$. A corresponding property does not appear for $j \neq \frac{1}{2}$. The last equality in (1.24″) also applies in the case $j = \frac{1}{2}$ only. This equality will be written more succinctly by using Latin indices = 1, 2, 3 in place of the cartesian indices. Then

$$\sigma_j\sigma_k = i\epsilon_{jkl}\sigma_l + \delta_{jk} \tag{1.25}$$

where ϵ_{jkl} is the antisymmetric third-rank tensor equal to $+1$ if j, k, l is an even permutation of 1, 2, 3 and equal to -1 if j, k, l is an odd permutation of 1, 2, 3; otherwise $\epsilon_{jkl} = 0$.

Another property which is extremely useful follows from the commutation rules (1.24″). If **A** and **B** are two vectors which commute with σ_k but not necessarily with each other, then

$$\boldsymbol{\sigma}\cdot\mathbf{A}\,\boldsymbol{\sigma}\cdot\mathbf{B} = \sigma_k A_k \sigma_l B_l = \mathbf{A}\cdot\mathbf{B} + (1 - \delta_{kl})\sigma_k\sigma_l A_k B_l$$

Using (1.24″), this becomes

$$\boldsymbol{\sigma}\cdot\mathbf{A}\,\boldsymbol{\sigma}\cdot\mathbf{B} = \mathbf{A}\cdot\mathbf{B} + i\boldsymbol{\sigma}\cdot(\mathbf{A} \times \mathbf{B}) \tag{1.26}$$

This is an example of the decomposition of the type (1.23). It is clear that no higher power of the Pauli spin matrices than the first need ever occur in the formalism. By repeated application of the rule (1.26) it is easy to construct the corresponding decomposition for the product of any number of factors $\boldsymbol{\sigma}\cdot\mathbf{A}_n$. In view of what has already been said it is trivial to see that this will always appear in the form $a + \mathbf{b}\cdot\boldsymbol{\sigma}$.

As was mentioned above, the form (1.22) of the Pauli matrices refers to a particular representation: σ_z diagonal. By a linear transformation with a non-singular matrix S it is possible to write the $\boldsymbol{\sigma}$-matrices in other representations. For example, in

$$\sigma_k' = S\sigma_k S^{-1} \tag{1.27}$$

S can be chosen so that any linear combination $\boldsymbol{\sigma}\cdot\mathbf{n}$, where $\mathbf{n}$ is an arbitrary vector, can be made diagonal. When $\mathbf{n}$ is a real (unit) vector the unitary transformation is a rotation in three-space. We shall return to this problem in the next section. At this juncture it is important to remember that all matrix equations are unchanged by the transformation (1.27). In particular, the commutation rules, (1.24′) and (1.24″), are unchanged in the sense that, if all σ_k in these equations are primed, the resulting equalities are valid. A few simple cases can be discussed immediately. For example, for $S = \sigma_x = S^{-1}$ we find $\sigma_x' = \sigma_x$, $\sigma_y' = -\sigma_y$, $\sigma_z' = -\sigma_z$, which corresponds to a rotation through π around the x-axis. On the other hand, a reflection (change of sign of an odd number of σ's) is not a unitary transformation because $-\boldsymbol{\sigma}$ does not fulfill the same commutation rules as does $\boldsymbol{\sigma}$.

The invariance of the commutation rules under the transformation (1.27) does not actually require S to be unitary. It is sufficient that S be non-singular so that S^{-1} exists. However, in the present instance, where σ_k' and σ_k are both hermitian, S can always be chosen to be unitary.

As another example consider a representation in which σ_x' is diagonal. Then, from the preceding it must have eigenvalues ± 1, and we write it in the form

$$\sigma_x' = \begin{pmatrix} 1 & 0 \\ 0 & -1 \end{pmatrix}$$

The linear transformation from the representation (1.22) to the $\boldsymbol{\sigma}'$ representation corresponds to a rotation which carries the z-axis into the x-axis. Since the positions of the z'- and y'-axes are not specified, there must be some arbitrariness in σ_y' and σ_z'. Setting

$$\sigma_y' = \begin{pmatrix} a & b \\ c & d \end{pmatrix}, \qquad \sigma_z' = \begin{pmatrix} a' & b' \\ c' & d' \end{pmatrix}$$

the requirement that $\sigma_x'\sigma_y' = i\sigma_z'$ implies that

$$a = ia', \qquad b = ib'$$
$$c = -ic', \qquad d = -id'$$

From $\sigma_y'\sigma_x' = -\sigma_x'\sigma_y'$ we find

$$a = d = 0$$

and

$$\sigma_y' = \begin{pmatrix} 0 & b \\ c & 0 \end{pmatrix}, \qquad \sigma_z' = \begin{pmatrix} 0 & -ib \\ ic & 0 \end{pmatrix}$$

From $\sigma_y'^2 = 1$ or $\sigma_z'^2 = 1$ we find

$$bc = 1$$

and, with this, results $\sigma_y'\sigma_z' = i\sigma_x' = -\sigma_z'\sigma_y'$ follow automatically. Also $\sigma_x'\sigma_z' = -i\sigma_y' = -\sigma_z'\sigma_x'$ is fulfilled. Hence

$$\sigma_y' = \begin{pmatrix} 0 & b \\ b^{-1} & 0 \end{pmatrix}, \qquad \sigma_z' = \begin{pmatrix} 0 & -ib \\ ib^{-1} & 0 \end{pmatrix}$$

The S-matrix effecting the $\boldsymbol{\sigma}$–$\boldsymbol{\sigma}'$ transformation is written

$$S = \begin{pmatrix} \alpha & \beta \\ \gamma & \delta \end{pmatrix}$$

where $\alpha\delta - \beta\gamma \neq 0$. From

$$\sigma_x' S = S\sigma_x$$

it follows that

$$\alpha = \beta, \qquad \delta = -\gamma$$

From $\sigma_y' S = S\sigma_y$ or $\sigma_z' S = S\sigma_z$ we find

$$\alpha i = b\gamma$$

and thus

$$S = \gamma\begin{pmatrix} -ib & -ib \\ 1 & -1 \end{pmatrix}, \qquad S^* = \gamma^\times\begin{pmatrix} ib^\times & 1 \\ ib^\times & -1 \end{pmatrix}$$

and

$$SS^* = 2|\gamma|^2\begin{pmatrix}|b|^2 & 0\\ 0 & 1\end{pmatrix}$$

Thus we can make $S^* = S^{-1}$ by setting $|\gamma|^2 = \frac{1}{2}$, $|b|^2 = 1$. For this choice of $|b|^2$ it is seen that $SS^* = S^*S = 1$. For $b = 1$, $\sigma'_y = \sigma_x$, $\sigma'_z = \sigma_y$, so that a cyclic interchange of indices has taken place.

The converse theorem that, if $S^* = S^{-1}$ and any matrix a is hermitian, then

$$a' = SaS^{-1}$$

is also hermitian is readily verified:

$$a'^* = (SaS^*)^* = SaS^* = SaS^{-1} = a'$$

as required. Notice that, if a sequence of unitary transformations is carried out, the resulting overall transformation is also unitary.

The converse statement regarding (1.27) is also true: if $\boldsymbol{\sigma}'$ and $\boldsymbol{\sigma}$ are two sets of three anticommuting matrices with $\sigma_i^2 = \sigma_i'^2 = 1$, then an S exists for which (1.27) is valid. The proof is identical with that given in section 13 for the Dirac matrices and will not be duplicated here. Finally, we note that the trace and determinant of a matrix is unchanged by a transformation of the type (1.27).

Throughout this book the notation $\boldsymbol{\sigma}$ or σ_i, where 2 by 2 matrices are implied, will refer to the representation (1.22).

The eigenvalue equations (1.12) for spin $\frac{1}{2}$ will be written in the form

$$\mathbf{s}^2\chi^m = s(s+1)\chi^m = \tfrac{3}{4}\chi^m$$

$$s_z\chi^m = m\chi^m, \qquad m = \pm\tfrac{1}{2} \tag{1.28}$$

There are two eigenfunctions $\chi^{\pm 1/2}$. From the matrix representation of s_z and $\mathbf{s}^2$ it follows that the χ^m must be *two-component* functions. In fact, with a simple choice of phases,

$$\chi^{1/2} = \begin{pmatrix}1\\0\end{pmatrix}; \qquad \chi^{-1/2} = \begin{pmatrix}0\\1\end{pmatrix} \tag{1.29}$$

These may be regarded as single column matrices. We verify that these form an orthonormal set.

$$(\chi^m, \chi^{m'}) = \delta_{mm'}$$

where the scalar product means that χ^{m*} is multiplied into $\chi^{m'}$. That is, χ^{m*} is the transpose, complex conjugate of χ^m:

$$\chi^{1/2*} = (1 \quad 0); \qquad \chi^{-1/2*} = (0 \quad 1)$$

so that χ^{m*} are single row matrices. In general, a scalar product will imply, unless explicitly stated to the contrary, integration over configuration space and summation over the column (or row) index labeling the components of the spin function χ^m. Of course, in the present case we are dealing with the eigenfunctions of the intrinsic spin, and they do not depend on the space coordinates x_k. Hence the first operation is here unnecessary.

The set of spin functions is obviously complete. Thus any two-component function can be written as a linear superposition of them:

$$\begin{pmatrix} a \\ b \end{pmatrix} = a\chi^{\frac{1}{2}} + b\chi^{-\frac{1}{2}}$$

and hence the only two-component function which is orthogonal to both $\chi^{\frac{1}{2}}$ and $\chi^{-\frac{1}{2}}$ is the trivial one which is identically zero.

The appearance of a multicomponent wave function is characteristic of the existence of a non-vanishing spin. Where the wave function ψ has a single component depending only on the space coordinates the spin is zero. In fact, the considerations of section 3 show that in this case

$$\mathbf{J} = -i\mathbf{r} \times \nabla = \mathbf{L} \tag{1.30}$$

where $\mathbf{L}$ is the orbital angular momentum operator. Of course, in the general case a particle with spin s ($s > 0$) may be characterized by a wave function ψ which has the form

$$\psi = \begin{pmatrix} \psi_1(x_k) \\ \psi_2(x_k) \\ \cdot \\ \cdot \\ \cdot \end{pmatrix}$$

In this case the prescription of section 3 shows that

$$\mathbf{J} = \mathbf{L} + \mathbf{s} \tag{1.30$'$}$$

where $\mathbf{s}$ is a vector-matrix with $2s + 1$ rows and columns and $\mathbf{L}$ is the direct product of $-i\mathbf{r} \times \nabla$ and a unit matrix of the same rank. This follows from the fact that under rotations each component of ψ must transform into a linear combination of components. If this were not so, the situation would arise in which rotations commute, contrary to fact.

For $s = \frac{1}{2}$

$$\mathbf{J} = \mathbf{L}I_2 + \tfrac{1}{2}\boldsymbol{\sigma}$$

which is usually written

$$\mathbf{J} = \mathbf{L} + \tfrac{1}{2}\boldsymbol{\sigma} \tag{1.31}$$

In the foregoing considerations we have $\psi_n(x_k) = 1$ or 0, and the resulting $\psi = \chi^m$ is a *pure spin* function. In section 7 we shall consider the problem of introducing orbital motion.

From this discussion it follows that the wave function ψ of a particle with spin $\frac{1}{2}$ is a function of the three x_k, which form a continuum, and in addition ψ depends on a fourth variable which is dichotomic. That is to say, the fourth variable has only two possible values and refers to the "direction of the spin" or, more exactly, to the eigenvalue of s_z. Thus the general form of ψ would be†

$$\psi(x_k, s_z') = \psi_1(x_k)\chi^{\frac{1}{2}} + \psi_2(x_k)\chi^{-\frac{1}{2}} = \begin{pmatrix} \psi_1(x_k) \\ \psi_2(x_k) \end{pmatrix}$$

The notation indicates that this ψ is a superposition of the two states $m = \pm\frac{1}{2}$. The interpretation of each term is: $|\psi_{1,2}|^2$ is the probability per unit volume that the particle is at the point x_k with $m = \frac{1}{2}, -\frac{1}{2}$ respectively. Note that there is no interference between these two states:

$$(\psi, \psi) = (\psi_1, \psi_1) + (\psi_2, \psi_2) = |\psi_1|^2 + |\psi_2|^2$$

where the scalar product implies only summation over the column (row) index of the spin functions. This in turn implies that (ψ, ψ) is the probability density when no observation of the spin (polarization measurement) is made. A more detailed discussion of polarization is given in section 6.

5. SPATIAL ROTATIONS

It has already been emphasized that we cannot ascribe any meaning to the statement that the spin vector is in a given direction. This would imply the three equations $\boldsymbol{\sigma}\psi = \hat{\mathbf{n}}\psi$ where $\hat{\mathbf{n}}$ is the spin direction. That this equality is impossible follows from the fact that $(\sigma_k, \sigma_l) \neq 0$. However, we can speak of the *average* spin direction. This is given by $(\psi, \boldsymbol{\sigma}\psi)$. If we introduce unit vectors $\hat{\mathbf{e}}_k$ along the coordinate axes,

$$\boldsymbol{\sigma} = \begin{pmatrix} \hat{\mathbf{e}}_3 & \hat{\mathbf{e}}_1 - i\hat{\mathbf{e}}_2 \\ \hat{\mathbf{e}}_1 + i\hat{\mathbf{e}}_2 & -\hat{\mathbf{e}}_3 \end{pmatrix}$$

For the pure spin functions,

$$(\chi^m, \boldsymbol{\sigma}\chi^m) = \pm\hat{\mathbf{e}}_3, \qquad \text{for } m = \pm\tfrac{1}{2}$$

† s_z' is a number distinguishing ψ from the orthogonal wave function:

$$\psi(x_k, -s_z') = \psi_2^\times\chi^{\frac{1}{2}} - \psi_1^\times\chi^{-\frac{1}{2}}$$

This result is obviously directly connected to the choice of representation in which $\sigma_z = \sigma_3$ is diagonal.

It is useful to investigate other representations in which the component of $\boldsymbol{\sigma}$ in any direction $\hat{\mathbf{n}}$, that is $\boldsymbol{\sigma}\cdot\hat{\mathbf{n}}$, is diagonal. Thus we write

$$\chi = \sum_m a_m \chi^m \tag{1.32a}$$

and

$$\boldsymbol{\sigma}\cdot\hat{\mathbf{n}}\,\chi = \lambda\chi \tag{1.32b}$$

It is evident that the average spin is†

$$(\chi_\pm, \boldsymbol{\sigma}\chi_\pm) = \pm\hat{\mathbf{n}} \tag{1.32c}$$

From the fact that $(\boldsymbol{\sigma}\cdot\hat{\mathbf{n}})^2 = 1$ (see Eq. 1.26), it follows that $\lambda = \pm 1$. Substituting (1.32a) into (1.32b), we find

$$\begin{pmatrix} \hat{n}_3 & \hat{n}_- \\ \hat{n}_+ & -\hat{n}_3 \end{pmatrix}(a_{1/2}\chi^{1/2} + a_{-1/2}\chi^{-1/2}) = \lambda(a_{1/2}\chi^{1/2} + a_{-1/2}\chi^{-1/2})$$

where $\hat{n}_\pm = \hat{n}_1 \pm i\hat{n}_2$. From (1.29) we obtain

$$\hat{n}_3 a_{1/2} + \hat{n}_- a_{-1/2} = \lambda a_{1/2}$$

$$\hat{n}_+ a_{1/2} - \hat{n}_3 a_{-1/2} = \lambda a_{-1/2}$$

or

$$\begin{vmatrix} \hat{n}_3 - \lambda & \hat{n}_- \\ \hat{n}_+ & -\hat{n}_3 - \lambda \end{vmatrix} = 0$$

giving $\lambda^2 = \hat{n}_3^2 + \hat{n}_+\hat{n}_- = \hat{\mathbf{n}}^2 = 1$ or $\lambda = \pm 1$ as mentioned. Also

$$a_{-1/2} = -\frac{\hat{n}_3 - \lambda}{\hat{n}_-}a_{1/2}$$

Writing $\hat{n}_3 = \cos\vartheta$, $\hat{n}_\pm = \sin\vartheta\, e^{\pm i\varphi}$, so that ϑ, φ are the polar and azimuth angles of $\hat{\mathbf{n}}$, and using the normalization condition

$$|a_{1/2}|^2 + |a_{-1/2}|^2 = 1$$

we find, for $\lambda = 1$,

$$|a_{1/2}|^2 = \cos^2\vartheta/2; \qquad a_{-1/2}/a_{1/2} = e^{i\varphi}\tan\vartheta/2$$

and, for $\lambda = -1$,

$$|a_{1/2}|^2 = \sin^2\vartheta/2; \qquad a_{-1/2}/a_{1/2} = -e^{i\varphi}\cot\vartheta/2$$

† We anticipate that there will be two eigenfunctions $\chi = \chi_\pm$; see (1.33a) and (1.33b) below.

We choose the phases as follows:

$$\lambda = 1: \qquad a_{1/2} = e^{-i\varphi/2}\cos\vartheta/2, \qquad a_{-1/2} = e^{i\varphi/2}\sin\vartheta/2 \tag{1.32d}$$

$$\lambda = -1: \qquad a_{1/2} = -e^{-i\varphi/2}\sin\vartheta/2, \qquad a_{-1/2} = e^{i\varphi/2}\cos\vartheta/2 \tag{1.32e}$$

Therefore the spin functions which diagonalize $\boldsymbol{\sigma}\cdot\hat{\mathbf{n}}$ with eigenvalue ± 1 are

$$\lambda = 1: \qquad \chi_+ = \begin{pmatrix} e^{-i\varphi/2}\cos\vartheta/2 \\ e^{i\varphi/2}\sin\vartheta/2 \end{pmatrix} \tag{1.33a}$$

$$\lambda = -1: \qquad \chi_- = \begin{pmatrix} -e^{-i\varphi/2}\sin\vartheta/2 \\ e^{i\varphi/2}\cos\vartheta/2 \end{pmatrix} \tag{1.33b}$$

These are, of course, a complete orthonormal set of spin functions. For ϑ, $\varphi \to 0$ the functions $\chi_\pm$ reduce to $\chi^{\pm 1/2}$.

The transformation just carried out can be written in another form. We consider the matrix elements of R (see Eq. 1.9), in the angular momentum representation and use the notation†

$$D^j_{mm'}(\alpha\beta\gamma) = (jm|R|jm') \tag{1.34}$$

Here α, β, and γ are the Euler angles of the rotation: (1) rotation through α around z, (2) rotation through β around resulting y-axis, (3) rotation through γ around final z-axis. Then under this rotation angular momentum eigenfunction ψ_j^m is transformed to

$$R\psi_j^m = \sum_{m'} D^j_{m'm}\psi_j^{m'} \tag{1.35}$$

It is important to notice that, if all rotations are expressed in the *original* coordinate system,[A]

$$R = e^{-i\alpha J_z}e^{-i\beta J_y}e^{-i\gamma J_z} \tag{1.35a}$$

In the present instance the rotation is one which carries the z-axis into the direction $\hat{\mathbf{n}}$. Hence the third Euler angle γ is irrelevant (it introduces a phase $e^{-im\gamma}$ in $D^{1/2}$). The preceding choice of phase is equivalent to setting $\gamma = 0$. It is clear then that

$$D^{1/2}(\varphi, \vartheta, 0) = \begin{pmatrix} e^{-i\varphi/2}\cos\vartheta/2 & e^{i\varphi/2}\sin\vartheta/2 \\ -e^{-i\varphi/2}\sin\vartheta/2 & e^{i\varphi/2}\cos\vartheta/2 \end{pmatrix} \tag{1.35b}$$

A two-component function which transforms under rotations by the $D^{1/2}$ matrix is called a *spinor*. Thus the pure spin functions χ^m and $\chi_\pm$ are spinors. They will be referred to as Pauli spinors. The index which labels the components will be referred to as the spinor index. It is seen that

$$D(\varphi + 2\pi n, \vartheta, 0) = D(\varphi, \vartheta + 2\pi n, 0) = (-)^n D(\varphi, \vartheta, 0)$$

† See Chapter IV of reference A.

where n is an integer. For odd n the complete rotation carries ψ to $-\psi$. This two-to-one correspondence of the unitary transformation D and three-space rotations is characteristic of spinors.

6. SPIN PROJECTION OPERATORS AND POLARIZATION

It was mentioned above that any set of two spinors like $\chi_\pm$ in (1.33) forms a complete set in the two-dimensional spin space. As we have seen, this means that any two-component function Ψ can be expanded as a linear combination of these two. Alternatively, there is no non-vanishing two-component function orthogonal to both χ_+ and χ_-.

If we write χ^α for $\chi_\pm$, so that α has two values, the statements above imply that for any spinor Ψ we can write

$$\Psi = \sum_\alpha c_\alpha \chi^\alpha = \sum_\alpha (\chi^\alpha, \Psi)\chi^\alpha$$

In terms of the spinor components,

$$\Psi_\rho = \sum_{\alpha\nu} \chi_\nu^{\alpha\times} \Psi_\nu \chi_\rho^\alpha = \sum_\nu \delta_{\rho\nu} \Psi_\nu$$

Therefore we obtain the completeness relation

$$\sum_\alpha \chi_\rho^\alpha \chi_\nu^{\alpha\times} = \delta_{\rho\nu} \tag{1.36}$$

or

$$\sum_\alpha \chi^\alpha \times \chi^{\alpha *} = 1 \tag{1.36'}$$

where $\times$ indicates a direct product of the two spinors.

Considering one term in (1.36), we define a pair of matrices P^α by

$$P^\alpha = \chi^\alpha \times \chi^{\alpha *} \tag{1.37}$$

or

$$P_{\rho\nu}^\alpha = \chi_\rho^\alpha \chi_\nu^{\alpha\times} \tag{1.37'}$$

Dropping the superscript α for the moment, we investigate the properties of P. First we observe that P is idempotent: that is, $P^2 = P$ and therefore $P^n = P$ $(n > 0)$; thus

$$(P^2)_{\sigma\lambda} = \sum_\rho P_{\sigma\rho} P_{\rho\lambda} = \sum_\rho \chi_\sigma \chi_\rho^\times \chi_\rho \chi_\lambda^\times$$
$$= \chi_\sigma \chi_\lambda^\times = P_{\sigma\lambda}$$

In order to understand this result we evaluate P for the spin function (1.33a, b). Clearly,

$$P = \tfrac{1}{2}[\mathrm{Tr}\, P + (\mathrm{Tr}\, P\boldsymbol{\sigma})\cdot\boldsymbol{\sigma}]$$

But

$$\mathrm{Tr}\, P = \sum_{\rho} \chi_\rho \chi_\rho^\times = 1$$

and

$$\mathrm{Tr}\, P\boldsymbol{\sigma} = \sum_{\rho\lambda} P_{\rho\lambda}\boldsymbol{\sigma}_{\lambda\rho} = \sum_{\rho\lambda} \chi_\lambda^\times \boldsymbol{\sigma}_{\lambda\rho}\chi_\rho$$
$$= (\chi, \boldsymbol{\sigma}\chi)$$

Here, as elsewhere, the subscripts on spinors are spinor indices and on matrices are corresponding row-column indices. With the results we find directly from (1.32c)

$$P^+ = \chi_+ \times \chi_+^* = \tfrac{1}{2}(1 + \boldsymbol{\sigma}\cdot\hat{\mathbf{n}}) \tag{1.37a}$$

$$P^- = \chi_- \times \chi_-^* = \tfrac{1}{2}(1 - \boldsymbol{\sigma}\cdot\hat{\mathbf{n}}) \tag{1.37b}$$

As expected,

$$P^+ + P^- = 1; \qquad (P^\pm)^2 = P^\pm \tag{1.38}$$

It is evident that

$$P^+P^- = P^-P^+ = 0 \tag{1.39}$$

and that

$$P_+\chi_- = 0, \qquad P_-\chi_+ = 0$$

The interpretation of these results is quite simple. If

$$\Psi = \sum c_\alpha \chi^\alpha \tag{1.40}$$

is an arbitrary superposition of the two spin states, then

$$P^+\Psi = c_+\chi_+, \qquad P^-\Psi = c_-\chi_-$$

and the operators $P^\pm$ project from Ψ the parts corresponding to + and − spin along $\hat{\mathbf{n}}$. Since $P^\pm\chi_\pm = \chi_\pm$, the idempotent property is obvious. The mutually exclusive character of P^+ and P^- (viz., 1.39), is an expression of the fact that there is no overlap in the portions of spin space projected by these two operators. The exhaustive property, $P^+ + P^- = 1$, is an evidence of the fact that the two projected subspaces together constitute the whole spin space. In other words, from a conglomerate of spin states P^+ projects or selects one state ($\lambda = 1$), P^- projects the other ($\lambda = -1$), and together these constitute the complete set of spin states.

In general terms, if a projection operator P exists, that is, $P^2 = P$, then $P' = 1 - P$ forms with P a complete set of projection operators. Thus

$$P + P' = 1, \qquad PP' = P'P = 0, \qquad P'^n = P' \quad (n \geqslant 1)$$

The projection operators given in (1.37a) and (1.37b) are Pauli spin projection operators. As is to be expected, they will be very closely related to the spin projection operators for a relativistic particle in the frame of reference in which the particle is at rest. In connection with this discussion it should be recognized that projection operators for other dynamical variables (for example, the energy) can be defined; see section 19. Finally, it is to be noted that for any matrix P which fulfills $P^2 = P$ and $P \neq I_2$, the determinant of P (det P) = 0 as will be readily verified by the reader. Thus P is singular and P^{-1} does not exist. In fact, the assumption that P^{-1} does exist leads to $P = I_2$ immediately, but this does not yield a sensible set of projection operators (that is, $P' = 0$ would follow in this case).

It should now be fairly clear how the polarization of a particle with spin $\frac{1}{2}$ is to be defined. If we again consider a state like (1.40) the polarization $\mathscr{P}$ will be defined by[5,6]

$$\mathscr{P} = \frac{(\Psi, \boldsymbol{\sigma}\Psi)}{(\Psi, \Psi)} = \frac{\operatorname{Tr} \boldsymbol{\sigma} P_\Psi}{\operatorname{Tr} P_\Psi} \tag{1.41}$$

where the projection operator P_Ψ is

$$(P_\Psi)_{\rho\lambda} = \Psi_\rho \Psi_\lambda^\times$$

If a beam of polarized particles is detected by a device which is sensitive only to spin projection along $\pm\hat{\mathbf{n}}$, the response of this device is proportional to

$$\mathscr{I}_\pm = (\Psi, P^+\Psi) = \tfrac{1}{2}(\Psi, \Psi)(1 \pm \mathscr{P}\cdot\hat{\mathbf{n}}) \tag{1.42}$$

where

$$\mathscr{I}_+ + \mathscr{I}_- = (\Psi, \Psi)$$

In general, the component of polarization in the direction $\hat{\mathbf{n}}$ is

$$\mathscr{P}\cdot\hat{\mathbf{n}} = \frac{(\Psi, \boldsymbol{\sigma}\cdot\hat{\mathbf{n}}\,\Psi)}{(\Psi, \Psi)} = \frac{|c_+|^2 - |c_-|^2}{|c_+|^2 + |c_-|^2} \tag{1.43}$$

so that $\mathscr{P}\cdot\hat{\mathbf{n}} = \pm 1$ for states with $\langle \boldsymbol{\sigma}\cdot\hat{\mathbf{n}} \rangle_{AV} = \pm 1$. It is to be emphasized that this definition of polarization does not carry over without modification to the relativistic case; cf. section 20.

7. ELECTRON IN A CENTRAL FIELD

Spin-Orbit Coupling

The main physical assumption of the Pauli theory is that the Hamiltonian describing a system of particles is just the usual Schrödinger Hamiltonian plus an additional term representing an interaction energy with the spin. For a single particle this term is

$$H_{\text{sp}} = -\boldsymbol{\mu}\cdot\mathscr{H} \tag{1.44}$$

where $\boldsymbol{\mu}$ is the magnetic moment operator (1.2) and $\mathscr{H}$ is the magnetic field at the position of the particle. Where there is only an external magnetic field $\mathscr{H}$, Eq. (1.44) gives the entire spin energy. However, when there is also an electric field an additional interaction term of relativistic origin arises. For an electron moving in an electrostatic field $\mathscr{E}$, as seen in the laboratory reference system or the reference system in which the atom as a whole is at rest, there is a contribution to the field $\mathscr{H}$ given by

$$\mathscr{H}_1 = \frac{\mathbf{v}}{c} \times \mathscr{E}$$

This corresponds to a precession of the spin axis around the field $\mathscr{H}_1$ with Larmor precession frequency

$$\boldsymbol{\omega}_1 = e\mathscr{H}_1/mc \tag{1.44$'$}$$

and a contribution

$$H'_{\text{sp}} = \hbar\boldsymbol{\omega}_1 \cdot \mathbf{s} \tag{1.44$''$}$$

to the coupling energy. However, this is not the total spin energy.† As the electron moves in the field $\mathscr{E}$, it undergoes an acceleration $\mathbf{a} \approx -e\mathscr{E}/m$ and in time dt the velocity changes from $\mathbf{v}$ to $\mathbf{v} + d\mathbf{v}$ with $d\mathbf{v} = \mathbf{a}\, dt$. This change of the electron reference frame with respect to the atom reference frame will introduce an additional precession of the spin axis. It is shown in Appendix B that in time dt the reference frame attached to the electron rotates through the angle

$$d\theta = \frac{\xi - 1}{v^2}(\mathbf{v} \times d\mathbf{v}) \approx \frac{1}{2c^2}(\mathbf{v} \times d\mathbf{v})$$

where $\xi = (1 - v^2/c^2)^{-\frac{1}{2}}$. Hence the additional precession frequency is

$$\boldsymbol{\omega}_2 = \frac{1}{2c^2}\mathbf{v} \times \mathbf{a} = -\frac{e}{2mc^2}(\mathbf{v} \times \mathscr{E})$$

Thus the total precession frequency is

$$\boldsymbol{\omega} = \boldsymbol{\omega}_1 + \boldsymbol{\omega}_2 = \frac{e}{2mc^2}(\mathbf{v} \times \mathscr{E}) = \tfrac{1}{2}\boldsymbol{\omega}_1$$

The total spin interaction energy is then

$$H_{\text{sp}} = \hbar\boldsymbol{\omega} \cdot \mathbf{s} = -\frac{\hbar}{2mc^2}\mathbf{v} \times \nabla V$$

where we use $e\mathscr{E} = -\nabla V$. If V is a potential energy arising from a central field,

$$\nabla V = \frac{1}{r}\frac{dV}{dr}\mathbf{r}$$

† The following discussion leading to Eq. (1.45) is based directly on the work of L. H. Thomas, reference 7.

Then, using $\mathbf{v} = \vec{\mathbf{p}}/m$ where

$$\vec{\mathbf{p}} = \frac{\hbar}{i}\nabla$$

is the linear momentum operator, we find

$$H_{\text{sp}} = \frac{\hbar}{2m^2c^2}\frac{1}{r}\frac{dV}{dr}\,\mathbf{s}\cdot(\mathbf{r}\times\vec{\mathbf{p}})$$

We use small letters for angular momentum operators of a single particle, and this becomes

$$H_{\text{sp}} = \frac{\hbar^2}{2m^2c^2}\frac{1}{r}\frac{dV}{dr}\,\mathbf{s}\cdot\mathbf{l} \qquad (1.45)$$

where $\mathbf{l}\hbar$ is the orbital angular momentum operator.

The total Hamiltonian is now†

$$H = \frac{\vec{p}^2}{2m} + V + H_{\text{sp}} \qquad (1.46)$$

and it is required to find the eigenfunctions of H. This will be done below in an exact manner for the spin and angle dependence of the wave function.

Pauli Spinors in a Central Field

In the absence of spin coupling the Hamiltonian

$$H_0 = \frac{\vec{p}^2}{2m} + V(r)$$

commutes with s_z and l_z. Therefore the wave functions for which H_0, $\mathbf{l}^2$, l_z, and s_z are simultaneously diagonal are of the form

$$\psi_0 = R(r)\,Y_l^m(\hat{\mathbf{r}})\,\chi^{m'} \qquad (1.47)$$

† By considering the limiting case of the Dirac equation, it will be shown in section 22 that there are two additional terms of the same order of magnitude as H_{sp} which should be added to (1.46). These are

$$\Delta H = [-ie\hbar\,\mathscr{E}\cdot\vec{\mathbf{p}} + V\vec{p}^2]/4m^2c^2$$

The first term has no classical analogue. The second is a correction due to the variation of mass with velocity, that is, a mechanical effect of relativity. Neither of these terms is spin-dependent, and for a central field they give merely a displacement but not a splitting of the unperturbed magnetic sublevels. For a Coulomb field the first term gives a level shift in first-order perturbation theory only for s-states and can be replaced by

$$\frac{\pi}{2}\frac{\hbar^2e^2Z}{m^2c^2}\,\delta(\mathbf{r})$$

where $\chi^{m'}$ are the Pauli spin functions defined in (1.29). In (1.47), $R(r)$ is a radial function, $Y_l^m(\hat{\mathbf{r}})$ is the spherical harmonic which is the eigenfunction of $\mathbf{l}^2$ and l_z with eigenvalues $l(l+1)$ and m respectively. The phase convention adopted is given by the explicit definition

$$Y_l^m = \left[\frac{2l+1}{4\pi}\frac{(l-m)!}{(l+m)!}\right]^{1/2} \frac{(-e^{i\varphi}\sin\vartheta)^m}{2^l l!}\left(\frac{d}{d\cos\vartheta}\right)^{l+m}(\cos^2\vartheta - 1)^l \tag{1.48}$$

and consequently

$$Y_l^{m\times} = (-)^m Y_l^{-m} \tag{1.48'}$$

These functions are orthonormal:

$$\int Y_{l_1}^{m_1\times} Y_{l_2}^{m_2} \sin\vartheta\, d\vartheta\, d\varphi = \delta_{l_1 l_2}\delta_{m_1 m_2}$$

With H_{sp} present, neither l_z nor s_z commutes with H. Writing

$$\mathbf{l}\cdot\mathbf{s} = l_z s_z + \tfrac{1}{2}(l_+ s_- + l_- s_+) \tag{1.49}$$

and using the algorithm

$$(A, BC) = (A, B)C + B(A, C) \tag{1.50}$$

we find

$$(s_z, \mathbf{s}\cdot\mathbf{l}) = i(l_x s_y - l_y s_x) = -(l_z, \mathbf{s}\cdot\mathbf{l})$$

Therefore $s_z + l_z = j_z$ does commute with H. In addition, $\mathbf{j}^2 = (\mathbf{l}+\mathbf{s})^2$ commutes with H, and this is readily seen from the fact that this operator commutes with H_0 and with any function of r while

$$2\mathbf{s}\cdot\mathbf{l} = \mathbf{j}^2 - \mathbf{l}^2 - \mathbf{s}^2 \tag{1.49'}$$

which commutes with $\mathbf{j}^2$ since $(\mathbf{l}^2, l_k) = 0$ and $(\mathbf{s}^2, s_k) = 0$. Consequently the required eigenfunctions simultaneously diagonalize H, $\mathbf{j}^2$, j_z as well as $\mathbf{l}^2$ and $\mathbf{s}^2$. Since the functions (1.47) form a complete set we write

$$\psi_j^\mu = R_j(r)\sum_m c_m(j)\, Y_l^{\mu-m}\chi^m; \qquad m = \pm\tfrac{1}{2} \tag{1.51}$$

where μ is the eigenvalue of j_z. Thus

$$J_z\psi_j^\mu = \mu\psi_j^\mu$$

automatically. Applying $\mathbf{j}^2$ to (1.51) and using (1.49), (1.49'), and (1.20'''), we obtain the result

$$\sum_m [l(l+1) - j(j+1) + \tfrac{3}{4} + 2m(\mu - m)]c_m\, Y_l^{\mu-m}\chi^m + [(l+\tfrac{1}{2})^2 - \mu^2]^{1/2}\sum_m c_{-m}\, Y_l^{\mu-m}\chi^m = 0$$

Since $Y_l^{\mu-m}\chi^m$ are linearly independent, we obtain two linear homogeneous equations in $c_{1/2}$, $c_{-1/2}$. Setting the determinant equal to zero gives the result

$$l(l+1) - j(j+1) + \tfrac{1}{4} = \pm(l+\tfrac{1}{2})$$

The two solutions are

$$j = l \pm \tfrac{1}{2} \geqslant \tfrac{1}{2}$$

which is the usual result of vector addition of angular momenta l and $\frac{1}{2}$. Also

$$\frac{c_{1/2}(j)}{c_{-1/2}(j)} = -\frac{[(l+\frac{1}{2})^2 - \mu^2]^{1/2}}{l(l+1) - j(j+1) + \mu + \frac{1}{4}}$$

Normalizing the radial and spin-angular functions separately, that is,

$$\sum_m |c_m(j)|^2 = 1$$

yields, with the conventional choice of phases,[B]

$$c_{1/2}(l+\tfrac{1}{2}) = \left(\frac{l+\mu+\frac{1}{2}}{2l+1}\right)^{1/2} = c_{-1/2}(l-\tfrac{1}{2})$$

$$c_{-1/2}(l+\tfrac{1}{2}) = \left(\frac{l-\mu+\frac{1}{2}}{2l+1}\right)^{1/2} = -c_{1/2}(l-\tfrac{1}{2})$$

Thus the required eigenfunctions are

$$\psi^{\mu}_{l+1/2} = \frac{R_{l+1/2}}{(2l+1)^{1/2}}\begin{pmatrix}(l+\mu+\frac{1}{2})^{1/2} & Y_l^{\mu-1/2}\\ (l-\mu+\frac{1}{2})^{1/2} & Y_l^{\mu+1/2}\end{pmatrix} \tag{1.51a}$$

$$\psi^{\mu}_{l-1/2} = \frac{R_{l-1/2}}{(2l+1)^{1/2}}\begin{pmatrix}-(l-\mu+\frac{1}{2})^{1/2} & Y_l^{\mu-1/2}\\ (l+\mu+\frac{1}{2})^{1/2} & Y_l^{\mu+1/2}\end{pmatrix} \tag{1.51b}$$

These are the Pauli central field spinors. In later discussions we shall also refer to the spin-angular part (ψ exclusive of the radial functions R) as central field spinors.

The spin-orbit energy is readily obtained by using first-order perturbation theory for the radial part of the problem. For a Coulomb field

$$V(r) = -Ze^2/r$$

and the additional energy due to H_{sp} is

$$H_{sp} = \frac{Ze^2\hbar^2}{2m_r^2c^2}\left\langle\frac{1}{r^3}\right\rangle\langle \mathbf{s}\cdot\mathbf{l}\rangle$$

where the angular brackets are diagonal matrix elements. Also m_r is the reduced mass of electron and nucleus. For hydrogen-like orbits of principal quantum number n one finds[C]

$$\left\langle \frac{1}{r^3} \right\rangle = \frac{(m_r e^2 Z/\hbar^2)^3}{n^3 l(l + 1)(l + \frac{1}{2})}$$

so that

$$H_{\text{sp}} = a\langle \mathbf{s}\cdot\mathbf{l} \rangle$$
$$= \tfrac{1}{2}a[j(j + 1) - l(l + 1) - \tfrac{3}{4}]$$

where

$$a = \frac{1}{2} \frac{(\alpha Z)^4 m_r c^2}{n^3 l(l + 1)(l + \frac{1}{2})}$$

and $\alpha = e^2/\hbar c$ is the fine structure constant. Each unperturbed level with quantum numbers n, l splits into a doublet with the lower level having $j = l - \frac{1}{2}$; that is, the doublet is *normal* for a single electron. The splitting is

$$\Delta E = \langle H_{\text{sp}} \rangle_{j=l+\frac{1}{2}} - \langle H_{\text{sp}} \rangle_{j=l-\frac{1}{2}} = a(l + \tfrac{1}{2})$$

and the center of gravity of the doublet is unshifted since

$$\sum_j (2j + 1)\langle H_{\text{sp}} \rangle_j = 0$$

Anomalous Zeeman Effect

In the presence of an external magnetic field $\mathcal{H} = \text{curl}\,\mathbf{A}$, the total Hamiltonian is

$$H = \frac{1}{2m}\left(\vec{\mathbf{p}} + \frac{e}{c}\mathbf{A}\right)^2 + V - \boldsymbol{\mu}\cdot\left(\mathcal{H} + \frac{1}{2c}\mathbf{v} \times \mathcal{E}\right) \tag{1.52}$$

In the Pauli approximation it is consistent to neglect the $\mathbf{A}^2$ term. Then, for a homogeneous field, $\mathbf{A} = \frac{1}{2}(\mathcal{H} \times \mathbf{r})$ and $\text{div}\,\mathbf{A} = 0$. Thus

$$H = H_0 + H'$$

$$H_0 = \frac{\vec{p}^2}{2m} + V$$

$$H' = \frac{e}{mc}\mathbf{A}\cdot\vec{\mathbf{p}} - \boldsymbol{\mu}\cdot\left(\mathcal{H} + \frac{1}{2c}\mathbf{v} \times \mathcal{E}\right) \tag{1.53}$$

The last term in H' gives the spin-orbit coupling. This can be written $a\mathbf{s}\cdot\mathbf{l}$ as before. The remaining terms due to the external field can be written in terms of $\mathbf{l}$ and $\mathbf{s}$ so that

$$H' = \mu_0 \mathcal{H}\cdot(\mathbf{l} + 2\mathbf{s}) + a\mathbf{l}\cdot\mathbf{s} \tag{1.54}$$

It is seen that with $\mathscr{H}$ along the z-axis j_z commutes with H' and H.

The secular determinant, using the representation (1.51), is

$$\begin{vmatrix} E_+ + \mu\dfrac{2l+2}{2l+1}\epsilon - E & \dfrac{\epsilon}{2l+1}[(l+\frac{1}{2})^2 - \mu^2]^{1/2} \\ \dfrac{\epsilon}{2l+1}[(l+\frac{1}{2})^2 - \mu^2]^{1/2} & E_- + \mu\dfrac{2\epsilon l}{2l+1} - E \end{vmatrix} = 0$$

where $\epsilon = \mu_0\mathscr{H}$ and $E_\pm$ are the (zero field) energies of the states with $j = l \pm \frac{1}{2}$. Also μ is the eigenvalue of j_z. The energy values are then

$$E = \tfrac{1}{2}(E_+ + E_-) + \epsilon\mu \pm \left[\left(\frac{\Delta E}{2}\right)^2 + \frac{\epsilon\mu}{2l+1}\Delta E + \left(\frac{\epsilon}{2}\right)^2\right]^{1/2} \tag{1.55}$$

where the $\pm$ sign is associated with the level for which $E = E_\pm$ in the limit $\mathscr{H} \to 0$: $E_+ = E_0 + \frac{1}{2}al$ and $E_- = E_0 - \frac{1}{2}a(l+1)$ and E_0 is the eigenvalue of H_0.

The result (1.55) shows that the member of the doublet with angular momentum j (in $\mathscr{H} = 0$ limit) splits into $2j + 1$ (non-degenerate) sub-levels. Levels with the same μ do not cross and, in general, E is an increasing function of μ. For an s-level ($l = 0$) Eq. (1.55) does not apply. Instead, from (1.54),

$$E = E_0 + 2\epsilon\mu, \qquad \mu = \pm\tfrac{1}{2}$$

and E_0 is the energy in the absence of the field. Thus for a $2p_{1/2} \to 1s_{1/2}$ transition the Zeeman pattern will consist of four separate lines instead of the Zeeman triplet expected without spin.[C]

8. COUPLING OF ANGULAR MOMENTA†

The Vector Addition Coefficients

The discussion of the preceding section shows how the eigenfunctions of orbital and spin-angular momentum can be coupled to form eigenfunctions of $\mathbf{j}^2$ and j_z where $\mathbf{j} = \mathbf{l} + \mathbf{s}$. This procedure can be generalized, and it will be useful to do so for subsequent considerations. Consider two vector angular momentum operators $\mathbf{j}_1$ and $\mathbf{j}_2$ operating in different spaces. The operators $\mathbf{j}_i^2$ and j_{iz} are diagonal with eigenvalues $j_i(j_i + 1)$ and m_i respectively in the decoupled representation

$$\psi_{j_1}^{m_1}\psi_{j_2}^{m_2}$$

Obviously $j_{1z} + j_{2z}$ is also diagonal with eigenvalue $m_1 + m_2$.

† See Chapter III of reference A.

The required representation must diagonalize $\mathbf{j}^2$ as well as $\mathbf{j}_1^2, \mathbf{j}_2^2, j_z$ where

$$\mathbf{j} = \mathbf{j}_1 + \mathbf{j}_2$$

is also a vector angular momentum operator. This coupled representation is obtained from the decoupled one by a unitary transformation where the elements of the unitary matrix depend on j_1, j_2, j, m_1, m_2, and m where the eigenvalue of $\mathbf{j}^2$ is $j(j+1)$ and m is the eigenvalue of j_z. They are denoted by $C(j_1 j_2 j; m_1 m_2 m)$, the Clebsch-Gordan or vector addition coefficients. For brevity they are sometimes referred to as C-coefficients. Thus

$$\psi_j^m = \sum_{m_1 m_2} C(j_1 j_2 j; m_1 m_2 m)\, \psi_{j_1}^{m_1} \psi_{j_2}^{m_2} \tag{1.56}$$

By applying $j_z = j_{1z} + j_{2z}$ to (1.52) we find that

$$\sum_{m_1 m_2} (m - m_1 - m_2) C(j_1 j_2 j; m_1 m_2 m)\, \psi_{j_1}^{m_1} \psi_{j_2}^{m_2} = 0$$

Since each term in this equation is linearly independent, it follows that $C(j_1 j_2 j; m_1 m_2 m) = 0$ unless

$$m_1 + m_2 = m$$

Hence one of the indices is redundant. For instance, the last projection number can be omitted with the understanding that it is the sum of the other two. Then

$$\psi_j^m = \sum_{m_1} C(j_1 j_2 j; m_1, m - m_1)\, \psi_{j_1}^{m_1} \psi_{j_2}^{m-m_1}$$

and only a single sum is involved.

From the unitary character of the transformation it follows that

$$\sum_{m_1} C(j_1 j_2 j; m_1, m - m_1)\, C(j_1 j_2 j'; m_1, m - m_1) = \delta_{jj'} \tag{1.57}$$

and

$$\sum_{j} C(j_1 j_2 j; m_1, m - m_1)\, C(j_1 j_2 j; m_1', m' - m_1') = \delta_{m_1 m_1'} \delta_{mm'} \tag{1.58}$$

Thus the matrix of C-coefficients with j labeling the rows and $m_2 = m - m_1$ labeling the columns is its own inverse.

The results of section 7 give the C-coefficients for $j_1 = l$, $j_2 = \frac{1}{2}$. Arranged in conventional form these are

$$C(l\tfrac{1}{2}j; m - m_2, m_2): \quad \begin{array}{c|cc} j \backslash m_2 & \frac{1}{2} & -\frac{1}{2} \\ \hline l + \frac{1}{2} & \left[\dfrac{l + m + \frac{1}{2}}{2l + 1}\right]^{1/2} & \left[\dfrac{l - m + \frac{1}{2}}{2l + 1}\right]^{1/2} \\ l - \frac{1}{2} & -\left[\dfrac{l - m + \frac{1}{2}}{2l + 1}\right]^{1/2} & \left[\dfrac{l + m + \frac{1}{2}}{2l + 1}\right]^{1/2} \end{array} \tag{1.59}$$

By enumerating the possible m values of all states which can be formed from the two states $j_1(-j_1 \leqslant m_1 \leqslant j_1)$ and $j_2(-j_2 \leqslant m_2 \leqslant j_2)$ it is seen that quite generally

$$|j_1 - j_2| \leqslant j \leqslant j_1 + j_2$$

and that all possible j values, differing by an integer, which occur between these limits are possible. This relation between j_1, j_2, and j is called a triangular relation. That is, the three numbers $j_1 j_2 j$ form the sides of a triangle and either all three are integers or one is an integer, the other two half-integers. The triangular relation is often abbreviated by the symbol $\Delta(j_1 j_2 j)$.

Properties of the Spin-Angular Functions

The wave function (1.51) is now written

$$\psi_j^\mu = R_j(r) \sum_m C(l\tfrac{1}{2}j; \mu - m, m)\, Y_l^{\mu-m} \chi^m \tag{1.60}$$

Of course, ψ_j^μ also depends on l, which is a good quantum number giving the parity as well as the orbital angular momentum. It is obvious from section 7 that ψ_j^μ is an eigenfunction of $\boldsymbol{\sigma}\cdot\mathbf{l} + 1$ with eigenvalue

$$j(j+1) - l(l+1) + \tfrac{1}{4} = (j + \tfrac{1}{2})^2 - l(l+1)$$

This number will be denoted by the symbol $-\kappa$. Thus

$$\kappa = \begin{matrix} l & \text{for } j = l - \tfrac{1}{2} \\ -l-1 & \text{for } j = l + \tfrac{1}{2} \end{matrix} \tag{1.61}$$

Therefore κ takes on all integer values except zero. We observe that $|\kappa| \equiv k$ gives the value of j according to

$$j = k - \tfrac{1}{2} \tag{1.62a}$$

In addition, specification of κ gives l or the parity of the wave function. The latter is

$$\pi_l = (-)^l = (-)^{j+\frac{1}{2}S_\kappa} \tag{1.62b}$$

where

$$S_\kappa \doteq \kappa/k \tag{1.62c}$$

is the sign of κ. It is now evident that the use of κ introduces an economy in the notation since its value gives both j and l:

$$l = \begin{matrix} \kappa & \text{for } \kappa > 0 \\ -\kappa - 1 & \text{for } \kappa < 0 \end{matrix} \tag{1.63}$$

Thus l is a function of κ. Where l appears in the sequel its value is defined by (1.63). In terms of spectroscopic notation $\kappa = -1, 1, -2, 2, \ldots$ corresponds to $s_{1/2}, p_{1/2}, p_{3/2}, d_{3/2}, \ldots$ states.

We also introduce $\bar{l} = l_{-\kappa}$; that is,

$$\bar{l} = \begin{array}{ll} \kappa - 1 & \text{for } \kappa > 0 \\ -\kappa & \text{for } \kappa < 0 \end{array} \tag{1.64}$$

For a given j the two possible κ values are $\pm(j + \frac{1}{2})$. It is also seen that

$$l - \bar{l} = S_\kappa$$

$$j = l - \tfrac{1}{2}S_\kappa$$

The spin-angular function in (1.60) is now written as χ_κ^μ:

$$\chi_\kappa^\mu = \sum_m C(l\tfrac{1}{2}j;\mu - m,m)\, Y_l^{\mu-m}\, \chi^m \tag{1.60'}$$

From the above,

$$(\boldsymbol{\sigma}\cdot\mathbf{l} + 1)\chi_\kappa^\mu = -\kappa\chi_\kappa^\mu \tag{1.65}$$

Another useful property of these spinors is

$$\sigma_r\chi_\kappa^\mu = -\chi_{-\kappa}^\mu \tag{1.65'}$$

where

$$r\sigma_r = \sum_i x_i\sigma_i$$

The proof of (1.65′) follows: σ_r is a scalar operator so that $\sigma_r\chi_\kappa^\mu$ must belong to the same j and μ as χ_κ^μ. That is, $\mathbf{j}^2$ clearly commutes with σ_r. For j_z we have

$$r(j_z, \sigma_r) = (l_z + s_z, x\sigma_x + y\sigma_y) = 0$$

since $(l_z, x) = iy$, $(l_z, y) = -ix$, $(s_z, \sigma_x) = i\sigma_y$, and $(s_z, \sigma_y) = -i\sigma_x$. Since σ_r has odd parity it follows that

$$\sigma_r\chi_\kappa^\mu = a\chi_{-\kappa}^\mu$$

where $a^2 = 1$ since $\sigma_r^2 = 1$ by (1.26). To evaluate a we can take $\hat{\mathbf{r}}$ along the z-axis. Then setting $\vartheta = 0$ in (1.48) we find

$$Y_l^m(\hat{\mathbf{e}}_3) = \left(\frac{2l+1}{4\pi}\right)^{1/2} \delta_{m0}$$

and we obtain

$$\chi_\kappa^\mu = \left(\frac{2l+1}{4\pi}\right)^{1/2} C(l\tfrac{1}{2}j;0\mu)\chi^\mu$$

Thus

$$a(2\bar{l}+1)^{1/2}\, C(\bar{l}\tfrac{1}{2}j;0\mu) = 2\mu(2l+1)^{1/2}\, C(l\tfrac{1}{2}j;0\mu)$$

For all four possible cases $j = l \pm \frac{1}{2}$, $\mu = \pm\frac{1}{2}$ we find $a = -1$, thus establishing (1.65′).

As an application we consider the expansion of a plane wave $\chi^m \exp(i\mathbf{k}\cdot\mathbf{r})$ into spherical waves. Such an expansion is useful in problems of scattering and angular correlation.[8] For a free particle the radial function, hitherto denoted by $R_j(r)$, is a spherical Bessel function:

$$R_j(r) = j_l(kr) = \left(\frac{\pi}{2kr}\right)^{1/2} J_{l+1/2}(kr) \tag{1.66}$$

and $J_{l+1/2}$ is the standard Bessel function. Thus we write

$$\chi^m \exp(i\mathbf{k}\cdot\mathbf{r}) = \sum_{\kappa\mu} a_{\kappa\mu} j_l(kr)\chi_\kappa^\mu \tag{1.67}$$

We use the Rayleigh expansion

$$\exp(i\mathbf{k}\cdot\mathbf{r}) = \sum_{L=0} i^L(2L+1)\, j_L(kr)\, P_L(\cos\Theta)$$

where Θ is the angle between $\hat{\mathbf{k}}$ and $\hat{\mathbf{r}}$; with the addition theorem of the spherical harmonics this becomes

$$\exp(i\mathbf{k}\cdot\mathbf{r}) = 4\pi \sum_{LM} i^L j_L(kr)\, Y_L^{M\times}(\hat{\mathbf{k}})\, Y_L^M(\hat{\mathbf{r}}) \tag{1.68}$$

From the orthonormality of the χ_κ^μ we obtain

$$j_l a_{\kappa\mu} = (\chi_\kappa^\mu, \chi^m \exp(i\mathbf{k}\cdot\mathbf{r}))$$

and with (1.68) and (1.60′) this gives

$$j_l a_{\kappa\mu} = 4\pi \sum_\tau C(l\tfrac{1}{2}j, \mu-\tau, \tau)\delta_{\tau m} \sum_{LM} i^L j_L Y_L^{M\times}(\hat{\mathbf{k}})\delta_{Ll}\delta_{M,\mu-\tau}$$

or

$$a_{\kappa\mu} = 4\pi i^l C(l\tfrac{1}{2}j;\mu-m,m)\, Y_l^{\mu-m\times}(\hat{\mathbf{k}}) \tag{1.69}$$

so that

$$\chi^m \exp(i\mathbf{k}\cdot\mathbf{r}) = 4\pi \sum_{\kappa\mu} i^l C(l\tfrac{1}{2}j;\mu-m,m)\, Y_l^{\mu-m\times}(\hat{\mathbf{k}})\, j_l(kr)\, \chi_\kappa^\mu \tag{1.70}$$

For $\hat{\mathbf{k}}$ along the z-axis this specializes to

$$\chi^m e^{ikz} = (4\pi)^{1/2} \sum_\kappa i^l(2l+1)^{1/2}\, C(l\tfrac{1}{2}j;0,m)\, j_l(kr)\, \chi_\kappa^m$$

$$= (2\pi)^{1/2} \sum_\kappa i^l S_\kappa^{m+1/2}(2j+1)^{1/2}\, j_l(kr)\, \chi_\kappa^m \tag{1.70′}$$

To obtain plane waves with the average spin direction along $\hat{\mathbf{n}}$, that is $\boldsymbol{\sigma}\cdot\hat{\mathbf{n}}$ diagonal, the transformation with the D matrix can be carried out just as in section 5. Then the χ^m is replaced by $\Sigma_{m'} D^{1/2}_{m'm}(\hat{\mathbf{n}})\chi^{m'}$ so that in (1.70′), for example, $S_\kappa^{m+1/2}\chi_\kappa^m$ is replaced by $D^{1/2}_{m'm} S_\kappa^{m'+1/2}\chi_\kappa^{m'}$ and the result summed over $m' = \pm\frac{1}{2}$.

PROBLEMS

1. Show that it is impossible to construct a non-vanishing 2 by 2 matrix which anticommutes with each of the three Pauli matrices.

2. (i) Evaluate

$$\boldsymbol{\sigma}\cdot\mathbf{A}_1\, \boldsymbol{\sigma}\cdot\mathbf{A}_2\, \boldsymbol{\sigma}\cdot\mathbf{A}_3$$

in the form $a + \mathbf{b}\cdot\boldsymbol{\sigma}$.

(ii) Find the trace of

$$\boldsymbol{\sigma}\cdot\mathbf{A}_1\, \boldsymbol{\sigma}\cdot\mathbf{A}_2\, \boldsymbol{\sigma}\cdot\mathbf{A}_3\, \boldsymbol{\sigma}\cdot\mathbf{A}_4$$

(iii) Show that

$$\boldsymbol{\sigma}\,\boldsymbol{\sigma}\cdot\mathbf{A} - \mathbf{A} = i\mathbf{A} \times \boldsymbol{\sigma} = \mathbf{A} - \boldsymbol{\sigma}\cdot\mathbf{A}\,\boldsymbol{\sigma}$$

3. Show that if a matrix is idempotent, i.e., $P^2 = P$ and $P \neq I_2$, then the determinant of P is zero. Thus a projection matrix is singular.

4. Solve the problem of the anomalous Zeeman effect using the decoupled wave functions (1.47) as zero-order solutions.

5. From Eq. (1.35b) it is seen that

$$D^{1/2}(0\,\vartheta\,0)\; D^{1/2}(\varphi\,0\,0) = D^{1/2}(\varphi\,\vartheta\,0)$$

but

$$D^{1/2}(\varphi\,0\,0)\; D^{1/2}(0\,\vartheta\,0) \neq D^{1/2}(\varphi\,\vartheta\,0)$$

Explain why both of these results should be expected.

6. Show that it is impossible to find a representation of the Pauli $\boldsymbol{\sigma}$-matrices in which (a) all three are real, (b) two are pure imaginary (i.e., $\sigma_k^{\times} = -\sigma_k$) and one is real.

7. If the numbers a_{ik} are the elements of a 3 by 3 orthogonal matrix, so that

$$\sum_k a_{ik}a_{jk} = \delta_{ji}$$

and

$$\sum_i a_{ij}a_{ik} = \delta_{jk}$$

then prove that

$$\sigma_i' = \sum_i a_{ij}\sigma_j$$

satisfies the same commutation rules as σ_i:

$$\sigma_i'^2 = 1, \qquad \sigma_j'\sigma_k' = -\sigma_k'\sigma_j' = i\epsilon_{jkl}\sigma_l' \qquad (j \neq k)$$

8. Show that there is no 2 by 2 matrix which commutes with $\boldsymbol{\sigma}\cdot\mathbf{A}$ other than the trivial cases of the unit matrix and a multiple of $\boldsymbol{\sigma}\cdot\mathbf{A}$ itself.

9. An electron in an atom interacts with the magnetic field produced by the nuclear magnetic moment $\boldsymbol{\mu}_N$. The vector potential of this magnetic field is

$$\mathbf{A} = \frac{\boldsymbol{\mu}_N \times \mathbf{r}}{r^3} = \frac{\boldsymbol{\mu}_N \times \hat{\mathbf{r}}}{r^2}$$

Show that the interaction energy is

$$H_{\text{sp}} = \frac{e\hbar}{mc}\left\{4\pi\boldsymbol{\mu}_N\cdot\mathbf{s}\,\delta(\mathbf{r}) + \frac{3\boldsymbol{\mu}_N\cdot\hat{\mathbf{r}}\,\mathbf{s}\cdot\hat{\mathbf{r}} - \boldsymbol{\mu}_N\cdot\mathbf{s}}{r^3}\right\}$$

10. From the fact that an arbitrary two-component spinor is an eigenfunction of $\mathbf{s}^2$ show that $\mathbf{s}^2$ must be diagonal.

11. Evaluate $\sigma_\nu \chi_\kappa^{\mu\times}$ where χ_κ^μ is the spin-angular function for central fields. In particular, show that $\sigma_\nu \chi_\kappa^{\mu\times}$ is, within a phase, $\chi_{\bar{\kappa}}^{-\mu}$.

REFERENCES

1. G. E. Uhlenbeck and S. A. Goudsmit, *Naturwiss.* **13,** 953 (1925); *Nature* **117,** 264 (1926).
2. W. Pauli, *Z. Physik* **43,** 601 (1927).
3. A. H. Compton, *J. Franklin Inst.* Aug. 1921, p. 145.
4. H. A. Kramers, *Quantum Mechanics*, North Holland Publishing Co., Amsterdam, 1957.
5. U. Fano, *Revs. Mod. Phys.* **29,** 74 (1957).
6. H. A. Tolhoek, *Revs. Mod. Phys.* **28,** 277 (1956).
7. L. H. Thomas, *Nature* **117,** 514 (1926); *Phil. Mag.* (VII) **3,** 1 (1927).
8. L. C. Biedenharn and M. E. Rose, *Revs. Mod. Phys.* **25,** 729 (1953).

II.

Relativistic Quantum Mechanics of Free Particles

9. POSTULATES OF THE THEORY

The postulational basis of the relativistic electron theory has been discussed by many authors. For example, for this as well as other questions reference may be made to the famous article of Pauli.[D] Although not generally stated explicitly, there are certain postulates which are common to quantum mechanical theories in general, and since they are of decisive importance in guiding us to a relativistic theory they are discussed below. For a more complete discussion the reader is referred to the work of Dirac.†

The postulates which follow apply quite generally to particles interacting with fields as well as to free particles. However, it is once more to be emphasized that these fields are taken as given quantities and are not quantized. The result is a single particle theory.‡ We list the postulates below, deferring the discussion of them to the end of this section.

1. The theory shall be formulated in terms of a field, quantitatively represented by an amplitude function ψ, in such a way that the customary statistical interpretation of quantum phenomena will be valid.
2. The description of physical phenomena in the theory will be based on an equation of motion describing the development in time of the system, or of the field amplitude ψ.
3. The superposition principle shall hold, and therefore the equation of motion must be linear in ψ.
4. The equation (or equations) of motion must be consistent with the

† Reference E, especially Chapter V.

‡ Often referred to as a c-number theory in contrast to the q-number theory with non-commuting fields in which creation and annihilation of particles is explicitly provided for.

principle of special relativity.† This, it will be seen in section 14, requires that they may be written in covariant form as, for example, the Maxwell equations of classical electrodynamics.

5. In view of postulate 1 it must be possible to define a probability density ρ such that ρ is positive definite:

$$\rho \geqslant 0 \tag{2.1}$$

and the space integral of ρ has the properties

$$\int \rho \, d^3x = \text{relativistic invariant} \tag{2.2a}$$

$$\frac{d}{dt}\int \rho \, d^3x = 0 \tag{2.2b}$$

These requirements permit a Lorentz-invariant meaning to a normalization condition such as

$$\int \rho \, d^3x = 1$$

6. The theory should be consistent with the correspondence principle and in the non-relativistic limit should reduce to the standard form of quantum mechanics already found applicable at low velocities. Furthermore, in the non-quantum limit the theory should yield the mechanics of special relativity.

Postulates 1 and 3 appear to be necessary in view of such experimental facts as scattering and the attendant diffraction effects observed in such phenomena. The ψ-function referred to will be again called a wave function. It will, in general, depend on the four space-time coordinates x_μ and may be a multicomponent wave function. The latter should be expected if the theory is to account for spin properties of the electron (cf. Chapter I).

Postulate 2 implies, as Dirac[E] has shown, that there exists an operator equation of the form

$$H\psi = i\hbar \frac{\partial \psi}{\partial t} \tag{2.3}$$

This gives for the time development of the system

$$\psi(t) = e^{-iHt/\hbar}\,\psi(0) \equiv \sum_{n=0}^{\infty} \frac{1}{n!}\left(\frac{-iHt}{\hbar}\right)^n \psi(0) \tag{2.3'}$$

where $\psi(0)$ refers to the function ψ at time $t = 0$. Thus $H/i\hbar$ is the time displacement operator; H itself has the dimensions of energy. From the general relation between time and energy in classical mechanics, including

† General relativity, so far as is known, plays an extremely negligible role in typical quantum mechanical processes. An outline of the necessary constructs of special relativity is given in Appendix B.

special relativity, we must expect H to be the energy operator. In (2.3′) we have assumed H to be explicitly independent of time; this assumption is necessary for a system in which energy is conserved. In view of postulate 1 the scale of ψ, as measured by its norm (ψ, ψ) for example, should not change as long as the system is left undisturbed. This implies that $\exp(-iHt/\hbar)$ is a unitary operator and therefore that H is hermitian. This is at least consistent with the energy identification since it is then assured that eigenvalues of H will be real.

In connection with postulate 4 it should be remarked that the occurrence of the first time derivative in the equation of motion will imply that the space derivatives must also occur to first order. The more or less obvious requirement of symmetry in all four space-time variables is clearly not fulfilled by the non-relativistic form of quantum mechanics. Although this symmetrical appearance of the four x_μ in the equations of motion will actually be realized in the form of the theory to which one arrives, it must be understood that it is not a sufficient condition for relativistic covariance and that this covariance must actually be demonstrated, as it will be.

Postulate 5 needs two comments. First, the positive definite character of ρ implies that we speak of a particle and not of a charge density. It is not clear *a priori*, in a given theory, whether the goal stipulated in (2.1) is attainable. For instance, for charged spin zero particles only a charge density can be defined.[1] The second remark is to the effect that (2.2b) is assured if a continuity equation exists and if ψ vanishes sufficiently strongly at the boundaries of the system. That is, a particle current density $\mathbf{j}$ must exist such that

$$\operatorname{div} \mathbf{j} + \frac{\partial \rho}{\partial t} = 0 \tag{2.4}$$

Then, by Gauss' theorem,

$$\frac{d}{dt} \int \rho \, d^3x = -\int \operatorname{div} \mathbf{j} \, d^3x = -\int j_n \, dS$$

where dS is an element of the bounding surface and j_n is the component of $\mathbf{j}$ along the outward normal. The requirement that this vanish can be stated explicitly only after $\mathbf{j}$ has been defined in terms of the wave functions. However, in a general way, the time independence of the volume integral of ρ is assured if j_n vanishes sufficiently strongly on the infinite surface bounding the physical region.

If, after $\mathbf{j}$ and ρ are defined, it can be shown that $\mathbf{j} = \mathbf{s}$ and $ic\rho = s_4$ form a four-vector, s_μ, the continuity equation can be written in the Lorentz invariant form,

$$\frac{\partial s_\mu}{\partial x_\mu} = 0 \tag{2.4′}$$

so that the relevant statements of postulate 5 will not depend on a particular reference frame. This requirement should therefore be added as an additional condition on **j**, ρ. Of course, (2.4) has the usual interpretation that a particle cannot disappear from a volume of space unless it crosses the surface bounding that volume. As we shall show later, it will be recognized that electrons can actually do this by means of pair annihilation

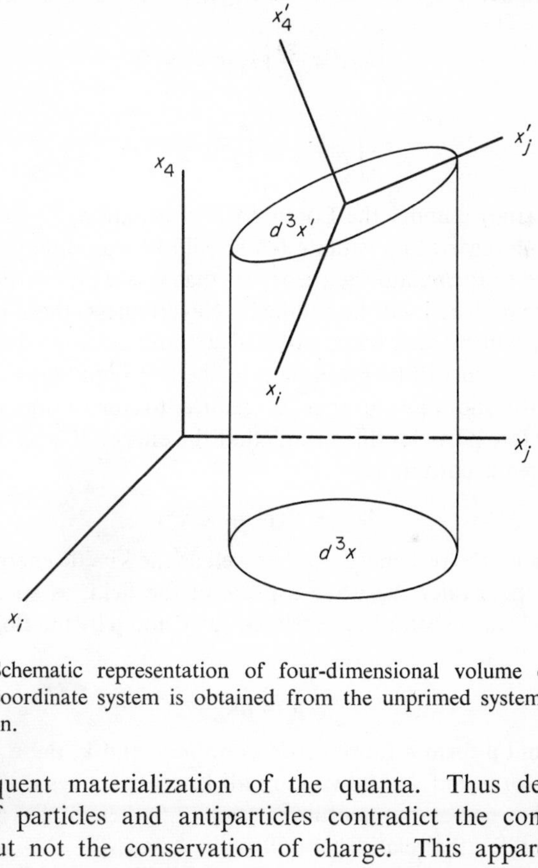

Figure 2.1 Schematic representation of four-dimensional volume of integration. The primed coordinate system is obtained from the unprimed system by a Lorentz transformation.

and subsequent materialization of the quanta. Thus destruction or creation of particles and antiparticles contradict the conservation of particles but not the conservation of charge. This apparent difficulty disappears in a quantized field theory. In the questions discussed in this book it raises no real problem.

The invariance of the volume integral of ρ can be demonstrated once the continuity equation (2.4′) is established. Assume that s_μ vanishes on the spatial boundaries of a closed four-dimensional space-time continuum. That is, for large x_k, $s_\mu \to 0$ for any x_4. Consider a closed four-dimensional volume in the form of a cylinder whose bases are $x_4 =$ constant and $x_4' =$ constant where x_4' refers to a second Lorentz frame (Fig. 2.1). The remaining surfaces correspond to x_k = constant, which we take to be large without limit. Then, by an application of Gauss' theorem, (2.4′) is transformed to a surface integral of the outward normal component of the four-vector s_μ. On the surfaces x_k = constant the vector vanishes and, it is assumed, sufficiently strongly that there is no contribution to the flux integral. On the surface x_4 = constant the normal component is $-s_4$ and on x_4' = constant it is s_4'. This is true if $dx_4/dx_4' > 0$. Then the flux integral is

$$-\int s_4\, d^3x + \int s_4'\, d^3x' = 0$$

or

$$\int \rho\, d^3x = \int \rho'\, d^3x'$$

implying invariance under the Lorentz transformation.

Finally, with regard to postulate 6 it should be stated that no deliberate effort is made to formulate the theory so that it is *a priori* evident that *all* the requirements listed will be fulfilled. Nevertheless, these requirements of the theory will be seen to be satisfied without additional assumptions. Particular attention will be given here to the last requirement mentioned: that the relativistic wave properties reduce to relativistic but classical orbits.† For free particles this means that the energy W and momentum $\mathbf{p}$ must be related according to

$$W^2 = c^2(p^2 + m^2c^2) \tag{2.5}$$

Here W includes the rest energy mc^2 as well as the kinetic energy $W - mc^2$. In quantum mechanics the wave aspects of the field, as specified by the frequency and wave vector $\mathbf{k}$, are related to W and $\mathbf{p}$ by the Bohr-deBroglie relations.

$$\begin{aligned} W &= \hbar\omega \\ \mathbf{p} &= \hbar\mathbf{k} \end{aligned} \tag{2.6}$$

Since iW/c and $\mathbf{p}$ form a four-vector as do $i\omega/c$ and $\mathbf{k}$, these relations are in covariant form and will be valid in all Lorentz frames if they are valid in any one. The energy-momentum relation (2.5) then implies the following dispersion law for the relativistic deBroglie waves:

$$\omega^2 = c^2(k^2 + k_0^2) \tag{2.7}$$

where

$$k_0 = mc/\hbar \tag{2.7′}$$

is the reciprocal Compton wavelength.

It will be seen that there are two branches for the waves under consideration: those corresponding to positive and also to negative

† A detailed discussion of the non-quantum limit is deferred until section 35.

frequencies. This existence of positive and negative frequencies is peculiar to every relativistic theory, and the consequences of this fact will be seen to be profound in the quantum theory.

In the limit $k \ll k_0$ the dispersion law is characteristic of non-relativistic quantum mechanics of free particles, as one should expect. Therefore, if the dispersion law is made the basis on which the theory is constructed, it may be expected that the appropriate limiting cases will automatically emerge in correct form.

10. THE WAVE EQUATION

The Second-Order Equation

The dispersion law (2.7) contains, as stated above, the frequency-wave number relationship applicable to non-relativistic deBroglie waves:

$$\omega - ck_0 = \omega' \cong \hbar k^2/2m \tag{2.8}$$

corresponding to

$$W - mc^2 = E \cong p^2/2m \tag{2.8'}$$

If one introduces a wave packet,

$$\psi = \int u(\mathbf{k}) \exp\,[i(\mathbf{k}\cdot\mathbf{r} - \omega' t)]\, d^3k \tag{2.9}$$

it follows from (2.8) that

$$i\hbar\frac{\partial\psi}{\partial t} = H_{nr}\psi = -\frac{\hbar^2}{2m}\nabla^2\psi$$

the usual non-relativistic wave equation for free particles.

Applying the same technique to (2.7) without the approximation of small k, we obtain with (2.9) the second-order wave equation,

$$\left(\nabla^2 - \frac{1}{c^2}\frac{\partial}{\partial t^2} - k_0^2\right)\psi = 0 \tag{2.10}$$

or

$$\left(\frac{\partial^2}{\partial x_\mu\,\partial x_\mu} - k_0^2\right)\psi = 0 \tag{2.10'}$$

This is known as the Klein-Gordon equation, and it has been proposed on a number of occasions.[1] The form (2.10′) clearly shows that the wave equation is relativistically covariant. Even though this equation does not have the form of (2.3), it will be instructive to examine it further. We write the equation for ψ^*:

$$\left(\nabla^2 - \frac{1}{c^2}\frac{\partial^2}{\partial t^2} - k_0^2\right)\psi^* = 0 \tag{2.10''}$$

By multiplying (2.10) with ψ^* on the left and (2.10″) by ψ on the right and subtracting, we obtain a continuity equation

$$\frac{\partial s_\mu}{\partial x_\mu} = 0 \tag{2.11a}$$

where

$$s_\mu = \text{const.}\left(\psi^* \frac{\partial \psi}{\partial x_\mu} - \frac{\partial \psi^*}{\partial x_\mu}\psi\right) \tag{2.11b}$$

Because the s_μ are evidently the components of a four-vector, (2.11a) is Lorentz invariant. However, we observe that

$$\rho \sim \psi^* \frac{\partial \psi}{\partial t} - \frac{\partial \psi^*}{\partial t}\psi$$

will not be positive definite if ψ obeys *only* the second-order equation (2.10). This is so because in that eventuality ψ and $\partial\psi/\partial t$ are independent. If at time $t = 0$ they are chosen so that ρ is positive, there is no guarantee that ρ will remain positive. For this reason the second-order equation is usually rejected as a description of the electron. It is correct to reject the Klein-Gordon description as far as electrons are concerned. However, the reasoning is somewhat misleading. First, one recognizes that, if ψ is a scalar (single-component) field, the second-order theory can apply to spin zero particles only. That it indeed does apply to such particles is well known. However, the difficulty concerning the non-positive definite character of ρ would appear to remain. The proper interpretation in the case of charged spin zero particles has already been mentioned:[1] ρ can be expressed as a *difference* of two positive definite bilinear quantities of the form $\varphi^*\varphi - \chi^*\chi$, where[2]

$$\begin{pmatrix}\varphi\\ \chi\end{pmatrix} \sim \begin{pmatrix}\psi - \dfrac{1}{k_0}\dfrac{\partial\psi}{\partial x_4}\\[2ex] \psi + \dfrac{1}{k_0}\dfrac{\partial\psi}{\partial x_4}\end{pmatrix} \tag{2.12}$$

In this form explicit recognition is made of the independence of ψ and $\partial\psi/\partial t$, which obey coupled *first*-order equations. The interpretation of ρ is then made correctly in terms of a charge density, and the two-component character of ψ is connected with the existence of positive and negative charges.

The assignment of the equation of motion (2.10) to spin zero particles does not entirely clear up the question at issue. The fact remains that according to postulate 6 the wave equation (2.10) must also apply for spin $\frac{1}{2}$, or for any spin. Thus, from (2.3), it would follow that

$$\frac{1}{c^2}\frac{\partial^2\psi}{\partial t^2} = -\frac{1}{\hbar^2 c^2} H^2\psi = (\nabla^2 - k_0^2)\psi$$

or

$$H^2 = c^2(\vec{\mathbf{p}}^2 + m^2c^2) \tag{2.13}$$

for free particles. If ψ is not a single-component function, (2.10) applies to each component. However, it is no longer true that each component of ψ is determined *only* by (2.10). In particular, it is not true that ψ and $\partial\psi/\partial t$ are independent. They are, in fact, related by (2.3). The existence of the continuity equation (2.11) is not to be interpreted in terms of a conservation theorem but is the direct result of the energy-momentum relation (2.5). Thus, for any ψ of the form

$$\psi = \int u_+(\mathbf{k}) \exp\left[i(\mathbf{k}\cdot\mathbf{r} - \omega t)\right] d^3k + \int u_-(\mathbf{k}) \exp\left[i(\mathbf{k}\cdot\mathbf{r} + \omega t)\right] d^3k$$

the continuity equation (2.11a) with s_μ given by (2.11b) is automatically fulfilled.

The Dirac Wave Equation[3]

The assumption is made that an equation of motion of the type (2.3) exists. Then the postulated property of ρ, that is, (2.2b), is automatically valid with H hermitian if

$$\rho = \psi^*\psi \tag{2.14}$$

Obviously, this ρ is positive definite. For, if (2.14) is assumed, we see that

$$\int \frac{\partial\rho}{\partial t}\, d^3x = -\frac{i}{\hbar}\int [\psi^* H\psi - (H\psi)^*\psi]\, d^3x = 0$$

by virtue of $H^* = H$.

Since the equation is linear in $\partial/\partial x_4$, the relativistic covariance implies that H is linear in the space derivatives $\partial/\partial x_k$ or the momentum operator $\vec{p}_k$. If we admit the possibility that ψ is a multicomponent function with components ψ_λ, H must have the form of a square matrix and the most general form of one of the elements of this matrix, in the absence of interactions, is

$$H_{\lambda\sigma} = c(\alpha_k)_{\lambda\sigma}\vec{p}_k + \beta_{\lambda\sigma}mc^2 \tag{2.15}$$

the constants have been chosen so that the numbers $(\alpha_k)_{\lambda\sigma}$ and $\beta_{\lambda\sigma}$ are dimensionless. For a particle at rest we must expect the first operator in

(2.15) to give zero when applied to ψ, and hence the second term would be associated with what remains: the rest energy. The first term should therefore be the kinetic energy operator.

The postulated wave equation is, in matrix form,

$$H\psi = [c\boldsymbol{\alpha}\cdot\vec{\mathbf{p}} + \beta mc^2]\psi = i\hbar\frac{\partial\psi}{\partial t} \tag{2.16}$$

which is a set of n equations where n is the number of components of ψ. The $\boldsymbol{\alpha}\cdot\vec{\mathbf{p}}$ term is an abbreviation for the sum of three terms,

$$\boldsymbol{\alpha}\cdot\vec{\mathbf{p}} = \sum_{k=1}^{3} \alpha_k \vec{p}_k$$

where, as mentioned, each of the three α_k is a square matrix. The same is true of β, and the hermiticity of H, each p_k being hermitian, requires that each of the four matrices $\boldsymbol{\alpha}$ and β are hermitian:

$$\alpha_k = \alpha_k^* \qquad (k = 1, 2, 3)$$
$$\beta = \beta^* \tag{2.17}$$

As stated above, this is sufficient for a continuity equation. To see this in detail and to identify the current density we write the hermitian conjugate of (2.16):

$$(H\psi)^* = \psi^* H = \psi^*[-c\boldsymbol{\alpha}\cdot\vec{\mathbf{p}} + \beta mc^2] = -i\hbar\frac{\partial\psi^*}{\partial t} \tag{2.18}$$

Multiplication of (2.16) by ψ^* on the left and of (2.18) by ψ on the right and subtraction give

$$i\hbar\frac{\partial\rho}{\partial t} = c(\psi^*\boldsymbol{\alpha}\cdot\vec{\mathbf{p}}\psi + \psi^*\boldsymbol{\alpha}\cdot\vec{\mathbf{p}}\psi)$$
$$= c\vec{\mathbf{p}}\cdot(\psi^*\boldsymbol{\alpha}\psi)$$

because $\vec{\mathbf{p}}$ is proportional to the gradient operator. Using $\vec{\mathbf{p}} = -i\hbar\nabla$, we obtain

$$\operatorname{div}\mathbf{j} + \frac{\partial\rho}{\partial t} = 0$$

where ρ is given by (2.14) and

$$\mathbf{j} = c\psi^*\boldsymbol{\alpha}\psi \tag{2.19}$$

The four-vector current density would be expected to be

$$(\mathbf{j}, ic\rho) = s_\mu = c\psi^* a_\mu \psi \tag{2.20}$$

where the four matrices a_μ are $\boldsymbol{\alpha}$ ($\mu = 1, 2, 3$) and $a_4 = i$ multiplied by the n by n unit matrix. Of course, it is yet to be proved that s_μ is a four-vector since the properties of ψ and ψ^* under Lorentz transformations have not yet been discussed. This question will be taken up in section 14.

We turn now to the connection with the second-order equation. From (2.13) it is required that

$$H^2 = c^2[(\alpha_i\alpha_k + \alpha_k\alpha_i)\vec{p}_i\vec{p}_k + mc(\alpha_i\beta + \beta\alpha_i)\vec{p}_i + \beta^2m^2c^2]$$
$$= c^2[\vec{p}_i\vec{p}_i + m^2c^2]$$

identically in the components of $\vec{\mathbf{p}}$. Consequently,

$$\alpha_i\alpha_k + \alpha_k\alpha_i = 2\delta_{ik} \tag{2.21a}$$

$$\alpha_i\beta + \beta\alpha_i = 0 \tag{2.21b}$$

$$\beta^2 = 1 \tag{2.21c}$$

That is, each of the four matrices α_i and β are their own inverse, in addition to being hermitian. They are therefore all unitary. Moreover the set of α_i, β constitutes *four* anticommuting matrices.†

The fact that the α_i and β cannot be taken to be unit matrices (or multiples thereof) means that ψ must be a multicomponent function. The process of linearization of the Klein-Gordon equation, which was Dirac's innovation,[3] has therefore led to the requirement of a multicomponent wave function, which, as may correctly be anticipated, is connected with the existence of spin. However, the first striking fact is that ψ cannot be a two-component function like the Pauli spinors, because then each α_i and β would be a 2 by 2 matrix and we have seen that there can be only three anticommuting 2 by 2 matrices: the Pauli $\boldsymbol{\sigma}$-matrices and their transforms. The dimensionality of the four Dirac matrices will be discussed in the following section. For the present we may observe that the number of components n must be even. To see this we observe that for each of the four Dirac matrices there is another matrix which anticommutes with it. Therefore, if b_μ is any one of the four matrices and b_ν is a matrix which anticommutes with b_μ, we have

$$\text{Tr}\, b_\mu = \text{Tr}\, b_\mu b_\nu^2 = \text{Tr}\, b_\nu b_\mu b_\nu = -\text{Tr}\, b_\mu b_\nu^2 = 0 \tag{2.21$'$}$$

since each $b_\nu^2 = 1$ and $\text{Tr}\, AB = \text{Tr}\, BA$. Thus each matrix has zero trace. There exists a representation in which any b_μ can be brought to diagonal form, and, since the results $b_\mu^2 = 1$ and $\text{Tr}\, b_\mu$ are independent of the representation, we conclude that the eigenvalues of b_μ in diagonal form

† Equations (2.21) can be written in more compact form by writing for example, $\beta = \alpha_4$. But this carries the unfortunate connotation that β is connected in some way with the fourth component of a four-vector whose space component is connected in the same way with $\boldsymbol{\alpha}$. The result (2.20) indicates that this is an incorrect interpretation, as it is indeed.

are ± 1 and that there are as many $+1$ as -1 eigenvalues. Thus the number of rows and columns must be even. The minimum possible number for n is 4, and it is easy to see that a 4 by 4 representation does, in fact, exist. For example,

$$\boldsymbol{\alpha} = \begin{pmatrix} 0 & \boldsymbol{\sigma} \\ \boldsymbol{\sigma} & 0 \end{pmatrix}, \qquad \beta = \begin{pmatrix} \mathrm{I}_2 & 0 \\ 0 & -\mathrm{I}_2 \end{pmatrix} \tag{2.22}$$

where each entry is a 2 by 2 matrix. In detail, for the representation of the Pauli $\boldsymbol{\sigma}$'s given in (1.22),

$$\alpha_1 = \begin{pmatrix} 0 & 0 & 0 & 1 \\ 0 & 0 & 1 & 0 \\ 0 & 1 & 0 & 0 \\ 1 & 0 & 0 & 0 \end{pmatrix}, \quad \text{etc.}$$

The matrices (2.22) will be referred to as the standard representation. That the standard representation fulfills all the rules (2.21) is readily verified. Of course, any transform

$$\boldsymbol{\alpha}' = S\boldsymbol{\alpha}S^{-1}, \qquad \beta' = S\beta S^{-1} \tag{2.22'}$$

also fulfills (2.21) and is equivalent. This type of transformation arises when a non-singular linear transformation from one ψ to another ψ' is made. Then

$$\psi' = S\psi, \qquad \psi = S^{-1}\psi'$$

and

$$H\psi = i\hbar\,(\partial\psi/\partial t)$$

becomes, with $\partial S/\partial t = 0$,

$$H'\psi' = SHS^{-1}\psi' = i\hbar\,(\partial\psi'/\partial t)$$

In the present instance

$$H' = c(\boldsymbol{\alpha}'\cdot\vec{\mathbf{p}} + \beta' mc)$$

where $\boldsymbol{\alpha}'$ and β' are related to $\boldsymbol{\alpha}$ and β by (2.22′). We compare the (spinor) expectation value (not necessarily integrated over coordinates) in two representations of a matrix Ω, where Ω is a sum of terms formed by constructing arbitrary products of α_k and β:

$$\psi'^*\Omega'\psi' = \psi^*S^*S\Omega S^{-1}S\psi = \psi^*S^*S\Omega\psi$$

If $S^*S = 1$, that is, if S is unitary,

$$\psi'^*\Omega'\psi' = \psi^*\Omega\psi$$

Another generalization which gives the same commutation rules is

$$\boldsymbol{\alpha} = \begin{pmatrix} \boldsymbol{\alpha}^{(4)} & 0 \\ 0 & \boldsymbol{\alpha}^{(4)} \end{pmatrix}, \qquad \beta = \begin{pmatrix} \beta^{(4)} & 0 \\ 0 & \beta^{(4)} \end{pmatrix} \tag{2.22''}$$

or

$$\boldsymbol{\alpha} = \begin{pmatrix} 0 & \boldsymbol{\alpha}^{(4)} \\ \boldsymbol{\alpha}^{(4)} & 0 \end{pmatrix}, \qquad \beta = \begin{pmatrix} 0 & \beta^{(4)} \\ \beta^{(4)} & 0 \end{pmatrix} \tag{2.22''}$$

where $\boldsymbol{\alpha}^{(4)}$ and $\beta^{(4)}$ are the matrices given by (2.22). Thus these alternatives are 8 by 8 matrices. But they correspond to writing the wave equation twice and yield nothing of additional significance.

The Covariant Form of the Wave Equation

It is clear that, although (2.16) and (2.18) are in Hamiltonian form, the time and space coordinates do not enter in a symmetric manner. Of course, (2.16) could be written in the form

$$\left(-i\hbar c\, \alpha_\mu \frac{\partial}{\partial x_\mu} + \beta mc^2\right)\psi = 0$$

where $\alpha_4 = i$. But, in order to construct a covariant operator, each term should be covariant and the rest energy term, in particular, should be simply mc^2. Therefore we multiply the preceding equation on the left by β and define

$$\begin{aligned} \gamma_k &= -i\beta\alpha_k \qquad (k = 1, 2, 3) \\ \gamma_4 &= \beta \end{aligned} \tag{2.23}$$

to obtain

$$\left(\gamma_\mu \frac{\partial}{\partial x_\mu} + k_0\right)\psi = 0 \tag{2.24}$$

This will be referred to as the *covariant* form of the wave equation. From (2.23) and (2.21) we obtain directly

$$\gamma_\mu\gamma_\nu + \gamma_\nu\gamma_\mu = 2\delta_{\mu\nu}; \qquad \mu, \nu = 1, 2, 3, 4 \tag{2.25}$$

for the commutation rule of the four Dirac γ-matrices. Of course, the right side of (2.25) implicitly contains a unit matrix. In Appendix D an alternative approach culminating in the same wave equation and commutation rules is presented.

It is clear by a preceding argument that the trace of anticommuting matrices vanishes. Therefore, for all μ,

$$\operatorname{Tr} \gamma_\mu = 0 \tag{2.26}$$

Also, by direct verification it is immediately seen that all γ_μ are hermitian:

$$\gamma_\mu = \gamma_\mu^* \tag{2.27}$$

For ψ^* the covariant equation of motion is

$$\frac{\partial \psi^*}{\partial x_k} \gamma_k - \frac{\partial \psi^*}{\partial x_4} \gamma_4 + k_0 \psi^* = 0 \qquad (2.24')$$

This extremely unsymmetrical form indicates that for Lorentz transformation properties it is not ψ^* which should be considered. Instead $\bar{\psi}$, the adjoint to ψ, is introduced (following Pauli[D]):

$$\bar{\psi} = \psi^* \gamma_4, \qquad \psi^* = \bar{\psi} \gamma_4 \qquad (2.28)$$

Then, inserting (2.28) in the equation for ψ^* and multiplying by γ_4 on the right yields

$$\frac{\partial \bar{\psi}}{\partial x_\mu} \gamma_\mu - k_0 \bar{\psi} = 0 \qquad (2.29)$$

In section 14 it will be shown that both equations of motion (2.24) and (2.29) are covariant under Lorentz transformations. That is, in two reference systems (2.24) and (2.29) are both valid if it is understood that the wave functions in the two systems are related to each other by a specified transformation.

11. THE DIRAC MATRICES[4]

In order to fix the dimensionality (rank) of the Dirac matrices we consider the complete set of matrices which can be constructed from them by multiplication. As will be seen presently, there are 16 different matrices γ_A $(A = 1, \ldots, 16)$ which can be formed in this way, and we shall choose a phase factor for each so that in all cases $\gamma_A^2 = 1$. Then also $\gamma_A = \gamma_A^*$ for all A. We divide the matrices γ_A into five groups as indicated below. The letters used to label these groups refer to Lorentz transformation properties discussed in section 14.

Group *S*. This consists of a single matrix, the identity or unit matrix. Obviously it can be formed from the γ_μ in at least four ways: $\gamma_\mu^2 = 1$ for each μ.

Group *V*. These are just the four matrices γ_μ.

Group *T*. These are the matrices formed by taking products in pairs. Since $\gamma_\mu^2 = 1$ and $\gamma_\mu\gamma_\nu = -\gamma_\nu\gamma_\mu$ when $\mu \neq \nu$, there are just six linearly independent matrices in this group:

$$i\gamma_\mu\gamma_\nu \qquad (\mu \neq \nu)$$

or, in detail,

$$i\gamma_1\gamma_2, \quad i\gamma_2\gamma_3, \quad i\gamma_3\gamma_1, \quad i\gamma_1\gamma_4, \quad i\gamma_2\gamma_4, \quad i\gamma_3\gamma_4$$

The first group of three can also be written, using (2.23), $i\alpha_1\alpha_2$, $i\alpha_2\alpha_3$, $i\alpha_3\alpha_1$. The second group is $-\alpha_1$, $-\alpha_2$, and $-\alpha_3$.

Group A. These are the four possible products formed by products of three γ_μ. Choosing the phase again as indicated above, these are: $i\gamma_2\gamma_3\gamma_4$, $i\gamma_3\gamma_1\gamma_4$, $i\gamma_1\gamma_2\gamma_4$, and $i\gamma_1\gamma_2\gamma_3$. These can be written in a more lucid fashion by using the γ_5 matrix, defined below, in the form $i\gamma_\mu\gamma_5$.

Group P. This is the single matrix formed by multiplying all four γ_μ:

$$\gamma_5 = \gamma_1\gamma_2\gamma_3\gamma_4$$

No other matrices can be formed from the γ's in view of (2.25).

The designation "group" used above does not mean that these 16 matrices form a group in the technical sense (for example, $i\gamma_1\gamma_2$ cannot be written as a product of two members of the set of 16). Moreover, if the factor i is omitted in the T group, then there are no inverses of these elements in the set. Nevertheless, the set of 16 matrices does form a mathematical entity: a Clifford algebra.[5] This is synonomous with statements 1 through 5 below.

We now prove a number of statements concerning the 16 Dirac matrices:[4,6]

Statement 1. For every $\gamma_A \neq 1$ there is at least one other matrix γ_B $(B \neq A)$ such that $\gamma_A\gamma_B = -\gamma_B\gamma_A$. This is obvious on inspection, and in fact, for every $\gamma_A \neq 1$, there are exactly 8 other γ_B which anticommute with γ_A and 8, counting γ_A itself, which commute with it. Obviously the unit matrix 1 is a member of the latter set.

Statement 2. For every $\gamma_A \neq 1$ we deduce that

$$\operatorname{Tr} \gamma_A = 0 \tag{2.30}$$

This follows exactly as in (2.21′).

Statement 3. The γ_A are linearly independent. This means that if

$$\sum_{A=1}^{16} c_A\gamma_A = 0 \tag{2.31}$$

then all $c_A = 0$. To prove this we multiply (2.31) by any one of the 16 γ's, say γ_B. Then

$$c_B + \sum_{A\neq B} c_A\gamma_B\gamma_A = 0$$

But $\gamma_B\gamma_A \neq 1$ or a multiple thereof when $A \neq B$. Therefore on taking the trace of this equation we find

$$c_B = 0$$

Since this applies for $B = 1, \ldots, 16$ the statement is demonstrated. Thus the 16 γ_A are distinct.

Statement 4. An arbitrary n by n matrix M can be written as a linear combination of the 16 γ_A. The truth of this statement is demonstrated by performing the decomposition. Thus

$$M = \sum_A m_A \gamma_A$$

and by multiplying by γ_B and taking the trace we find

$$m_A = \frac{1}{n} \operatorname{Tr} \gamma_A M \tag{2.32}$$

Statement 5. If a matrix M commutes with all 16 γ_A it must be a multiple of the unit matrix. We first write M in the form

$$M = m_B \gamma_B + \sum_{A \neq B} m_A \gamma_A \tag{2.33}$$

where $\gamma_B \neq 1$ but is otherwise arbitrary. Since a γ_C can always be chosen such that $\gamma_B \gamma_C = -\gamma_C \gamma_B$, where γ_C is one of the 16 γ_A matrices, we can write

$$\begin{aligned} M = \gamma_C M \gamma_C &= m_B \gamma_C \gamma_B \gamma_C + \sum_{A \neq B} m_A \gamma_C \gamma_A \gamma_C \\ &= -m_B \gamma_B + \sum_{A \neq B} \epsilon_A m_A \gamma_A ; \qquad \epsilon_A = \pm 1 \end{aligned}$$

since, for each A, $\gamma_C \gamma_A \gamma_C = \pm \gamma_A$. Multiplying this equation and (2.33) by γ_B and taking the trace, we obtain

$$\operatorname{Tr} \gamma_B M = n m_B = -n m_B$$

where the first equality follows from (2.33). It is then evident that

$$m_B = 0$$

Since γ_B was any member of the set excluding 1, it follows that M contains no γ-matrices other than 1. This demonstrates the validity of statement 5.†

Under the circumstance which has been established—that only one element of the Dirac algebra commutes with all the rest—it is a property of the algebra that it can be represented by n by n matrices where n^2 is the number of elements of the set. Thus since $n^2 = 16$ we conclude that, aside from trivial generalizations, the Dirac matrices have four rows and columns. The wave function is a four-component function.

The matrices (2.22) do indeed constitute a 4 by 4 representation for the α_i and β. In this representation, the standard representation,

$$\boldsymbol{\gamma} = \begin{pmatrix} 0 & -i\boldsymbol{\sigma} \\ i\boldsymbol{\sigma} & 0 \end{pmatrix}, \qquad \gamma_4 = \begin{pmatrix} 1 & 0 \\ 0 & -1 \end{pmatrix} \tag{2.34}$$

† This result is a special case of Schur's lemma.[7]

and all equivalent representations are obtained from (section 13)

$$\gamma'_\mu = S\gamma_\mu S^{-1} \tag{2.35}$$

For the T group described above we find

$$i\gamma_j\gamma_k = \begin{pmatrix} i\sigma_j\sigma_k & 0 \\ 0 & i\sigma_j\sigma_k \end{pmatrix} = -\begin{pmatrix} \sigma_l & 0 \\ 0 & \sigma_l \end{pmatrix} \tag{2.36}$$

where j, k, l are a cyclic permutation of 1, 2, 3. The matrix in (2.36) will be designated by σ_l. That is, in general,

$$\boldsymbol{\sigma} = \begin{pmatrix} \boldsymbol{\sigma} & 0 \\ 0 & \boldsymbol{\sigma} \end{pmatrix}$$

or

$$\sigma_1 = \begin{pmatrix} 0 & 1 & 0 & 0 \\ 1 & 0 & 0 & 0 \\ 0 & 0 & 0 & 1 \\ 0 & 0 & 1 & 0 \end{pmatrix}, \qquad \sigma_2 = \begin{pmatrix} 0 & -i & 0 & 0 \\ i & 0 & 0 & 0 \\ 0 & 0 & 0 & -i \\ 0 & 0 & i & 0 \end{pmatrix},$$

$$\sigma_3 = \begin{pmatrix} 1 & 0 & 0 & 0 \\ 0 & -1 & 0 & 0 \\ 0 & 0 & 1 & 0 \\ 0 & 0 & 0 & -1 \end{pmatrix} \tag{2.37}$$

Each one of these three 4 by 4 matrices is a direct product of a unit matrix and a Pauli spin matrix. The fact that the same notation is used for both four- and two-dimensional matrices should cause no confusion since the context will distinguish between them.

It will be noted that all the Dirac matrices can be written as direct products of two 2 by 2 matrices: one of these operating in the "Dirac space" refers to the four areas of the 4 by 4 matrices delineated by dotted lines below:

$$\left(\begin{array}{cc|cc} x & x & x & x \\ x & x & x & x \\ \hline x & x & x & x \\ x & x & x & x \end{array}\right) \tag{*}$$

The other which operates in the "Pauli space" refers to the four elements within each of these four areas. Thus

$$\alpha_i = \rho_1\sigma_i, \qquad \beta = \rho_3 I_2 \tag{2.38a}$$

where

$$\rho_1 = \begin{pmatrix} 0 & 1 \\ 1 & 0 \end{pmatrix}, \qquad \rho_3 = \begin{pmatrix} 1 & 0 \\ 0 & -1 \end{pmatrix} \tag{2.38b}$$

operate in Dirac space. It is to be understood that the direct product is always implied for matrices operating in different spaces. A third matrix operating in Dirac space is evidently

$$\rho_2 = \begin{pmatrix} 0 & -i \\ i & 0 \end{pmatrix} \tag{2.38c}$$

so that 1, ρ_1, ρ_2, ρ_3 form a complete set like 1, σ_1, σ_2, σ_3.

The Dirac matrices which have zero elements in the upper right and lower left quadrants in the 4 by 4 array (*) are called even in the Dirac sense; those with zeroes in the upper left and lower right quadrants are called odd. Evidently matrices which are formed with ρ_1 and ρ_2 are odd and those formed with ρ_3 are even. In a corresponding way the wave function is written in the form

$$\psi = \begin{pmatrix} \psi_1 \\ \psi_2 \\ \psi_3 \\ \psi_4 \end{pmatrix} = \begin{pmatrix} \psi^u \\ \psi^l \end{pmatrix}$$

where u and l refer to "upper" and "lower":

$$\psi^u = \begin{pmatrix} \psi_1 \\ \psi_2 \end{pmatrix}, \qquad \psi^l = \begin{pmatrix} \psi_3 \\ \psi_4 \end{pmatrix}$$

are each two-component spinors. Then, for example,

$$\rho_2\psi = \begin{pmatrix} -i\psi^l \\ i\psi^u \end{pmatrix}$$

while

$$\boldsymbol{\alpha}\psi = \rho_1\boldsymbol{\sigma}\psi = \begin{pmatrix} \boldsymbol{\sigma}\psi^l \\ \boldsymbol{\sigma}\psi^u \end{pmatrix}$$

From these examples it is clear that the matrices operating in the Dirac space act on ψ^u and ψ^l while the matrices operating in Pauli space act on the two components in $\psi^u(\psi_1, \psi_2)$ and in $\psi^l(\psi_3, \psi_4)$. Odd Dirac matrices couple ψ^u and ψ^l while even ones couple ψ^u with ψ^u and ψ^l with ψ^l. The four-component ψ, sometimes referred to as a bispinor, will here be called a spinor (or four-spinor). This nomenclature is justified since the four-component functions transform under rotations in exactly the same way as the Pauli spinors; see section 19.

12. SPIN AND CONSTANTS OF THE MOTION

From the form (2.3) of the equation of motion it follows for any operator Ω that†

$$\frac{d\Omega}{dt} = \frac{i}{\hbar}(H\Omega - \Omega H) = \frac{i}{\hbar}(H, \Omega) \tag{2.39}$$

From the interpretation of ψ provided by the density ρ as given in (2.14) one must calculate expectation values according to

$$\langle\Omega\rangle = \int d^3x\, \psi^* \Omega \psi \tag{2.40}$$

Hence it follows that the time derivative of the expectation value is the expectation value of the time derivative.

$$\left\langle \frac{d\Omega}{dt} \right\rangle = \frac{d}{dt}\langle\Omega\rangle \tag{2.41}$$

This forms the basis of the connection with the realm of classical physics via the correspondence principle.

For our present purpose it is more pertinent to recognize that by (2.39) constants of the motion exist for a set of commuting operators if and only if they commute with H. In connection with the angular momentum of the electron we first calculate the commutator of $l_j = -i(\mathbf{r} \times \nabla)_j$ with H. Only the kinetic energy term $c\boldsymbol{\alpha}\cdot\vec{\mathbf{p}}$ is relevant since β commutes with l_j. We find

$$(l_1, \boldsymbol{\alpha}\cdot\vec{\mathbf{p}}) = \alpha_2(l_1, \vec{p}_2) + \alpha_3(l_1, \vec{p}_3) = i(\alpha_2\vec{p}_3 - \alpha_3\vec{p}_2)$$

or

$$(\mathbf{l}, \boldsymbol{\alpha}\cdot\vec{\mathbf{p}}) = i(\boldsymbol{\alpha} \times \vec{\mathbf{p}}) \neq 0 \tag{2.42}$$

For the commutator with the square of the orbital angular momentum $\mathbf{l}^2$ we use (1.50) and obtain

$$(\mathbf{l}^2, \boldsymbol{\alpha}\cdot\vec{\mathbf{p}}) = -i\{\alpha_1[(l_2, \vec{p}_3)_+ - (l_3, \vec{p}_2)_+] + \alpha_2[(l_3, \vec{p}_1)_+ - (l_1, \vec{p}_3)_+] \\ + \alpha_3[(l_1, \vec{p}_2)_+ - (l_2, \vec{p}_1)_+]\} \tag{2.43}$$

† Time-dependent operators are discussed in Appendix C.

Here we use a subscript + to designate the anticommutator:

$$(A, B)_+ = AB + BA$$

It will be seen that none of the quantities in square brackets in (2.43) vanishes. For example,

$$\begin{aligned}(l_3, \vec{p}_1)_+ - (l_1, \vec{p}_3)_+ &= -i\vec{p}_2 + 2l_3\vec{p}_1 - (i\vec{p}_2 + 2l_1\vec{p}_3) \\ &= -2i\vec{p}_2 + 2(\mathbf{l} \times \vec{\mathbf{p}})_2 \\ &= -2i\vec{p}_2 + \frac{1}{\hbar}(\mathbf{r}\cdot\vec{\mathbf{p}}\,\vec{p}_2 - r_2\vec{\mathbf{p}}^2) \neq 0\end{aligned}$$

The condition that (2.43) vanishes is that the coefficient of each α_i vanishes. It follows that the orbital angular momentum is not a constant of the motion. On the other hand, we expect the total angular momentum to be a constant of the motion since no direction in space is preferred. We identify the vector operator for the total angular momentum as†

$$\mathbf{j} = \mathbf{l} + \tfrac{1}{2}\boldsymbol{\sigma} \tag{2.44}$$

where $\boldsymbol{\sigma}$ is the 4 by 4 matrix vector. This will certainly give the Pauli result when the non-relativistic limit is taken. The commutator of j_1 with H is $c(j_1, \boldsymbol{\alpha}\cdot\vec{\mathbf{p}})$ since all components of $\boldsymbol{\sigma}$ commute with β in the standard representation and therefore in all representations. Thus

$$(j_1, \boldsymbol{\alpha}\cdot\vec{\mathbf{p}}) = (l_1, \boldsymbol{\alpha}\cdot\vec{\mathbf{p}}) + \tfrac{1}{2}(\sigma_1, \boldsymbol{\alpha}\cdot\vec{\mathbf{p}})$$

Using

$$\boldsymbol{\sigma} = -\gamma_5\boldsymbol{\alpha} = -\boldsymbol{\alpha}\gamma_5 \tag{2.45a}$$

or

$$\boldsymbol{\alpha} = -\gamma_5\boldsymbol{\sigma} = -\boldsymbol{\sigma}\gamma_5 \tag{2.45b}$$

we find

$$\tfrac{1}{2}(\sigma_1, \boldsymbol{\alpha}\cdot\vec{\mathbf{p}}) = i(\vec{p}_2\alpha_3 - \vec{p}_3\alpha_2)$$

and two similar equations obtained by cyclic permutation of the indices. From (2.42) it follows that

$$(\mathbf{j}, \boldsymbol{\alpha}\cdot\vec{\mathbf{p}}) = 0 \tag{2.46}$$

Therefore $\mathbf{j}^2$ and any component of $\mathbf{j}$, say j_3, may be made diagonal simultaneously with the energy H.

As a result of the foregoing consideration we must identify $\frac{1}{2}\boldsymbol{\sigma} \equiv \mathbf{s}$ as the spin operator in the relativistic theory. Obviously $\mathbf{s}^2$ is diagonal with eigenvalue $s(s + 1) = \frac{3}{4}$ or $s = \frac{1}{2}$. This interpretation of the spin is therefore in agreement with the empirical results.

† The context should clearly distinguish between the symbol **j** used as the total angular momentum operator and as the Dirac current density.

Since $\mathbf{j}^2$ and $\mathbf{s}^2$ commute with H while $\mathbf{l}^2$ does not, it follows that the spin-orbit coupling operator $\mathbf{s}\cdot\mathbf{l} = \frac{1}{2}\boldsymbol{\sigma}\cdot\mathbf{l}$ also does not commute with H. However, there is an operator related to $\boldsymbol{\sigma}\cdot\mathbf{l}$ which is precisely the relativistic analogue of (1.65), which does commute with H and with each component of $\mathbf{j}$. This is the operator

$$K = \beta(\boldsymbol{\sigma}\cdot\mathbf{l} + 1) \tag{2.47}$$

Obviously K commutes with β. Therefore, for the commutator with H, consider

$$(\beta\,\boldsymbol{\sigma}\cdot\mathbf{l}, \boldsymbol{\alpha}\cdot\vec{\mathbf{p}}) + (\beta, \boldsymbol{\alpha}\cdot\vec{\mathbf{p}}) = (\beta\,\boldsymbol{\sigma}\cdot\mathbf{l}, \boldsymbol{\alpha}\cdot\vec{\mathbf{p}}) + 2\beta\,\boldsymbol{\alpha}\cdot\vec{\mathbf{p}}$$

But

$$(\beta\,\boldsymbol{\sigma}\cdot\mathbf{l}, \boldsymbol{\alpha}\cdot\vec{\mathbf{p}}) = \beta(\boldsymbol{\sigma}\cdot\mathbf{l}, \boldsymbol{\alpha}\cdot\vec{\mathbf{p}})_+$$

To evaluate this we note that the extension of (1.26) to the 4 by 4 $\boldsymbol{\sigma}$-matrices is immediate. That is,

$$\boldsymbol{\sigma}\cdot\mathbf{A}\,\boldsymbol{\sigma}\cdot\mathbf{B} = \mathbf{A}\cdot\mathbf{B} + i\boldsymbol{\sigma}\cdot\mathbf{A}\times\mathbf{B} \tag{2.48}$$

This relation will be used very frequently in the sequel. Multiplying by $-\gamma_5$ we get

$$\boldsymbol{\alpha}\cdot\mathbf{A}\,\boldsymbol{\sigma}\cdot\mathbf{B} = \boldsymbol{\sigma}\cdot\mathbf{A}\,\boldsymbol{\alpha}\cdot\mathbf{B} = -\gamma_5\mathbf{A}\cdot\mathbf{B} + i\boldsymbol{\alpha}\cdot(\mathbf{A}\times\mathbf{B}) \tag{2.48$'$}$$

For completeness we record the important result

$$\boldsymbol{\alpha}\cdot\mathbf{A}\,\boldsymbol{\alpha}\cdot\mathbf{B} = \boldsymbol{\sigma}\cdot\mathbf{A}\,\boldsymbol{\sigma}\cdot\mathbf{B} \tag{2.48$''$}$$

Therefore, from (2.48′),

$$(\boldsymbol{\sigma}\cdot\mathbf{l}, \boldsymbol{\alpha}\cdot\vec{\mathbf{p}})_+ = -\gamma_5[\mathbf{l}\cdot\vec{\mathbf{p}} + \vec{\mathbf{p}}\cdot\mathbf{l} + i\,\boldsymbol{\sigma}\cdot(\mathbf{l}\times\vec{\mathbf{p}} + \vec{\mathbf{p}}\times\mathbf{l})]$$

But $\mathbf{l}\cdot\vec{\mathbf{p}} = \vec{\mathbf{p}}\cdot\mathbf{l} = 0$ and

$$\hbar\,\mathbf{l}\times\vec{\mathbf{p}} = -\mathbf{r}\vec{p}^2 + (\mathbf{r}\cdot\vec{\mathbf{p}})\vec{\mathbf{p}}$$

while

$$\hbar\,\vec{\mathbf{p}}\times\mathbf{l} = \mathbf{r}\vec{p}^2 - (\vec{\mathbf{p}}\cdot\mathbf{r})\vec{\mathbf{p}} - i\hbar\vec{\mathbf{p}}$$

Then we get

$$\mathbf{l}\times\vec{\mathbf{p}} + \vec{\mathbf{p}}\times\mathbf{l} = 2i\vec{\mathbf{p}}$$

and

$$(K, \boldsymbol{\alpha}\cdot\vec{\mathbf{p}}) = 2\beta\,\boldsymbol{\alpha}\cdot\vec{\mathbf{p}} + 2\beta\gamma_5\,\boldsymbol{\sigma}\cdot\vec{\mathbf{p}} = 0 \tag{2.49}$$

The commutator of K and $\mathbf{j}$ is obtained in a similar way. Again β commutes with $\mathbf{j}$ and we need only consider

$$(\beta\,\boldsymbol{\sigma}\cdot\mathbf{l}, \mathbf{l} + \tfrac{1}{2}\boldsymbol{\sigma}) = \beta(\boldsymbol{\sigma}\cdot\mathbf{l}, \mathbf{l}) + \tfrac{1}{2}\beta(\boldsymbol{\sigma}\cdot\mathbf{l}, \boldsymbol{\sigma})$$

From (2.48) we obtain

$$(\boldsymbol{\sigma}\cdot\mathbf{l}, \boldsymbol{\sigma}) = 2i\boldsymbol{\sigma}\times\mathbf{l}$$

From $\mathbf{l}\times\mathbf{l} = i\mathbf{l}$ the first term is

$$\beta(\boldsymbol{\sigma}\cdot\mathbf{l}, \mathbf{l}) = -i\beta(\boldsymbol{\sigma}\times\mathbf{l})$$

Hence

$$(K, \mathbf{j}) = 0 \tag{2.50}$$

The connection between K^2 and $\mathbf{j}^2$ is revealed by

$$K^2 = (\boldsymbol{\sigma}\cdot\mathbf{l} + 1)^2 = \mathbf{l}^2 + i\boldsymbol{\sigma}\cdot\mathbf{l} \times \mathbf{l} + 2\boldsymbol{\sigma}\cdot\mathbf{l} + 1$$
$$= \mathbf{l}^2 + \boldsymbol{\sigma}\cdot\mathbf{l} + 1 = j^2 + \tfrac{1}{4}$$

Therefore the eigenvalue κ^2 of K^2 is $(\mathbf{j} + \frac{1}{2})^2$ or

$$\kappa = \pm(j + \tfrac{1}{2})$$

just as in (1.62). More will be said about K in sections 26 and 42.

The Hamiltonian $H = c(\boldsymbol{\alpha}\cdot\vec{\mathbf{p}} + \beta mc)$ does not commute with the operation of space inversion $\mathbf{r} \rightarrow -\mathbf{r}$. The term $\boldsymbol{\alpha}\cdot\vec{\mathbf{p}}$ is odd under inversion, while β is even. Hence the operator β times space inversion does commute with H. This will be called the parity operator and will be denoted by βI_s. Since $\mathbf{j}$ and K contain axial vector operators which commute with β, it follows that the parity operator commutes with H, $\mathbf{j}$, K. It is seen that K gives the eigenvalue of $\mathbf{j}^2$, and in section 26 it will be seen that it also gives the eigenvalue of the parity operator in the angular momentum representation. This situation is therefore reminiscent of what was seen to apply in the Pauli theory. The problem of space inversion will be discussed at greater length in section 25.

There is another very obvious and very important representation. This is the plane wave representation in which the set of commuting operators is H and $\vec{\mathbf{p}} = -i\hbar\nabla$. Because the eigenvalues of $\vec{\mathbf{p}}$ constitute the vector momentum, the relativistic plane wave of fixed energy W is

$$\psi(\mathbf{r}, t) = u(\mathbf{p}) \exp\left[\frac{i}{\hbar}(\mathbf{p}\cdot\mathbf{r} - Wt)\right] \tag{2.51}$$

In Chapter III, where the plane wave solutions are studied in greater detail, it will be seen that there is another operator (there called $\mathcal{O}$) connected with the spin (analogous to $\boldsymbol{\sigma}$) the component of which in any direction can be made simultaneously diagonal with H and $\vec{\mathbf{p}}$.

Of course, $\vec{\mathbf{p}}$ does not commute with K or $I_s\beta$. Therefore the two representations described are alternative ones and they are connected by a linear transformation; see section 27.

13. THE FUNDAMENTAL THEOREM OF PAULI[4,6]

In what follows, extensive use is made of the fundamental theorem of Pauli. The content of the theorem is: If two sets of matrices γ_μ and γ'_μ ($\mu = 1, 2, 3, 4$) obey the commutation rules

$$\gamma_\mu\gamma_\nu + \gamma_\nu\gamma_\mu = 2\delta_{\mu\nu}; \qquad \gamma'_\mu\gamma'_\nu + \gamma'_\nu\gamma'_\mu = 2\delta_{\mu\nu}$$

then there must exist a non-singular matrix S which connects the two sets according to

$$\gamma'_\mu S = S\gamma_\mu$$

From each set γ_μ and γ'_μ we can build a set of 16 matrices in a parallel way. Typical members of sets are called γ_A and γ'_A respectively.† The theorem also implies that

$$\gamma'_A S = S\gamma_A \tag{2.52}$$

for each A.

It is first shown that (2.52) is valid if one makes the choice

$$S = \sum_{B=1}^{16} \gamma'_B F \gamma_B \tag{2.52'}$$

where F is arbitrary. Then

$$\gamma'_A S \gamma_A = \sum_{B=1}^{16} \gamma'_A \gamma'_B F \gamma_B \gamma_A \tag{2.52''}$$

Each product $\gamma_A\gamma_B$ is, within a factor ± 1 or $\pm i$, equal to some other member of the set, say γ_C. Thus

$$\gamma_B\gamma_A = \lambda_C\gamma_C \tag{2.53a}$$

where $\lambda_C = \pm 1$ or $\pm i$. For each A as B ranges from 1 to 16, the γ_C which result constitute the complete set of 16 four by four Dirac matrices. To see this, we assume the contrary. That is, let

$$\gamma_B\gamma_A = \lambda_C\gamma_C$$

and

$$\gamma_D\gamma_A = \rho_D\gamma_C, \qquad B \neq D$$

so that one particular matrix γ_C occurs at least twice. Then

$$\gamma_B = \lambda_C\gamma_C\gamma_A = (\lambda_C/\rho_D)\gamma_D$$

This is contrary to the proven linear independence of the 16 γ-matrices and so is impossible.

From (2.53a) it follows that

$$\gamma'_B\gamma'_A = \lambda_C\gamma'_C \tag{2.53b}$$

since the rules for forming all the γ'-matrices from γ'_μ are exactly the same as those for forming the γ-matrices from γ_μ, and the commutation rules are the same for both sets. From (2.53b) we find

$$\gamma'_A\gamma'_B = \lambda_C^{-1}\gamma'_C$$

† The previous statement implies that a one-to-one correspondence between members of the two sets exists such that for $\gamma_A\gamma_B = \gamma_C$ there corresponds the relation $\gamma'_A\gamma'_B = \gamma'_C$.

by taking the inverse. Introducing (2.53a) and (2.53b) into (2.52″), we find

$$\gamma'_A S \gamma_A = \sum_{C=1}^{16} \lambda_C^{-1} \gamma'_C F \lambda_C \gamma_C$$

$$= \sum_{C=1}^{16} \gamma'_C F \gamma_C = S$$

By multiplying on the right by γ_A we obtain (2.52).

It now remains to be shown that F can be chosen so that S^{-1} exists. To do this it is necessary to show first that F can be chosen so that $S \neq 0$. If S were exactly a null matrix for all F, we could choose F to be a matrix with only one element different from zero:

$$F_{\mu\nu} = \delta_{\mu\mu_0} \delta_{\nu\nu_0}$$

where μ_0, ν_0 are an arbitrary index pair. Then $S = 0$ implies that

$$\sum_{B=1}^{16} (\gamma'_B)_{\lambda\mu_0} (\gamma_B)_{\nu_0\sigma} = 0$$

Since this would follow for all ν_0 and σ, each element of the matrix

$$\sum_{B=1}^{16} (\gamma'_B)_{\lambda\mu_0} \gamma_B$$

would vanish. This again contradicts the linear independence of the γ_B. Hence there must be some F for which $S \neq 0$.

To demonstrate the existence of S^{-1} it is shown that a non-zero matrix $\bar{S}$ exists such that $\bar{S}S = k$, where k is a multiple of the unit matrix. Consider

$$\bar{S} = \sum_{B=1}^{16} \gamma_B G \gamma'_B \tag{2.54}$$

where G is, for the moment, arbitrary. This is constructed in a way similar to (2.52′) except for the interchange of γ_B and γ'_B. From precisely the same argument as led to (2.52) from (2.52′) we deduce that

$$\gamma_A \bar{S} = \bar{S} \gamma'_A \tag{2.55}$$

This equation with (2.52) gives

$$\gamma_A \bar{S} S = \bar{S} \gamma'_A S = \bar{S} S \gamma_A$$

Since $\bar{S}S$ commutes with all γ_A it is a multiple of a unit matrix by statement 5 of section 11. Thus

$$\bar{S} S = k \tag{2.56}$$

Now G can be chosen so that $\bar{S} \neq 0$ just as was done for S. Also F can be chosen so that $k \neq 0$ since the assumption that $k = 0$ for all F leads to

$$\sum_{B=1}^{16} \bar{S}\gamma'_B F \gamma_B = 0$$

by (2.56) and (2.52′). Again, if the choice $F_{\mu\nu} = \delta_{\mu\mu_0}\delta_{\nu\nu_0}$ is made, one obtains

$$\sum_{B=1}^{16} (\bar{S}\gamma'_B)_{\lambda\mu_0}\gamma_B = 0$$

But this is impossible in view of the linear independence of the γ_B and the fact that at least one coefficient in the sum above does not vanish: $\bar{S} \neq 0$ and γ'_B includes the unit matrix. Thus $k \neq 0$ is possible for some F. Also, from (2.56),

$$\det \bar{S} \det S \neq 0$$

and S^{-1} therefore exists. From (2.52) it follows that

$$\gamma'_A = S\gamma_A S^{-1} \tag{2.57}$$

as was stated originally.

It can be further demonstrated that S is determined to within a numerical factor by the two sets γ_μ and γ'_μ. If there were two matrices S_1 and S_2 for which

$$\gamma'_\mu = S_1\gamma_\mu S_1^{-1}$$
$$\gamma'_\mu = S_2\gamma_\mu S_2^{-1}$$

then

$$S_1\gamma_\mu S_1^{-1} = S_2\gamma_\mu S_2^{-1}$$

or

$$S_2^{-1}S_1\gamma_\mu = \gamma_\mu S_2^{-1}S_1$$

Thus $S_2^{-1}S_1$ commutes with the entire set of 16 matrices and is a multiple of a unit matrix: $S_2 = kS_1$ follows at once. It is customary to choose the arbitrary multiplicative factor so that $\det S = 1$. Then S is unique except for a factor of modulus unity: explicitly, ± 1 or $\pm i$.

14. LORENTZ TRANSFORMATIONS AND RELATIVISTIC COVARIANCE

In this section we shall consider the Lorentz transformations as they affect the equations of motion. Our explicit considerations are for the moment restricted to the proper continuous group of transformations, since the improper transformations are best studied in conjunction with other considerations which are taken up in section 25. In this connection it should be realized that covariance under the discontinuous transformation does not have quite so strong a basis of experimental justification as do the continuous transformations. It will also appear subsequently that the discussion of the present section is fully applicable to an electron in an electromagnetic field.

As outlined in Appendix B, the Lorentz transformation is defined by a matrix a which connects the space-time variables in two reference systems (primed and unprimed):

$$x'_\mu = a_{\mu\nu} x_\nu \tag{2.58}$$

and invariance of $x_\mu x_\mu$ implies that a is an orthogonal matrix

$$a_{\mu\nu} a_{\mu\lambda} = \delta_{\nu\lambda}, \qquad a_{\mu\nu} a_{\rho\nu} = \delta_{\mu\rho} \tag{2.59}$$

or

$$\tilde{a} = a^{-1} \quad \text{and} \quad \det a = \pm 1$$

For transformations continuous with the identity $\det a = 1$. Since the x_k are real and x_4 is pure imaginary and the same is true in the primed system, it follows that a_{jk}, ia_{4j}, ia_{j4}, and a_{44} are real. For continuous transformations as well as for space reflection $a_{44} \geqslant 0$. In the first case, since $\Sigma_\mu (a_{\mu 4})^2 = 1$, it is seen that $a_{44} \geqslant 1$ for space-time rotations.

Covariance of the Equations of Motion

We now consider equations (2.24) and (2.29) and investigate the conditions under which relativistic covariance under proper Lorentz transformations obtains. That is, if (2.24) and (2.29) apply in the unprimed system, then it is necessary that $\psi'(x')$ and $\bar{\psi}'(x')$ exist such that

$$\left(\gamma_\mu \frac{\partial}{\partial x'_\mu} + k_0\right) \psi(x') = 0 \tag{2.24''}$$

and

$$\frac{\partial \bar{\psi}'}{\partial x'_\mu} \gamma_\mu - k_0 \bar{\psi}'(x') = 0 \tag{2.29'}$$

We do not alter the γ_μ because these matrices are simply a device for writing four equations for the components of ψ as a single matrix equation (2.24). In the same way they permit the four complex conjugate equations to be written in the compact form (2.29). If these four equations in the components of ψ are written in detailed or expanded form in the unprimed system, the corresponding equations in the primed system, if Lorentz covariance is to obtain, are realized by priming each component of ψ and by replacing x_μ by x'_μ in both $\partial/\partial x_\mu$ and in the argument of the wave function. Then (2.24″) and (2.29′) are the compact form of such equations with same γ_μ as in the system of unprimed equations.

For $a_{44} \geqslant 0$ we write

$$\psi'(x') = \Lambda\psi(x) \tag{2.60}$$

where, it is assumed, Λ does not contain the coordinates. It is also assumed, subject to verification, that the inverse Λ^{-1} exists. Starting with (2.24″) we obtain

$$\gamma_\mu a_{\mu\nu} \frac{\partial}{\partial x_\nu} \Lambda\psi + k_0\Lambda\psi = 0 \tag{2.24‴}$$

where we have used

$$\frac{\partial}{\partial x'_\mu} = \frac{\partial x_\nu}{\partial x'_\mu}\frac{\partial}{\partial x_\nu} = a^{-1}_{\nu\mu}\frac{\partial}{\partial x_\nu} = a_{\mu\nu}\frac{\partial}{\partial x_\nu}$$

That is, the four-gradient is a polar four-vector.

If we multiply (2.24‴) by Λ^{-1} on the left it becomes the same as (2.24) provided that

$$\Lambda^{-1}\gamma_\mu a_{\mu\nu}\Lambda = \gamma_\nu \tag{2.60a}$$

Using (2.59), we may write this alternatively in the form

$$\Lambda^{-1}\gamma_\mu\Lambda = a_{\mu\nu}\gamma_\nu \tag{2.60b}$$

The existence of a Λ which satisfies this condition is apparent from the following. Let

$$\gamma'_\mu = a_{\mu\nu}\gamma_\nu$$

Then

$$\begin{aligned}\gamma'_\mu\gamma'_\lambda + \gamma'_\lambda\gamma'_\mu &= a_{\mu\nu}a_{\lambda\rho}\gamma_\nu\gamma_\rho + a_{\lambda\rho}a_{\mu\nu}\gamma_\rho\gamma_\nu \\ &= 2a_{\mu\nu}a_{\lambda\rho}\delta_{\nu\rho} = 2a_{\mu\rho}a_{\lambda\rho} \\ &= 2\delta_{\mu\lambda}\end{aligned}$$

Therefore by Pauli's fundamental theorem there exists an S such that $S\gamma_\mu S^{-1} = \gamma'_\mu$. By comparison with (2.60b) it is clear that $\Lambda = S^{-1}$ within a multiplicative factor. Since the $a_{\mu\nu}$ are not all real, the γ'_μ defined above need not be hermitian. Hence Λ (also S^{-1} and therefore S in this case) will not be unitary in general.

Turning to the transformation of the adjoint equation, we write

$$\begin{aligned}\bar{\psi}'(x') &= \psi'^*(x')\gamma_4 \\ &= \psi^*(x)\Lambda^*\gamma_4 \\ &= \bar{\psi}(x)\gamma_4\Lambda^*\gamma_4\end{aligned} \tag{2.61}$$

The operator $\gamma_4\Lambda^*\gamma_4$ can be related to Λ^{-1} as follows. Writing (2.60b) for the two cases $\mu = j = 1, 2, 3$ and $\mu = 4$, we have

$$a_{jk}\gamma_k + a_{j4}\gamma_4 = \Lambda^{-1}\gamma_j\Lambda$$

$$a_{4k}\gamma_k + a_{44}\gamma_4 = \Lambda^{-1}\gamma_4\Lambda$$

Taking the hermitian conjugate of these equations results in

$$a_{jk}\gamma_k - a_{j4}\gamma_4 = \Lambda^*\gamma_j\Lambda^{-1*}$$

$$-a_{4k}\gamma_k + a_{44}\gamma_4 = \Lambda^*\gamma_4\Lambda^{-1*}$$

These can be combined into

$$a_{\mu\rho}\gamma_4\gamma_\rho\gamma_4 = \Lambda^*\gamma_4\gamma_\mu\gamma_4\Lambda^{-1*}$$

as is verified by setting $\mu = j$ and $\mu = 4$. Then we multiply (2.60b) on the left and right by γ_4 and substitute in the above to obtain

$$\gamma_4\Lambda^{-1}\gamma_\mu\Lambda\gamma_4 = \Lambda^*\gamma_4\gamma_\mu\gamma_4\Lambda^{-1*}$$

By multiplying by $\Lambda\gamma_4$ on the left and by $\Lambda^*\gamma_4$ on the right, the result is

$$\gamma_\mu\Lambda\gamma_4\Lambda^*\gamma_4 = \Lambda\gamma_4\Lambda^*\gamma_4\gamma_\mu$$

Therefore $\Lambda\gamma_4\Lambda^*\gamma_4$ commutes with all γ_μ and is a multiple of 1.

$$\Lambda\gamma_4\Lambda^*\gamma_4 = k \tag{2.62}$$

By taking the hermitian conjugate of this equation we find

$$\gamma_4\Lambda\gamma_4\Lambda^* = k^\times$$

and multiplying by γ_4 on right and left results in

$$\Lambda\gamma_4\Lambda^*\gamma_4 = k^\times$$

Therefore $k = k^\times$ and k is real. Since (2.60) does not fix a multiplicative factor in Λ, k can be chosen to have modulus unity. Later we show that k has the same sign as a_{44} so that in the present case $k = 1$. This result can be very easily established by noting that Λ is a function of a set of parameters defining the rotation in the space-time continuum. One of these parameters is θ the angle of rotation, real for space rotations and pure imaginary for space-time rotations. Examples are given in Eqs. (2.69) and (2.71) below. As θ varies in a continuous way, k cannot change discontinuously, and for $\theta = 0$, $\Lambda = 1$ and from (2.62) we deduce that $k = 1$. Then, from (2.61),

$$\bar{\psi}(x') = \bar{\psi}(x)\Lambda^{-1} \tag{2.63}$$

From (2.62) with $k = \pm 1$ it follows that

$$|\det \Lambda|^2 = 1$$

The transformation of (2.29′) into (2.29) is now achieved by the condition

$$a_{\mu\nu}\Lambda^{-1}\gamma_\mu\Lambda = \gamma_\nu$$

which is identical with (2.60a).

The Transformation Matrix

To determine Λ for particular continuous transformations we consider first an infinitesimal transformation

$$x'_\mu = x_\mu + \epsilon_{\mu\nu}x_\nu$$

or

$$a_{\mu\nu} = \delta_{\mu\nu} + \epsilon_{\mu\nu}$$

The orthogonal character of the transformation means that to first order

$$a\tilde{a} = 1 + \epsilon + \tilde{\epsilon} = 1$$

so that ϵ is an antisymmetric matrix: $\epsilon_{\mu\nu} = -\epsilon_{\nu\mu}$. The Λ matrix which is determined by the $a_{\mu\nu}$ or $\epsilon_{\mu\nu}$ is now of the form

$$\Lambda = 1 + \tfrac{1}{2}\epsilon_{\mu\nu}T^{\mu\nu} \tag{2.64}$$

where $T^{\mu\nu}$ constitutes a set of matrices one for each pair of indices μ, ν and $T^{\mu\nu} = -T^{\nu\mu}$. The inverse of Λ is

$$\Lambda^{-1} = 1 - \tfrac{1}{2}\epsilon_{\mu\nu}T^{\mu\nu} \tag{2.65}$$

Inserting (2.64) and (2.65) in (2.60b) gives

$$(1 - \tfrac{1}{2}\epsilon_{\rho\nu}T^{\rho\nu})\gamma_\mu(1 + \tfrac{1}{2}\epsilon_{\lambda\tau}T^{\lambda\tau}) = \gamma_\mu + \epsilon_{\mu\nu}\gamma_\nu$$

Neglecting, as usual, the term of second order in ϵ, we find

$$\epsilon_{\lambda\nu}(\gamma_\mu T^{\lambda\nu} - T^{\lambda\nu}\gamma_\mu) = \epsilon_{\lambda\nu}(\gamma_\nu\delta_{\mu\lambda} - \gamma_\lambda\delta_{\nu\mu})$$

or

$$(\gamma_\mu, T^{\lambda\nu}) = \gamma_\nu\delta_{\mu\lambda} - \gamma_\lambda\delta_{\nu\mu} \tag{2.66}$$

A solution sufficiently general for our purpose is

$$T^{\lambda\nu} = \tfrac{1}{2}\gamma_\lambda\gamma_\nu \qquad (\lambda \neq \nu) \tag{2.67}$$

For $\lambda = \nu$ Eq. (2.66) is trivially valid. For $\lambda \neq \mu \neq \nu \neq \lambda$ both sides of the equation vanish with the solution (2.67) since γ_μ commutes with $T^{\lambda\nu}$ in that case. Finally, it is easily verified that, if $\mu = \nu \neq \lambda$ or $\mu = \lambda \neq \nu$, an identity is obtained.

We now write

$$\begin{aligned}\psi'(x') - \psi(x) = \delta\psi &= (\Lambda - 1)\psi \\ &= \tfrac{1}{2}\epsilon_{\mu\nu}T^{\mu\nu}\psi\end{aligned}$$

For a finite transformation, $\psi' = \Lambda\psi$ results with

$$\Lambda = \exp\left(\tfrac{1}{4}\epsilon_{\mu\nu}\gamma_\mu\gamma_\nu\right)$$

Example 1. Consider a rotation around the x_3-axis through an angle θ. Then

$$a = \begin{pmatrix} \cos\theta & \sin\theta & 0 & 0 \\ -\sin\theta & \cos\theta & 0 & 0 \\ 0 & 0 & 1 & 0 \\ 0 & 0 & 0 & 1 \end{pmatrix} \tag{2.68}$$

and, for an infinitesimal transformation $\theta \ll 1$,

$$\epsilon_{12} = -\epsilon_{21}$$

and all other $\epsilon_{\mu\nu} = 0$. Since $T_{12} = -T_{21} = \frac{1}{2}\gamma_1\gamma_2$, we obtain

$$\Lambda = e^{\frac{1}{2}\gamma_1\gamma_2\theta} = \cos\frac{\theta}{2} + \gamma_1\gamma_2\sin\frac{\theta}{2} \tag{2.69a}$$

$$\Lambda^{-1} = e^{-\frac{1}{2}\gamma_1\gamma_2\theta} = \cos\frac{\theta}{2} - \gamma_1\gamma_2\sin\frac{\theta}{2} \tag{2.69b}$$

The expanded form of the exponential operator follows because

$$(\gamma_1\gamma_2)^{2n} = (-)^n$$

and, of course, $(\gamma_1\gamma_2)^{2n+1} = (-)^n\gamma_1\gamma_2$. We check these results by inserting (2.69) into (2.60b) and obtain $\gamma_\nu = a_{\nu\rho}\gamma_\rho$ for $\nu = 3, 4$ and

$$\gamma_1\cos\theta + \gamma_2\sin\theta = a_{1\rho}\gamma_\rho = a_{11}\gamma_1 + a_{12}\gamma_2$$

$$-\gamma_1\sin\theta + \gamma_2\cos\theta = a_{2\rho}\gamma_\rho = a_{21}\gamma_1 + a_{22}\gamma_2$$

from which (2.68) is recovered. It will be noted that

$$\Lambda = \exp\left(\frac{i}{2}\sigma_3\theta\right) \tag{2.69c}$$

In general, for a rotation through an angle θ around the direction $\hat{\mathbf{n}}$,

$$\Lambda = \exp\left(\frac{i}{2}\boldsymbol{\sigma}\cdot\hat{\mathbf{n}}\theta\right) \tag{2.69d}$$

The Λ-matrix is then seen to be identical with the matrix of the Cayley-Klein parameters.[8] On comparison with $D^{1/2}(\varphi, \theta, 0)$ in Eq. (1.35b), it is seen from (2.69d) that $\Lambda = D^{1/2}(0, \theta, 0)$ if and only if $\hat{\mathbf{n}}$ is a unit vector along the y-axis, as expected from the definition of the Euler rotation.

Example 2. Consider a Lorentz transformation corresponding to a uniform motion with velocity v along the x_3-axis. Since this is a rotation in the x_3–x_4 plane, the results are in complete parallel with the first example except that the angle θ is pure imaginary. In fact,

$$\sin\theta = i\frac{v}{c}\xi \qquad \xi = (1 - v^2/c^2)^{-1/2} \qquad \cos\theta = \xi \tag{2.70}$$

and with $\theta = i\omega$

$$\Lambda = e^{\frac{1}{2}\gamma_3\gamma_4\theta} = \cos\frac{\theta}{2} + i\alpha_3\sin\frac{\theta}{2}$$

$$= \cosh\frac{\omega}{2} - \alpha_3\sinh\frac{\omega}{2} \tag{2.71a}$$

$$= \left(\frac{\xi+1}{2}\right)^{1/2} - \alpha_3\left(\frac{\xi-1}{2}\right)^{1/2}$$

$$\Lambda^{-1} = \left(\frac{\xi+1}{2}\right)^{1/2} + \alpha_3\left(\frac{\xi-1}{2}\right)^{1/2}$$

The coordinate transformation obtained is just the familiar one corresponding to uniform motion along the x_3-axis:

$$x_1' = x_1, \qquad x_2' = x_2$$
$$x_3' = \xi(x_3 - vt) \tag{2.72}$$
$$t' = \xi\left(t - \frac{vx_3}{c^2}\right)$$

It is of interest to observe that for $v^2/c^2 \ll 1$, $\Lambda \to 1$ so that $\psi'(x') = \psi(x)$ and (2.72) reduces to the Galilean transformation: $x_\nu' = x_\nu$ $(\nu = 1, 2, 4)$ and $x_3' = x_3 - vt$.

Bilinear Covariants

Under the Lorentz transformation, $f(x) \to f'(x')$. Then the following covariant quantities are of interest and occur in the Dirac theory.

(1) Scalar: $f'(x') = f(x)$

(2) Vector (polar): $f_\mu'(x') = a_{\mu\nu}f_\nu(x)$

(3) Tensor: $f_{\mu\nu}'(x') = a_{\mu\lambda}a_{\nu\sigma}f_{\lambda\sigma}(x)$

(4) Axial or pseudovector: $f_\mu'(x') = (\det a)a_{\mu\nu}f_\nu(x)$

(5) Pseudoscalar: $f'(x') = (\det a)f(x)$

Under proper transformations (det $a = 1$) there is no distinction between (1) and (5) or between (2) and (4).

That only these tensors and pseudotensors of rank 0, 1, and 2 occur is a consequencc of the existence of the five groups into which the 16 Dirac matrices were classified in the discussion of section 11. We proceed to the construction of these five covariant quantities in terms of bilinear combinations of the Dirac wave functions.

Scalar S. From (2.60) and (2.63) it follows that $S(x) \equiv \bar{\psi}(x)\psi(x)$ is a scalar.

$$S'(x') = \bar{\psi}'(x')\,\psi'(x') = \bar{\psi}(x)\Lambda^{-1}\Lambda\,\psi(x) = S(x) \tag{2.73}$$

Vector V. We define four quantities $V_\mu(x)$ by

$$V_\mu(x) = \bar{\psi}(x)\gamma_\mu\,\psi(x) \tag{2.74}$$

Then

$$\begin{aligned} V'_\mu(x') &= \bar{\psi}'(x')\gamma_\mu\,\psi'(x') = \bar{\psi}(x)\Lambda^{-1}\gamma_\mu\Lambda\,\psi(x) \\ &= a_{\mu\nu}\bar{\psi}(x)\gamma_\nu\,\psi(x) = a_{\mu\nu}V_\nu(x) \end{aligned} \tag{2.74$'$}$$

Therefore V_μ are the components of a four-vector which transforms exactly like x_μ. It will be verified that the vector $\mathbf{ij}/c$ and ρ (see Eq. 2.20), is just V_μ. This justifies the reference to s_μ as a four-vector and demonstrates the invariance of the continuity equation.

Tensor T. Again we define a second-rank antisymmetric array by

$$T_{\mu\nu}(x) = i\bar{\psi}(x)\gamma_\mu\gamma_\nu\,\psi(x) \qquad (\mu \neq \nu) \tag{2.75}$$

The transformation of $T_{\mu\nu}$ is

$$\begin{aligned} T'_{\mu\nu}(x') &= i\bar{\psi}'(x')\gamma_\mu\gamma_\nu\,\psi'(x') = i\bar{\psi}(x)\Lambda^{-1}\gamma_\mu\Lambda\Lambda^{-1}\gamma_\nu\Lambda\,\psi(x) \\ &= ia_{\mu\rho}a_{\nu\sigma}\,\bar{\psi}(x)\gamma_\rho\gamma_\sigma\,\psi(x) \\ &= a_{\mu\rho}a_{\nu\sigma}\,T_{\rho\sigma}(x) \end{aligned} \tag{2.75$'$}$$

Note that in the second last line the terms $\rho = \sigma$ do not contribute because $\mu \neq \nu$. Hence $T_{\mu\nu}$ is a four-tensor antisymmetric in the tensor indices.

Axial vector A. This set of four quantities is defined by

$$A_\mu = i\bar{\psi}(x)\gamma_\mu\gamma_5\,\psi(x) \tag{2.76}$$

The transformation law is most easily studied by first evaluating

$$\Lambda^{-1}\gamma_5\Lambda = \Lambda^{-1}\gamma_1\gamma_2\gamma_3\gamma_4\Lambda$$

By introducing $\epsilon_{\alpha\beta\alpha'\beta'}$ an antisymmetrical fourth-rank tensor which vanishes unless all indices are different and is $+1$ (-1) for α, β, α', β', an even (odd) permutation of 1, 2, 3, 4 we can write

$$\gamma_5 = \frac{1}{4!}\,\epsilon_{\alpha\beta\alpha'\beta'}\gamma_\alpha\gamma_\beta\gamma_{\alpha'}\gamma_{\beta'}$$

since each of the 4! terms in the sum is γ_5 by virtue of the fact that with α, β, α', β' all different $\gamma_\alpha\gamma_\beta\gamma_{\alpha'}\gamma_{\beta'} = \pm\gamma_5$ according to whether $\epsilon_{\alpha\beta\alpha'\beta'} = \pm 1$. Hence

$$\begin{aligned}\Lambda^{-1}\gamma_5\Lambda &= \frac{1}{4!}\,\epsilon_{\alpha\beta\alpha'\beta'}(\Lambda^{-1}\gamma_\alpha\Lambda)(\Lambda^{-1}\gamma_\beta\Lambda)(\Lambda^{-1}\gamma_{\alpha'}\Lambda)(\Lambda^{-1}\gamma_{\beta'}\Lambda)\\ &= \frac{1}{4!}\,\epsilon_{\alpha\beta\alpha'\beta'}a_{\alpha\mu}a_{\beta\nu}a_{\alpha'\mu'}a_{\beta'\nu'}\gamma_\mu\gamma_\nu\gamma_{\mu'}\gamma_{\nu'}\\ &= \frac{1}{4!}\,(\det a)\epsilon_{\mu\nu\mu'\nu'}\gamma_\mu\gamma_\nu\gamma_{\mu'}\gamma_{\nu'}\\ &= (\det a)\gamma_5 \end{aligned} \tag{2.77}$$

Returning to A_μ, we now see that

$$A'_\mu(x') = i\bar{\psi}(x)\Lambda^{-1}\gamma_\mu\Lambda\Lambda^{-1}\gamma_5\Lambda\,\psi(x) = (\det a)\,a_{\mu\nu}A_\nu(x)$$

so that A_μ is a pseudo or axial vector.

Finally, the fact that

$$P(x) = \bar{\psi}(x)\gamma_5\,\psi(x) \tag{2.78}$$

is a pseudoscalar is already evident from (2.77). That is,

$$P'(x') = (\det a)\,P(x) \tag{2.78$'$}$$

It is clear that we can generalize the covariants discussed above by replacing $\psi(x)$, but not $\bar{\psi}(x)$, by the wave function of another particle which, however, transforms just as ψ does. If the two particles are referred to by labels a and b then, as an example,

$$\bar{\psi}^a(x)\,\psi^b(x)$$

is a scalar.

These covariant quantities play an important role in the problem of formulating the weak interaction of four fermions.[9–11] When this interaction energy is to be a Lorentz invariant it can evidently be constructed by contracting the tensors of the five groups. Thus if, for example,

$$V_\mu^{ab} = \bar{\psi}^a(x)\gamma_\mu\,\psi^b(x)$$

where a and b are labels of different spin $\frac{1}{2}$ particles, the contraction of two vectors V_μ^{ab}, V_μ^{cd} is evidently a scalar. Similar scalars are constructed from $S^{ab}S^{cd}$, $T_{\mu\nu}^{ab}T_{\mu\nu}^{cd}$, $A_\mu^{ab}A_\mu^{cd}$, and $P^{ab}P^{cd}$.

To facilitate comparison with the form in which these often appear in the literature of nuclear beta decay the covariants are listed below in terms of ψ^* instead of $\bar{\psi}$ and in terms of the $\boldsymbol{\alpha}$, β matrices.

$$\begin{aligned} S &= \psi^*\beta\psi \\ V_4 &= \psi^*\psi, \qquad V_k = -i\psi^*\alpha_k\psi \\ T_{jk} &= -\psi^*\beta\sigma_l\psi, \qquad T_{4k} = \psi^*\beta\alpha_k\psi \\ A_k &= -\psi^*\sigma_k\psi, \qquad A_4 = i\psi^*\gamma_5\psi \\ P &= \psi^*\gamma_4\gamma_5\psi \end{aligned} \tag{2.79}$$

Here j, k, and l are a cyclic permutation of x, y, z or 1, 2, 3. Note that in this form the tensor components appear as $\psi^*\Omega\psi$, where Ω need not be hermitian. Those Ω which are not hermitian are, however, antihermitian (i times a hermitian matrix) and on contraction of the covariants a factor i appears twice. It should also be remarked that in many references a representation in which $\boldsymbol{\alpha}$, β are replaced by $-\boldsymbol{\alpha}$, $-\beta$ appears in the literature. Again, on contraction, this sign difference would not appear.

The notation S, V, T, A, P used above is based on the terminology of the theory of beta decay; see section 21. In this theory it is necessary to work with quantized field operators because particles are created and/or destroyed in the decay process. However, after the formalism of the perturbation theory is carried through, it is possible to evaluate the observable results predicted by the theory in terms of wave functions of the type discussed here.

PROBLEMS

1. Find the transformation matrix S for which

$$\boldsymbol{\alpha}' = S\boldsymbol{\alpha}S^{-1} = -\boldsymbol{\alpha}$$

$$\beta' = S\beta S^{-1} = -\beta$$

Can S be chosen to be unitary? If ψ is a solution of the wave equation in the $\boldsymbol{\alpha}$, β representation and is written in the form

$$\psi = \begin{pmatrix} \psi_1 \\ \psi_2 \\ \psi_3 \\ \psi_4 \end{pmatrix}$$

express ψ'_λ ($\lambda = 1, 2, 3, 4$) in terms of ψ_λ. Compare the four-density ρ and $\mathbf{j}$ calculated by explicit matrix multiplication in the two represenations.

2. Show that if

$$\gamma_\mu\gamma_\nu + \gamma_\nu\gamma_\mu = \gamma'_\nu\gamma'_\mu + \gamma'_\mu\gamma'_\nu = 2\delta_{\mu\nu}$$

and, with all γ_μ hermitian,

$$\gamma'_\mu = S\gamma_\mu S^{-1}$$

S^*S commutes with all γ_μ and SS^* commutes with all γ'_μ. Consequently S^*S and SS^* must both be multiples of a unit matrix, and in particular it is possible to choose $SS^* = 1$.

3. Consider two Lorentz transformations defined by

$$x'_\mu = a_{\mu\nu}x_\nu, \qquad x''_\mu = b_{\mu\nu}x'_\nu$$

with corresponding matrices Λ_a and Λ_b transforming the wave functions. If

$$\Lambda_a\gamma_4\Lambda_a^*\gamma_4 = a_{44}/|a_{44}|$$

$$\Lambda_b\gamma_4\Lambda_b^*\gamma_4 = b_{44}/|b_{44}|$$

show that

$$\Lambda_b\Lambda_a\gamma_4(\Lambda_b\Lambda_a)^*\gamma_4 = (b_{44}/|b_{44}|)\,(a_{44}/|a_{44}|)$$

4. From the conditions of problem 3 show that

$$|\det \Lambda_a|^2 = |\det \Lambda_b|^2 = 1$$

Give an argument to show that for transformations continuous with the identity the only possible value is

$$\det \Lambda = 1$$

5. Show that the tensor covariants discussed in section 14 have the stipulated transformation properties even when they are defined in terms of two types of Dirac particles (for example, electron and mu meson); that is,

$$V_\nu(x) = \bar{\psi}^e(x)\gamma_\nu\,\psi^\mu(x)$$

transforms like a four-vector.

6. Show that the complete contraction of two covariant tensors of the same rank is a Lorentz invariant.

7. Consider a Lorentz transformation for which $a_{4\rho} = a_{\rho4} = \delta_{\rho4}$, as in a space rotation. Show that Λ commutes with γ_4 and that in the representation (2.22) it must have the form

$$\Lambda = \begin{pmatrix} \Lambda_1 & 0 \\ 0 & \Lambda_2 \end{pmatrix}$$

where Λ_1, Λ_2, and 0 are here 2 by 2 matrices. A matrix of this type is called even (Dirac). Write the inverse matrix Λ^{-1} in terms of Λ_1^{-1} and Λ_2^{-1}.

8. Referring to problem 7, carry out a similar investigation of the Lorentz transformation in which $a_{3\rho} = \delta_{3\rho}$. With what matrix does Λ commute in this case? In the representation (2.22) can Λ be an even matrix?

9. A matrix of the form

$$\begin{pmatrix} 0 & A \\ B & 0 \end{pmatrix}$$

where A, B, and 0 are 2 by 2 matrices is called an odd Dirac matrix. Referring to problem 7, show that the product of two odd or two even matrices is even while the product of an odd and an even matrix taken in either order is odd.

10. Consider the matrices

$$P_{\pm} = \tfrac{1}{2}(1 \pm \beta)$$

Write these matrices in the representation (2.22). Show that in any representation

$$\det P_{\pm} = 0$$

Show also that in any representation

$$P_{\pm}^2 = P_{\pm}, \qquad P_+P_- = P_-P_+ = 0, \qquad P_+ + P_- = 1$$

so that P_+ and P_- form a complete set of projection operators. Can you suggest an interpretation of these projection operators?

11. Is it possible to construct a representation of the four γ_μ in which they are all real? Show that it is impossible for all γ_μ to be even in the Dirac sense.

12. Demonstrate that in every representation $\det \gamma_A = 1$ for all 16 Dirac matrices.

13. Prove the relations

$$\gamma_\mu\gamma_5 + \gamma_5\gamma_\mu = 0, \qquad \mu = 1, 2, 3, 4$$

$$\gamma_5^* = \gamma_5, \qquad \gamma_5^2 = 1, \qquad \gamma_5^* = \gamma_5^{-1}$$

Are there any other matrices which anticommute with all four of the γ_μ?

14. Show that the four components A_μ defined by

$$A_\mu(x) = i\bar{\psi}(x)\gamma_\mu\gamma_5\,\psi(x)$$

transform like a third-rank tensor antisymmetric in all index pairs.

15. Show that $\gamma'_\mu = \tilde{\gamma}_\mu$ can always be obtained from γ_μ by

$$\gamma'_\mu = S\gamma_\mu S^{-1}$$

Can S be unitary in this case? If S is unitary explain why S must also be hermitian.

16. A and B are two 4 by 4 matrices which can be written in the form

$$A = \begin{pmatrix} a^{11} & a^{12} \\ a^{21} & a^{22} \end{pmatrix}$$

and similarly for B, where a^{ik} and b^{ik} are all 2 by 2 matrices. Show that $C = AB$ can be written in the form

$$C = \begin{pmatrix} c^{11} & c^{12} \\ c^{21} & c^{22} \end{pmatrix}$$

where the 2 by 2 matrix c^{ik} is given by

$$c^{ik} = \sum_j a^{ij}b^{jk}$$

17. An invariant quadrilinear combination of the wave functions of four different Dirac particles (a, b, c, d) is constructed by contracting the covariant forms as discussed in section 14. Write J_n, $n = 1, 2, 3, 4, 5$ for $S^{ab}S^{cd}$, $V^{ab}\cdot V^{cd}$, $T^{ab}:T^{cd}$, $A^{ab}\cdot A^{cd}$, $P^{ab}P^{cd}$, where the dots indicate the number of indices contracted, Evidently, interchange of particles a and c would also give an invariant quadrilinear form. Call these five invariants L_n. Then show that

$$L_n = A_{nm}J_m$$

where the 5 by 5 matrix A (Fierz matrix)[12] is

$$A = \frac{1}{4}\begin{pmatrix} 1 & 1 & 1 & 1 & 1 \\ 4 & -2 & 0 & 2 & -4 \\ 6 & 0 & -2 & 0 & 6 \\ 4 & 2 & 0 & -2 & -4 \\ 1 & -1 & 1 & -1 & 1 \end{pmatrix}$$

Verify that $A^2 = 1$, as it should. Find the eigenvalues and corresponding eigenvectors of A. The latter are linear combinations of the five J_n which are equal, to within a factor, to the same linear combinations of L_n.

18. Consider a representation which differs from the standard one by interchange of γ_4 and γ_5. Show that in this representation the Dirac equations can be written as two coupled equations involving two-component spinors and that the coupling is broken for zero rest mass.

19. Write each of the 16 Dirac matrices as the direct product of 2 by 2 matrices in Dirac space and Pauli space.

REFERENCES

1. E. Schrödinger, *Ann. Physik* **79,** 489 (1926); O. Klein, *Z. Physik* **37,** 895 (1926); W. Gordon, *Z. Physik* **40,** 117 (1926); V. Fock, *Z. Physik* **38,** 242 (1926); **39,** 226 (1926); J. Kudar, *Ann. Physik* **81,** 632 (1926); Th. deDonder and H. Van Dingen, *Compt. rend.*, July 1926.
2. H. Feshbach and F. Villar, *Revs. Mod. Phys.* **30,** 24 (1958).
3. P. A. M. Dirac, *Proc. Roy. Soc.* (*London*) **A117,** 610 (1928); **A118,** 351 (1928).
4. W. Pauli, *Ann. Inst. Henri Poincaré* **6,** 109 (1936).
5. W. K. Clifford, *Am. J. Math.* **1,** 350 (1878).
6. R. H. Good, Jr., *Revs. Mod. Phys.* **27,** 187 (1955).
7. I. Schur, *Berliner Sitzber.* 406 (1905).
8. H. Goldstein, *Classical Mechanics*, Addison-Wesley, Cambridge, Mass., 1950, p. 116.
9. E. J. Konopinski, *Revs. Mod. Phys.* **15,** 209 (1943).
10. L. Michel and A. Wightman, *Phys. Rev.* **93,** 354 (1954).
11. R. W. King and D. C. Peaslee, *Phys. Rev.* **94,** 1284 (1954).
12. M. Fierz, *Z. Physik* **104,** 553 (1937).

III.

Dirac plane waves

15. THE FOUR PLANE WAVE STATES

The Wave Functions

The eigenfunctions of definite energy have a time dependence

$$i\hbar \frac{\partial \psi}{\partial t} = W\psi \tag{3.1}$$

and are therefore eigenfunctions of H with eigenvalue W. This is the energy including the rest energy. We shall use rational relativistic units wherein $\hbar = m = c = 1$. The rest energy, for example, has the value 1. The time-independent wave equation is then

$$H\psi = (\boldsymbol{\alpha}\cdot\vec{\mathbf{p}} + \beta)\psi = W\psi \tag{3.2}$$

This is valid for the time-dependent or time-independent wave function.

The plane wave states are eigenfunctions of the momentum operator, the eigenvalues p_1, p_2, p_3 constituting the components of the vector momentum $\mathbf{p}$. Note that without the arrow $\mathbf{p}$ is a set of three numbers. We have

$$\vec{\mathbf{p}}\psi = \mathbf{p}\psi \tag{3.3}$$

Hence we write

$$\psi = U(\mathbf{p}) \exp\left[i(\mathbf{p}\cdot\mathbf{r} - Wt)\right] \tag{3.3$'$}$$

where $U(\mathbf{p})$ is a four-component spinor which satisfies the equation

$$hU = (\boldsymbol{\alpha}\cdot\mathbf{p} + \beta)U = WU \tag{3.4}$$

This is the abridged notation for four linear algebraic equations in the components of $U(\mathbf{p})$.

The upper and lower two-component spinors in U are introduced by

$$U = \begin{pmatrix} u \\ v \end{pmatrix} \tag{3.4'}$$

This corresponds to the decomposition of the wave function in Dirac space. Then (3.4) in the representation (2.22) becomes

$$\boldsymbol{\sigma}\cdot\mathbf{p}u = (W + 1)v \tag{3.5a}$$

$$\boldsymbol{\sigma}\cdot\mathbf{p}v = (W - 1)u \tag{3.5b}$$

Eliminating v, we find

$$(\boldsymbol{\sigma}\cdot\mathbf{p})^2 u = p^2 u = (W^2 - 1)u$$

where (1.26) has been used. In the same way, eliminating u would give

$$(\boldsymbol{\sigma}\cdot\mathbf{p})^2 v = p^2 v = (W^2 - 1)v$$

Therefore the four roots of the secular determinant of the eigenvalue problem under consideration are

$$\begin{aligned} W &= p_0 \equiv (p^2 + 1)^{1/2}, &&\text{occurring twice} \\ W &= -p_0 = -(p^2 + 1)^{1/2}, &&\text{occurring twice} \end{aligned} \tag{3.6}$$

Consequently, there are four eigenstates of the energy operator H and these are degenerate in pairs: two with positive energy p_0 and two with negative energy equal to $-p_0$. The significance of this strange result—that eigenstates with negative energies occur—will be discussed in the next section.

Considering first the positive energy solutions, there are, in general, two linearly independent solutions. This fact is not altered by the existence of the two-fold degeneracy. The degeneracy simply means that in the 4 by 4 determinant obtained by writing out the four linear equations corresponding to (3.4) each minor vanishes when the determinant vanishes; that is, when (3.6) is fulfilled. Therefore the general solution is given in terms of two constants $a_{\pm}$:

$$u = \begin{pmatrix} a_+ \\ a_- \end{pmatrix} = a_+\chi^{1/2} + a_-\chi^{-1/2}$$

which is the most general form of a two-component spinor. Alternatively, the positive energy wave functions define a two-dimensional space with the basis

$$U_+ \sim \begin{pmatrix} \chi^{1/2} \\ \dfrac{\boldsymbol{\sigma}\cdot\mathbf{p}}{p_0+1}\,\chi^{1/2} \end{pmatrix}$$

$$U_- \sim \begin{pmatrix} \chi^{-1/2} \\ \dfrac{\boldsymbol{\sigma}\cdot\mathbf{p}}{p_0+1}\,\chi^{-1/2} \end{pmatrix}$$

These are unnormalized. The normalization to one particle per unit volume, that is,

$$\psi^*\psi = 1$$

gives the normalized amplitudes

$$U_\pm = \left(\frac{p_0+1}{2p_0}\right)^{1/2} \begin{pmatrix} \chi^{\pm 1/2} \\ \dfrac{\boldsymbol{\sigma}\cdot\mathbf{p}}{p_0+1}\,\chi^{\pm 1/2} \end{pmatrix} \tag{3.7}$$

This normalization also corresponds to a current density equal to $\mathbf{j} = \mathbf{p}/p_0 = \mathbf{v}$, the *average* velocity. The proof is easily obtained by direct calculation:

$$\mathbf{j} = \psi^*\boldsymbol{\alpha}\psi = U^*\boldsymbol{\alpha}U = \frac{1}{2p_0}[(\chi^m, \boldsymbol{\sigma}\,\boldsymbol{\sigma}\cdot\mathbf{p}\,\chi^m) + (\boldsymbol{\sigma}\cdot\mathbf{p}\,\chi^m, \boldsymbol{\sigma}\chi^m)]$$

$$= \frac{1}{2p_0}[(\chi^m, (\boldsymbol{\sigma}, \boldsymbol{\sigma}\cdot\mathbf{p})_+\,\chi^m)] = \frac{2\mathbf{p}}{2p_0}(\chi^m, \chi^m) = \frac{\mathbf{p}}{p_0} \tag{3.8}$$

In (3.8) we have used the hermitian property of $\boldsymbol{\sigma}\cdot\mathbf{p}$. Obviously, other normalizations are possible. For normalization to unit current the wave functions are obtained from (3.7) by multiplication by $v^{-1/2}$. Normalization per unit energy range requires multiplication of (3.7) by the square root of ρ_E, the density of states per unit range of E:

$$\rho_E = \frac{4\pi p p_0}{(2\pi)^3} = \frac{p p_0}{2\pi^2}$$

The Spin Operator

In order to understand the physical significance of the spin in the relativistic theory we first consider the non-relativistic limit. Then $p \ll 1$ and p_0 is replaced by 1. Consequently, from (3.5) we see that in this limit

$u \gg v$. Therefore for positive energy states u is the so-called *large* component, v the *small* component. Then

$$U_\pm \rightarrow U_\pm(0) = \begin{pmatrix} \chi^{\pm 1/2} \\ 0 \end{pmatrix} \tag{3.9}$$

so that we recover the Pauli spin functions. For the non-relativistic wave function $\psi_{nr} = U_\pm(0) \exp [i(\mathbf{p}\cdot\mathbf{r} - p_0 t)]$ it is seen that

$$\beta \psi_{nr} = \psi_{nr}$$

Therefore in this limit β can be replaced by 1, the unit matrix. In the general case the non-relativistic amplitude function, except for a normalization factor, can be obtained from U by application of the projection operator $\frac{1}{2}(1 + \beta)$:

$$\tfrac{1}{2}(1 + \beta)U = \left(\frac{p_0 + 1}{2p_0}\right)^{1/2} U_{nr}$$

It is also seen that odd Dirac matrices couple large with small components while even ones couple large with large and small with small. Consequently, in the non-relativistic limit the large contribution to quantities like $\psi^*\Omega\psi$ come from even Ω operators.

From the result (3.9) it would appear that the two solutions $U_\pm$ and $\psi_\pm$ correspond to two spin orientations. However, unlike the Pauli spin case where σ_z is diagonal, we have

$$\sigma_z U_\pm = \left(\frac{p_0 + 1}{2p_0}\right)^{1/2} \begin{pmatrix} \sigma_z \chi^{\pm 1/2} \\ \dfrac{\sigma_z \,\boldsymbol{\sigma}\cdot\mathbf{p}}{p_0 + 1} \chi^{\pm 1/2} \end{pmatrix}$$

and, while $\sigma_z \chi^{\pm 1/2} = \pm \chi^{\pm 1/2}$, in the small (or lower) component σ_z does not commute with $\boldsymbol{\sigma}\cdot\mathbf{p}$ unless $\mathbf{p}$ is in the z-direction. In that case it is true that σ_z is diagonal: $\sigma_z U_\pm = \pm U_\pm$ for $\mathbf{p} = p_z \hat{\mathbf{e}}_z$. But in general neither ψ nor U is an eigenfunction of σ_z. Since, in the case that $p = p_z$ it is true that $\sigma_z = \boldsymbol{\sigma}\cdot\hat{\mathbf{p}}$, it appears that $\boldsymbol{\sigma}\cdot\mathbf{p}$ is diagonal in this special case. In fact $\boldsymbol{\sigma}\cdot\mathbf{p}$ does commute with the Hamiltonian. However, (3.7) is not an eigenstate of $\boldsymbol{\sigma}\cdot\mathbf{p}$ in general:

$$\boldsymbol{\sigma}\cdot\hat{\mathbf{p}}\, U_\pm = \left(\frac{p_0 + 1}{2p_0}\right)^{1/2} \begin{pmatrix} \boldsymbol{\sigma}\cdot\hat{\mathbf{p}}\, \chi^{\pm 1/2} \\ \dfrac{p}{p_0 + 1} \chi^{\pm 1/2} \end{pmatrix}$$

In fact we observe that for any unit vector $\hat{\mathbf{n}}$

$$(\boldsymbol{\sigma}\cdot\hat{\mathbf{n}}, H) = (\boldsymbol{\sigma}\cdot\hat{\mathbf{n}}, \boldsymbol{\alpha}\cdot\mathbf{p}) = 2i\boldsymbol{\alpha}\cdot\hat{\mathbf{n}} \times \mathbf{p}$$

and the commutator is zero only if $\hat{\mathbf{n}} \times \mathbf{p} = 0$. This implies that there is a linear combination of U_+ and U_- which is an eigenfunction of $\boldsymbol{\sigma}\cdot\mathbf{p}$, and we shall subsequently discuss this in detail. However, we are interested in the interpretation of U_+ or U_- alone. For this purpose we note that

$$(\beta\boldsymbol{\sigma}\cdot\hat{\mathbf{n}}, H) = (\beta\boldsymbol{\sigma}\cdot\hat{\mathbf{n}}, \boldsymbol{\alpha}\cdot\mathbf{p}) = \beta(\boldsymbol{\sigma}\cdot\hat{\mathbf{n}}, \boldsymbol{\alpha}\cdot\mathbf{p})_+$$
$$= -2\beta\gamma_5\hat{\mathbf{n}}\cdot\mathbf{p}$$

and this vanishes if $\hat{\mathbf{n}}\cdot\mathbf{p} = 0$. Therefore, if we introduce two unit vectors $\hat{\mathbf{e}}_1$ and $\hat{\mathbf{e}}_2$ which together with $\hat{\mathbf{p}}$ form a right-handed coordinate system, we can construct an operator†

$$\mathcal{O} = \boldsymbol{\sigma}\cdot\hat{\mathbf{p}}\,\hat{\mathbf{p}} + \beta\boldsymbol{\sigma}\cdot\hat{\mathbf{e}}_1\,\hat{\mathbf{e}}_1 + \beta\boldsymbol{\sigma}\cdot\hat{\mathbf{e}}_2\,\hat{\mathbf{e}}_2 \tag{3.10}$$

and the commutator

$$(\mathcal{O}, H) = 0 \tag{3.11}$$

Of course, the three terms in $\mathcal{O}$ do not commute with each other, so only one of them can be made diagonal. This is the relativistic generalization of the spin operator which was $\boldsymbol{\sigma}$ in the Pauli theory. In the non-relativistic limit

$$\mathcal{O} \to \boldsymbol{\sigma} = \boldsymbol{\sigma}\cdot\hat{\mathbf{p}}\,\hat{\mathbf{p}} + \boldsymbol{\sigma}\cdot\hat{\mathbf{e}}_1\,\hat{\mathbf{e}}_1 + \boldsymbol{\sigma}\cdot\hat{\mathbf{e}}_2\,\hat{\mathbf{e}}_2$$

It will now be shown that the representation (3.7) diagonalizes $\mathcal{O}_z$. The reason for the preference for the z-axis is the choice σ_z diagonal on which (3.7) is based. In the following we note that

$$\hat{\mathbf{p}} \times \hat{\mathbf{e}}_1 = \hat{\mathbf{e}}_2, \qquad \hat{\mathbf{e}}_2 \times \hat{\mathbf{p}} = \hat{\mathbf{e}}_1, \qquad \hat{\mathbf{e}}_1 \times \hat{\mathbf{e}}_2 = \hat{\mathbf{p}}$$

Then

$$\boldsymbol{\sigma}\cdot\hat{\mathbf{e}}_1\,U_\pm = \left(\frac{p_0+1}{2p_0}\right)^{1/2}\begin{pmatrix} \boldsymbol{\sigma}\cdot\hat{\mathbf{e}}_1\,\chi^{\pm 1/2} \\ -\dfrac{ip\boldsymbol{\sigma}\cdot\hat{\mathbf{e}}_2}{p_0+1}\chi^{\pm 1/2} \end{pmatrix}$$

and

$$\boldsymbol{\sigma}\cdot\hat{\mathbf{e}}_2\,U_\pm = \left(\frac{p_0+1}{2p_0}\right)^{1/2}\begin{pmatrix} \boldsymbol{\sigma}\cdot\hat{\mathbf{e}}_2\,\chi^{\pm 1/2} \\ \dfrac{ip\boldsymbol{\sigma}\cdot\hat{\mathbf{e}}_1}{p_0+1}\chi^{\pm 1/2} \end{pmatrix}$$

Then

$$\mathcal{O}_z U_\pm = \left(\frac{p_0+1}{2p_0}\right)^{1/2}\begin{pmatrix} a \\ b \end{pmatrix}$$

where

$$a = [\boldsymbol{\sigma}\cdot\hat{\mathbf{p}}\,\hat{p}_z + \boldsymbol{\sigma}\cdot\hat{\mathbf{e}}_1\,\hat{e}_{1z} + \boldsymbol{\sigma}\cdot\hat{\mathbf{e}}_2\,\hat{e}_{2z}]\chi^{\pm 1/2} = \sigma_z\chi^{\pm 1/2} = \pm\chi^{\pm 1/2}$$
$$(p_0+1)b = p[\hat{p}_z + i\boldsymbol{\sigma}\cdot\hat{\mathbf{e}}_2\,\hat{e}_{1z} - i\boldsymbol{\sigma}\cdot\hat{\mathbf{e}}_1\,\hat{e}_{2z}]\chi^{\pm 1/2}$$

are each two-component spinors.

† See also section 20. We refer to the components of $\mathcal{O}$ as spin operators in the sense that they correspond to the Pauli operators $\boldsymbol{\sigma}$ and not $\frac{1}{2}\boldsymbol{\sigma}$. An alternative nomenclature for $\mathcal{O}$ is the "polarization operator" since, as will be clear from the sequel, the polarization of an electron beam is the ensemble average of $\mathcal{O}$.

For $\chi^{+1/2}$ we use

$$\boldsymbol{\sigma}\cdot\mathbf{V}\,\chi^{1/2} = \begin{pmatrix} V_z \\ V_+ \end{pmatrix}$$

for any vector $\mathbf{V}$ and $V_+ = V_x + iV_y$. Then

$$(p_0 + 1)b = p\begin{pmatrix} \hat{p}_z \\ i(\hat{e}_{1z}\hat{e}_{2+} - \hat{e}_{2z}\hat{e}_{1+}) \end{pmatrix}$$

But $i(\hat{e}_{1z}\hat{e}_{2+} - \hat{e}_{2z}\hat{e}_{1+}) = i(\hat{\mathbf{e}}_1 \times \hat{\mathbf{e}}_2)_y + (\hat{\mathbf{e}}_1 \times \hat{\mathbf{e}}_2)_x = \hat{\mathbf{p}}_+$. Thus

$$(p_0 + 1)b = \boldsymbol{\sigma}\cdot\mathbf{p}\,\chi^{\pm 1/2}$$

and we obtain

$$\mathcal{O}_z U_+ = U_+ \tag{3.12}$$

Similarly, for $\chi^{-1/2}$ we use

$$\boldsymbol{\sigma}\cdot\mathbf{V}\,\chi^{-1/2} = \begin{pmatrix} V_- \\ -V_z \end{pmatrix}$$

where $V_- = V_x - iV_y$, and so in this case

$$(p_0 + 1)b = p\begin{pmatrix} i(\hat{e}_{1z}\hat{e}_{2-} - \hat{e}_{2z}\hat{e}_{1-}) \\ \hat{p}_z \end{pmatrix}$$

$$= p\begin{pmatrix} i(\hat{e}_1 \times \hat{\mathbf{e}}_2)_y - (\hat{e}_1 \times \hat{\mathbf{e}}_2)_x \\ \hat{p}_z \end{pmatrix}$$

$$= \begin{pmatrix} -p_- \\ p_z \end{pmatrix} = -\boldsymbol{\sigma}\cdot\mathbf{p}\,\chi^{-1/2}$$

Therefore

$$\mathcal{O}_z U_- = -U_- \tag{3.13}$$

The interpretation of (3.12) and (3.13) is that the z-component of the relativistic spin operator $\mathcal{O}$ is a constant of the motion and for the states $U_\pm$ the eigenvalues of $\mathcal{O}_z$ are ± 1.

Since $\boldsymbol{\sigma}\cdot\hat{\mathbf{p}}$, $\boldsymbol{\sigma}\cdot\hat{\mathbf{e}}_1$, and $\boldsymbol{\sigma}\cdot\hat{\mathbf{e}}_2$ all anticommute, we note that $\mathcal{O}^2 = 3$ and $(\mathcal{O}\cdot\hat{\mathbf{n}})^2 = 1$ for any unit vector $\hat{\mathbf{n}}$. Hence the eigenvalues of $\mathcal{O}\cdot\hat{\mathbf{n}}$ are ± 1 in general.

We can also interpret the spin properties of the state (3.7) in terms of the average spin; that is,

$$(\psi^*, \mathcal{O}\psi) = (U_\pm^*, \mathcal{O}U_\pm) = \langle\mathcal{O}\rangle_\pm$$

The expectation value $\langle\mathcal{O}\rangle_\pm$ is readily calculated:

$$\langle\mathcal{O}\rangle_\pm = [\hat{\mathbf{p}}\,\langle\boldsymbol{\sigma}\cdot\hat{\mathbf{p}}\rangle + \hat{\mathbf{e}}_1\,\langle\beta\boldsymbol{\sigma}\cdot\hat{\mathbf{e}}_1\rangle + \hat{\mathbf{e}}_2\,\langle\beta\boldsymbol{\sigma}\cdot\hat{\mathbf{e}}_2\rangle]_\pm$$

Here we use

$$\langle\boldsymbol{\sigma}\cdot\hat{\mathbf{p}}\rangle_\pm = \pm\hat{p}_z, \qquad \langle\beta\boldsymbol{\sigma}\cdot\hat{\mathbf{e}}_i\rangle_\pm = \pm\hat{e}_{iz}, \qquad i = 1, 2$$

and again $\boldsymbol{\sigma}\cdot\hat{\mathbf{p}}$, $\boldsymbol{\sigma}\cdot\hat{\mathbf{e}}_1$, and $\boldsymbol{\sigma}\cdot\hat{\mathbf{e}}_2$ have the same commutation rules as σ_z, σ_x, and σ_y. Thus

$$\langle \mathcal{O} \rangle_{\pm} = \pm(\hat{p}_z\hat{\mathbf{p}} + \hat{e}_{1z}\hat{\mathbf{e}}_1 + \hat{e}_{2z}\hat{\mathbf{e}}_2) = \pm\hat{\mathbf{e}}_z$$

That is, the average value of the spin operator has unit length and is in the z-direction for U_+ and in the $-z$-direction for U_-. This is what is meant by the usual terminology: "spin up" (U_+), "spin down" (U_-). In section 19 the generalization to an arbitrary representation where $\langle \mathcal{O} \rangle$ is an arbitrary unit vector will be considered.

Since U_+ and U_- are eigenfunctions of the hermitian operator $\mathcal{O}_z$, having different eigenvalues, it follows that they must be orthogonal. This is verified by direct calculation from (3.7):

$$(U_+, U_-) = (U_-, U_+) = 0$$

The same, of course, applies to $(\psi_+, \psi_-) = (\psi_-, \psi_+)$. The two spinor amplitudes $U_{\pm}$ constitute a complete set of positive energy plane waves. The fact that the Dirac wave functions have four and not two components will be interpreted in the next section.

16. NEGATIVE ENERGY SOLUTIONS. THE POSITRON

The occurrence of negative energy solutions is characteristic of a relativistic theory because of the two possible solutions of (2.5); namely $W = \pm p_0$. Obviously, a negative energy state would imply properties unlike those of any observed particle. For instance, in a classical theory, and a quantum theory as well, the average velocity† is

$$v_k = \frac{\partial W}{\partial p_k} = -\frac{p_k}{p_0}$$

† The velocity operator, in ordinary units, is (see Appendix C)

$$\dot{\mathbf{x}} = \frac{i}{\hbar}(H, \mathbf{x}) = c\boldsymbol{\alpha}$$

and, since the eigenvalues of each component of $\boldsymbol{\alpha}$ have modulus unity, it might appear that the velocity has the value $\pm c$. This is indeed the instantaneous velocity but not the measured velocity. In a representation in which the energy is constant in time none of the α_k can be made diagonal. In fact,

$$\dot{\boldsymbol{\alpha}} = i(H, \boldsymbol{\alpha}) = -2i(\boldsymbol{\alpha}H - \vec{\mathbf{p}}) = -2\boldsymbol{\sigma} \times \vec{\mathbf{p}} + 2i\beta\boldsymbol{\alpha}$$

with $\hbar = c = 1$. In physical terms this is a reflection of the fact that a precise velocity measurement requires precise time and position measurements, so that the energy and momentum, in that case, could not be constants of the motion. The average velocity divided by c is $\langle\boldsymbol{\alpha}\rangle = \mathbf{p}/p_0$ for a plane wave of positive energy.

where the last equality applies for the negative energy states. Thus the momentum and velocity would be in opposite directions. In a classical theory the negative energy states cause no trouble because no transitions between positive and negative energy states occur. Therefore, if a particle occupies a positive energy state at any time, it will never appear in a negative energy state. The anomalous negative energy states are then eliminated as a result of initial conditions which stipulate that no such state occurred in the past. In a quantum theory this device is no longer admissible. Although the problem of coupling of Dirac electrons with an electromagnetic field has not yet been discussed, it is fairly obvious that spontaneous emission of radiation can occur as long as a state of lower energy is unoccupied and as long as conservation of angular momentum and linear momentum can be fulfilled. These conservation principles can always be fulfilled under appropriate conditions (for example, the presence of another particle to take up recoil momentum is necessary in bremsstrahlung). Thus there is nothing to prevent an electron from radiating energy in making a transition from a positive energy state to a negative energy state. What is more, there is nothing to prevent it from continuing to radiate, making transitions to lower and lower negative energy states. This behavior is evidently to be rejected in a reasonable description of nature, and the negative energy states are unphysical so far as observed states are concerned.†

The solution of the difficulty of the negative energy states is due to Dirac.[1] One defines the vacuum to consist of no occupied positive energy states and all negative energy states completely filled. This means that each negative energy state contains two electrons. An electron therefore is a particle in a positive energy state with all negative energy states occupied. No transitions to these states can occur because of the Pauli principle. The interpretation of a single unoccupied negative energy state is then a particle with *positive* energy, p_0 if the observed momentum is $\mathbf{p}$, and with (average) velocity

$$\mathbf{v} = \mathbf{p}/p_0$$

parallel to the momentum. This follows because to produce the vacuum where all observables have zero expectation value requires the addition of an electron with energy $-p_0$ and (average) velocity $-\mathbf{p}/p_0$. It will be apparent that a hole in the negative energy states is equivalent to a particle with the same mass as the electron, and this mass, m, which may be defined by

$$\mathbf{p} = m\mathbf{v}(1 - v^2/c^2)^{-1/2}$$

† They may and do occur as intermediate states in the usual description of such processes as Compton scattering; see section 37.

is positive. When one examines the behavior of the particle (unoccupied negative energy state) in an electromagnetic field it is seen that its charge is e where the electron charge (that of the particle in the occupied positive energy state) is $-e$; see section 21. The theory therefore predicts the existence of a particle, the positron, with the same mass and opposite charge as compared to an electron. It is well known that this particle was discovered in 1933 by Anderson.[2]

Although the prediction of the positron is certainly a brilliant success of the Dirac theory, some rather formidable questions still arise. With a completely filled "negative energy sea" the complete theory (hole theory) can no longer be a single-particle theory. The treatment of the problems of electrodynamics is seriously complicated by the requisite elaborate structure of the vacuum. The filled negative energy states need produce no observable electric field. However, if an external field is present the shift in the negative energy states produces a polarization of the vacuum and, according to the theory, this polarization is infinite. In a similar way it can be shown that an electron acquires infinite inertia (self-energy) by the coupling with the electromagnetic field which permits emission and absorption of virtual quanta. More recent developments show that these infinities, while undesirable, are removable in the sense that they do not contribute to observed results.[3,4] For example, it can be shown that starting with the parameters e and m for a bare Dirac particle the effect of the "crowded" vacuum is to change these to new constants e' and m', which must be identified with the observed charge and mass. The difference between e and e' as well as between m and m' arises principally from coupling between the electron and the electromagnetic field wherein transitions to states of very high momentum p' can occur and the divergences mentioned arise from the contribution from states with $p' \to \infty$. If these contributions were cut off in any reasonable manner, $m' - m$ and $e' - e$ would be of order $\alpha = e^2/\hbar c \cong 1/137$. No rigorous justification for such a cut-off has yet been proposed.

All this means that the present theory of electrons and fields is not complete. This is, of course, a characteristic of many theories in physics. The particles—the electron and its antiparticle the positron, or positive and negative mu mesons—are treated as "bare" particles. For problems involving electromagnetic field coupling this approximation will result in an error of order α. As an example, in section 22 it will be shown that the Dirac theory predicts a magnetic moment $\mu = \mu_0$ for the electron, whereas a more complete treatment[5] of radiative effects gives $\mu = \mu_0(1 + \alpha/2\pi)$, which agrees very well with the very accurate measured value[6] of $\mu/\mu_0 = 1.001146 \pm 0.000012$. This example is typical in the sense that it tells us that the Dirac theory can be useful in a certain domain, a very broad domain, of physical problems. In other words, we can prescribe a method for obtaining results which are consistent with experiment. It is only fair to add that this is not an *ad hoc* procedure and that a reasonable physical picture emerges from the theory. So far as the treatment of dynamic processes is concerned, it should be stressed that even when a quantized field is necessary, as in decay processes, the present theory is not only useful but also essential in obtaining results with which experiment can be confronted.

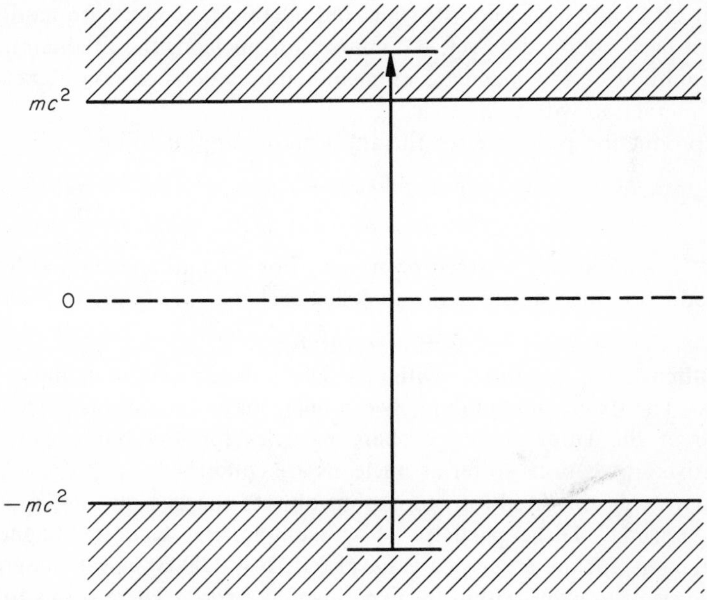

Figure 3.1 Energy spectrum showing positive and negative energy continua. A transition, indicated by the vertical arrow, of a negative energy electron from the initially completely filled negative energy states to a positive energy state represents the creation of a positron-electron pair.

In radiative problems such as bremsstrahlung, photoelectric effect, internal conversion, pair annihilation, and pair formation the theory is used to obtain results in the lowest non-vanishing order of the perturbation theory. The process of pair production, for example, is then regarded as the absorption of a photon with a transition of an electron from a negative to a positive energy state. Annihilation is the reverse process except that in the absence of a (nuclear) field only two quantum annihilation is permitted by the requirements of energy and momentum conservation. The simple diagram of Fig. 3.1 shows the envisaged transition. The shaded region gives the possible continuum energy states in the absence of external fields.

Another brilliant success of the Dirac hypothesis is the prediction of antinucleons, negative proton or antiproton and the antineutron. These particles, which were discovered in recent years in high energy nuclear reactions,[7] have (within the experimental error) the predicted properties that: (i) the charge of particle and that of antiparticle are opposite; (ii) their mass is the same; and (iii) they are produced and annihilate in pairs. The spins should be the same and their magnetic moments (section 22) should have opposite signs, but reliable data on these quantities have not been obtained as yet. Of course, for nucleons the prediction of the magnitude of the magnetic moment requires detailed consideration of the interaction with pi mesons.

The production processes for the antiproton $\bar{p}$ appear to be

$$p + p \rightarrow 3p + \bar{p}$$

$$\pi^- + p \rightarrow p + n + \bar{p}$$

Here π^- is a negatively charged pi meson. For the antineutron $\bar{n}$ at least one production mechanism is the so-called exchange scattering of $\bar{p}$ on p:

$$\bar{p} + p \rightarrow n + \bar{n}$$

The antiparticles annihilate with particles giving predominantly $\pi^{\pm}$ mesons. The strong interaction between nucleons and π mesons precludes the use of the Dirac theory of bare particles for any but essentially qualitative applications so far as nucleons are concerned.

In contrast to this situation mu mesons of both charge signs, $\mu^{\pm}$, appear to be "normal" Dirac particles. For example, the accurate magnetic measurement[8] for the μ^+ gives a value $(1.00122 \pm 0.0008)\ \mu_0$ which agrees with the electron value within the experimental error.† There seems to be little doubt that the physical properties of the μ meson can be explained by the Dirac theory as well as in the case of electrons.[9] The distinction between the particles seems to be entirely in the much larger mass of the μ mesons $(207m)$ which permits the decay process of $\mu^{\pm} \rightarrow e^{\pm}$ + neutrinos whereas, of course, $e^{\pm}$ are stable except for annihilation with each other.

17. THE PROPERTIES OF FREE POSITRONS

From the results of section 15 it is seen that the normalized wave functions of a negative energy electron with the eigenvalue of $\vec{\mathbf{p}} = \mathbf{p}$ are

$$\psi_{\pm}(-p_0) = V_{\pm}(-\mathbf{p}) \exp\left[i(\mathbf{p}\cdot\mathbf{r} + p_0 t)\right]$$

† Here μ_0 is the magneton unit defined with the meson mass.

and

$$V_{\pm}(-\mathbf{p}) = \left(\frac{p_0 + 1}{2p_0}\right)^{1/2} \begin{pmatrix} -\dfrac{\boldsymbol{\sigma}\cdot\mathbf{p}}{p_0 + 1}\chi^{\pm 1/2} \\ \chi^{\pm 1/2} \end{pmatrix} \tag{3.7'}$$

Here $H\psi_{\pm}(-p_0) = -p_0\psi_{\pm}(-p_0)$. The argument $(-p_0)$ is to indicate a negative energy state. The large component is the lower spinor. Thus in this case $p_0 \rightarrow 1$ gives

$$V_{\pm}(0) = \begin{pmatrix} 0 \\ \chi^{\pm 1/2} \end{pmatrix} = V_{nr}$$

and β can be replaced by -1. Also

$$\tfrac{1}{2}(1 - \beta)V_{\pm}(-\mathbf{p}) = \left(\frac{p_0 + 1}{2p_0}\right)^{1/2} V_{nr}$$

The projection operators $\frac{1}{2}(1 \pm \beta)$ constitute a complete set.

The results given here and above for the positive energy states clarify the problem of interpretation of the four-component wave function. The occurrence of an "upper" and "lower" spinor is evidently connected with the appearance of positive and negative energy states or, in more physical terms, with the existence of positive and negative charge. This corresponds to the decomposition of the wave function in Dirac space. The decomposition in Pauli space is clearly associated with double-valued spin orientation. This interpretation is brought out more explicitly in the diagonal representation discussed in section 19.

The physical particle is not the negative energy state electron but the positron. The corresponding positron has energy p_0 and momentum $-\mathbf{p}$. We change the notation so that for the positron $\mathbf{p}$ has the meaning of the physical momentum of the particle. Hence the positron wave function is

$$\psi_{\pm} = V_{\pm}(\mathbf{p}) \exp\left[-i(\mathbf{p}\cdot\mathbf{r} - p_0 t)\right] \tag{3.14}$$

where

$$V_{\pm}(\mathbf{p}) = \left(\frac{p_0 + 1}{2p_0}\right)^{1/2} \begin{pmatrix} \dfrac{\boldsymbol{\sigma}\cdot\mathbf{p}}{p_0 + 1}\chi^{\pm 1/2} \\ \chi^{\pm 1/2} \end{pmatrix} \tag{3.14a}$$

The large component is again the lower two-component spinor, while the small component is the upper two-spinor. Even Dirac matrices have the property of coupling large with large and small with small components, just as for the electron. Similarly, odd matrices couple small and large components as before.

The $V_\pm$ are normalized and orthogonal

$$(V_+, V_-) = (V_-, V_+) = 0$$

for both $V_\pm(\mathbf{p})$ and $V_\pm(-\mathbf{p})$. Between the U and V amplitudes the following relations hold:

$$(U_m, V_{m'}(-\mathbf{p})) = 0, \qquad (U_m, V_{m'}) = \frac{1}{p_0}(\chi^m, \boldsymbol{\sigma}\cdot\mathbf{p}\,\chi^{m'})$$

where unless otherwise indicated the argument of U and V is $\mathbf{p}$; for brevity m and m' are used as indices in place of $\pm$. The first of these results shows that the four amplitudes $U_\pm(\mathbf{p})$, $V_\pm(-\mathbf{p})$ are linearly independent and constitute an orthonormal set. This is obvious from the following facts: (1) they are eigenfunctions of H with different eigenvalues; (2) $U_\pm(\mathbf{p})$ are eigenfunctions of the hermitian $\mathcal{O}_z$ with different eigenvalues; and (3) $V_\pm(-\mathbf{p})$ are eigenfunctions of the hermitian operator:

$$\mathcal{O}'_z = \mathcal{O}'\cdot\hat{\mathbf{e}}_z = -\boldsymbol{\sigma}\cdot\hat{\mathbf{p}}\hat{p}_z + \beta\boldsymbol{\sigma}\cdot\hat{\mathbf{e}}_1\,\hat{e}_{1z} + \beta\boldsymbol{\sigma}\cdot\hat{\mathbf{e}}_2\,\hat{e}_{2z}$$

with eigenvalues ∓ 1. On comparing with $\mathcal{O}_z$, the change of sign in the first term should be noted. This result is obtained in the following way: We have

$$V_\pm(-\mathbf{p}) = -i\rho_2 U_\pm(\mathbf{p})$$

and ρ_2 commutes with $\boldsymbol{\sigma}$ and anticommutes with β. Therefore

$$\begin{aligned}\mathcal{O}'_z V_\pm(-\mathbf{p}) &= i\rho_2\mathcal{O}_z U_\pm(\mathbf{p})\\ &= \pm i\rho_2 U_\pm(\mathbf{p}) = \mp V_\pm(-\mathbf{p})\end{aligned}$$

Between $V_\pm(\mathbf{p})$ and $V_\pm(-\mathbf{p})$ we obtain the scalar products

$$[V_m(\mathbf{p}), V_{m'}(-\mathbf{p})] = \frac{1}{p_0}\,\delta_{mm'}$$

since, as is seen in the next paragraph, $V_\pm(\mathbf{p})$ are also eigenfunctions of $\mathcal{O}'_z$ with the same eigenvalue as $V_\pm(-\mathbf{p})$. This result is, in fact, evident since $\mathcal{O}$ and $\mathcal{O}'$ do not change under the transformation $\mathbf{p} \to -\mathbf{p}$. It follows from the foregoing that $U_\pm(\mathbf{p})$, $V_\pm(\mathbf{p})$ are four linearly independent amplitudes.

It is of considerable importance that there exists an operation which converts an electron wave function into a positron wave function and vice versa. We distinguish between these by writing them, for the moment, as $\psi(-e)$ and $\psi(e)$ respectively. Then, with the standard representation used here,

$$\psi(e) = \eta i\beta\alpha_2\psi^\times(-e) \tag{3.15}$$

where η is a phase factor: $|\eta| = 1$. To prove this, it is only necessary to show that

$$V(\mathbf{p}) = \eta i\beta\alpha_2 U^{\times}(\mathbf{p})$$

where, as indicated, a real phase factor $\eta = \pm 1$ may occur. Since

$$i\beta\alpha_2 = \begin{pmatrix} 0 & i\sigma_2 \\ -i\sigma_2 & 0 \end{pmatrix}$$

we find

$$i\beta\alpha_2 U_{\pm}^{\times} = \left(\frac{p_0+1}{2p_0}\right)^{1/2} \begin{pmatrix} \dfrac{i\sigma_2\boldsymbol{\sigma}^{\times}\cdot\mathbf{p}}{p_0+1}\chi^{\pm 1/2} \\ -i\sigma_2\chi^{\pm 1/2} \end{pmatrix}$$

since $\chi^{\pm 1/2}$ is real. Now $i\sigma_2\boldsymbol{\sigma}^{\times}\cdot\mathbf{p} = -\boldsymbol{\sigma}\cdot\mathbf{p}i\sigma_2$ and

$$i\sigma_2\chi^{\pm 1/2} = \mp\chi^{\mp 1/2}$$

Then, combining these results,

$$V_{\pm}(\mathbf{p}) = \pm i\beta\alpha_2 U_{\mp}^{\times}(\mathbf{p}) \tag{3.16}$$

The operation of complex conjugation and multiplication by $i\beta\alpha_2$ which occurs in (3.15) and (3.16) is called *charge conjugation.* It appears here in the standard representation, but it will be discussed in a general representation in section 24. It is seen to interchange a positron and electron and at the same time to reverse the spin state. This fact will be investigated further below. Clearly, the charge conjugation operation works in both directions. That is,

$$\psi_{\pm}(e) = \pm i\beta\alpha_2\psi_{\mp}^{\times}(-e) \tag{3.17a}$$

implies

$$\psi_{\pm}(-e) = \pm i\beta\alpha_2\psi_{\mp}^{\times}(e) \tag{3.17b}$$

The spin reversal is another way of saying that $\mathcal{O}$ and $\mathcal{O}'$, the spin operators for electron and positron, have opposite eigenvalues; see also below.

The notation will be simplified by introducing the charge conjugation matrix C:

$$C^{-1} = \pm i\beta\alpha_2 = C \tag{3.18}$$

and writing

$$\psi_{\pm}^{c} = C\psi_{\mp}^{\times} \tag{3.19}$$

We refer to ψ^c as the charge conjugate wave function. Then any operator equation of the form

$$\Omega\psi_{\pm} = \omega\psi_{\pm}$$

where Ω is hermitian, ω real, becomes

$$C^{-1}\Omega^{\times}C\psi^{c}_{\mp} = \omega\psi^{c}_{\mp}$$

In the present case

$$C^{-1} = C \tag{3.20}$$

and this, it will be seen, is a consequence of choosing the phase so as to make C real. The operator

$$C^{-1}\Omega^{\times}C = \Omega^{c} \tag{3.21}$$

is the charge conjugate operator. Similarly, for a hermitian operator which is not diagonal we consider the (necessarily real) expectation value

$$\omega = (\psi_{\pm}, \Omega\psi_{\pm})$$

Then the charge conjugate equation is

$$\omega^{c} = (\psi^{c}_{\pm}, \Omega^{c}\psi^{c}_{\pm}) = (\psi_{\mp}, \tilde{C}^{-1}C^{\times -1}\Omega\psi_{\mp})^{\times} = \omega^{\times} = \omega$$

since $\tilde{C} = C = C^{\times} = C^{-1}$.

Applying these results we find $\boldsymbol{\alpha}^{c} = \boldsymbol{\alpha}$, $\beta^{c} = -\beta$, $\boldsymbol{\sigma}^{c} = -\boldsymbol{\sigma}$ and

(a) Energy operator: $H^{c} = -H = -(\boldsymbol{\alpha}\cdot\vec{\mathbf{p}} + \beta)$
(b) Momentum operator: $\vec{\mathbf{p}}^{c} = -\vec{\mathbf{p}} = i\nabla$
(c) Spin operator: $\mathcal{O}^{c} = -\boldsymbol{\sigma}\cdot\hat{\mathbf{p}}\,\hat{\mathbf{p}} + \beta\boldsymbol{\sigma}\cdot\hat{\mathbf{e}}_1\hat{\mathbf{e}}_1 + \beta\boldsymbol{\sigma}\cdot\hat{\mathbf{e}}_2\hat{\mathbf{e}}_2 = \mathcal{O}'$
(d) Angular momentum: $\mathbf{J}^{c} = \mathbf{l}^{c} + \frac{1}{2}\boldsymbol{\sigma}^{c} = -\mathbf{J} = -(\mathbf{l} + \frac{1}{2}\boldsymbol{\sigma})$
(e) Current four-vector: $\mathbf{j}^{c} = \mathbf{j}$, $\rho^{c} = \rho$

We proceed to a discussion of these results. In connection with the energy operator we recognize that

$$i\frac{\partial\psi^{c}}{\partial t} = i\frac{\partial C^{-1}\psi^{\times}}{\partial t} = -C^{-1}H^{\times}\psi^{\times} = -C^{-1}H^{\times}C\psi^{c} = -H^{c}\psi^{c}$$

or

$$i\frac{\partial\psi^{c}}{\partial t} = -p_0\psi^{c}$$

so p_0 is the eigenvalue of H^{c}. Therefore we are justified in calling H^{c} the energy operator. Similarly,

$$\vec{\mathbf{p}}^{c}\psi^{c} = i\nabla\psi^{c} = \mathbf{p}\psi^{c}$$

and so $\vec{\mathbf{p}}^{c}$ is the momentum operator. For the spin operator we note that the component of spin along the momentum has reversed in sign. This is related to the *helicity* of the particle; that is, the expectation value $\langle\boldsymbol{\sigma}\cdot\hat{\mathbf{p}}\rangle$. The result that electrons and positrons have opposite helicity is well known as an experimental result in beta decay. The angular momentum operators of the positron are the negative operators of the electron. For the positron, then, the commutation rules are

$$\mathbf{J}^c \times \mathbf{J}^c = -i\mathbf{J}^c$$

The operator $K^c = \beta^c(\boldsymbol{\sigma}^c \cdot \mathbf{l}^c + 1)$ is equal to $-K$. The connection between this result and the relative parity of positron and electron states will be clarified in section 26. Finally, the result for the current four-vector is fairly obvious. The space part of particle current density is in the direction of the average velocity or momentum, and the particle density is positive definite. These results are precisely what one obtains from the hole theory.

18. THE DIAGONAL REPRESENTATION

Plane Waves

A special representation to which considerable interest is attached is that in which the energy matrix h for plane waves is transformed to diagonal form. Since the eigenvalues of h are $\pm p_0$ the diagonal form of h must be

$$h' = ShS^{-1} = p_0\beta \tag{3.22}$$

This corresponds to the transformation from U to $U' = U_0$, where

$$U = S^{-1}U_0 \tag{3.23}$$

and

$$h'U_0 = ShS^{-1}U_0 = p_0\beta U_0 = p_0U_0$$

or

$$\beta U_0 = U_0 \tag{3.24}$$

Here we confine our attention to positive energy states. The extension to negative energy states will be obvious. The result (3.24) corresponds to an electron in the rest frame, and therefore the results of this section should correspond to the non-relativistic limit. We return to a consideration of this question below.

It is evident that if S_1 and S_2 are solutions of (3.22), that is

$$S_ih = p_0\beta S_i, \qquad i = 1, 2 \tag{3.22$'$}$$

then any linear combination of S_1 and S_2 is also a solution. All the solutions can be generated in the following way. First, a particular solution is constructed. This is

$$\beta + k\boldsymbol{\alpha} \cdot \mathbf{p}$$

where k is a constant. Insertion in (3.22′) shows that

$$k = \frac{1}{p_0 + 1}$$

and $p_0^2 = p^2 + 1$. We now consider a solution of (3.22′) in the form

$$S_A = \gamma_A(\beta + k\boldsymbol{\alpha}\cdot\mathbf{p})$$

where k may now be different from the value found above. Here γ_A is one of the 16 matrices previously discussed, and it either commutes or anticommutes with β. Insertion of S_A in (3.22′) shows that S_A satisfies this equation provided that

$$k = \frac{1}{1 + \epsilon p_0}$$

where $\epsilon = +1$ if $(\gamma_A, \beta) = 0$ and $\epsilon = -1$ if $(\gamma_A, \beta)_+ = 0$. It follows that the most general solution of (3.22′) is

$$S = \sum_A c_A[\gamma_A(1 + \epsilon p_0)\beta + \gamma_A\boldsymbol{\alpha}\cdot\mathbf{p}]$$

where c_A are 16 arbitrary constants not all zero. If we write

$$M = \sum_A c_A\gamma_A$$

then

$$S = Mh + p_0\beta M \tag{3.25}$$

independently of ϵ. Direct substitution in (3.22′) verifies that this S does indeed satisfy this equation since $h^2 = p_0^2$ times the unit matrix.

If the normalization of U_0 to

$$(U_0, U_0) = 1$$

is to be retained, it is necessary that $S^*S = SS^* = 1$. But

$$SS^* = p_0^2MM^* + p_0[(MhM^*, \beta)_+ + p_0\beta MM^*\beta]$$

It is sufficiently general to consider the two cases: (i) M and β commute and (ii) M and β anticommute. In the first case we set $M = M_0$ and in the second $M = -\gamma_5M_0$, where $(M_0, \beta) = 0$ but M_0 is otherwise arbitrary. When M is a linear combination of M_0 and $-\gamma_5M_0$, the result for S and therefore for U_0 is a corresponding combination of the results for cases (i) and (ii).

It is now seen that

$$SS^* = MM^*(2p_0^2 \pm 2p_0)$$

where the upper sign corresponds to case (i) and the lower to case (ii). The general form of M_0 is

$$M_0 = \begin{pmatrix} a & 0 \\ 0 & b \end{pmatrix}$$

where, if we take $a^*a = b^*b = 1$, it follows that $M_0^* M_0 = 1$. Therefore in case (i) we choose S to be

$$S = [2p_0(p_0 + 1)]^{-\frac{1}{2}}[M_0 h + p_0 \beta M_0] \tag{3.26a}$$

and $M_0^* M_0 = 1$. In case (ii)

$$S = -[2p_0(p_0 - 1)]^{-\frac{1}{2}} \gamma_5 [M_0 h - p_0 \beta M_0] \tag{3.26b}$$

Substitution of S given by (3.26a) into $U_0 = SU$ gives

$$U_0 = \begin{pmatrix} a\chi^m \\ 0 \end{pmatrix} \tag{3.27}$$

where, as usual, $m = \pm\frac{1}{2}$. The general form of a is $\boldsymbol{\sigma}\cdot\hat{\mathbf{n}}_1$, where $\hat{\mathbf{n}}_1$ is a unit vector. The result (3.27) is a unitary transformation (with a which is unitary) on the wave function

$$U(0) = \begin{pmatrix} \chi^m \\ 0 \end{pmatrix}$$

representing the electron in the rest frame.

For case (ii) we find similarly

$$U_0 = \begin{pmatrix} b\boldsymbol{\sigma}\cdot\hat{\mathbf{p}}\, \chi^m \\ 0 \end{pmatrix} \tag{3.28}$$

which is again a unitary transformation on $U(0)$.

For negative energy or positron states it is readily seen that the diagonal representation results in

$$V = \begin{pmatrix} 0 \\ c\chi^m \end{pmatrix}$$

where $cc^* = c^*c = 1$. The demonstration will be left as an exercise for the reader.

It is natural to think, in connection with these results, of the Lorentz transformation which brings the electron to rest. To see the relation of this with the unitary transformation used in the foregoing, we generalize the transformation of Eq. (2.71a). This gives

$$\Lambda = \left(\frac{\xi + 1}{2}\right)^{1/2} - \boldsymbol{\alpha}\cdot\hat{\mathbf{p}}\left(\frac{\xi - 1}{2}\right)^{1/2} = \exp\left[-\boldsymbol{\alpha}\cdot\hat{\mathbf{p}} \cosh^{-1}\left(\frac{\xi + 1}{2}\right)^{1/2}\right]$$

and

$$\Lambda^{-1} = \left(\frac{\xi + 1}{2}\right)^{1/2} + \boldsymbol{\alpha}\cdot\hat{\mathbf{p}}\left(\frac{\xi - 1}{2}\right)^{1/2} \tag{3.29}$$

Here $\hat{\mathbf{p}}$ is a unit vector in the direction of the velocity vector $\mathbf{v}$ of the transformation. The correctness of (3.29) is verified by using (2.60b), which can be written in the form

$$4a_{\mu\nu} = \mathrm{Tr}\,(\gamma_\nu \Lambda^{-1} \gamma_\mu \Lambda)$$

or

$$8a_{\mu\nu} = \mathrm{Tr}\,\gamma_\nu[(\xi + 1)\gamma_\mu - (\xi - 1)\boldsymbol{\alpha}\cdot\hat{\mathbf{p}}\,\gamma_\mu\,\boldsymbol{\alpha}\cdot\hat{\mathbf{p}} + (\xi^2 - 1)^{1/2}(\boldsymbol{\alpha}\cdot\hat{\mathbf{p}}, \gamma_\mu)]$$

When this is evaluated for the various cases, $\mu \neq 4, \nu \neq 4$; $\mu = 4, \nu \neq 4$; $\mu = \nu = 4$, it is seen that the Lorentz transformation generated,

$$x'_\mu = a_{\mu\nu} x_\nu$$

agrees exactly with Eqs. (B.6) and (B.7) of Appendix B.

Now Λ given in (3.29) may be applied to $\psi = U \exp i(\mathbf{p}\cdot\mathbf{r} - p_0 t)$. The exponential factor is the scalar product of two four-vectors and is therefore a Lorentz invariant. Then using $\xi = p_0$ we obtain

$$\Lambda U = \frac{p_0^{-1/2}}{2}\begin{pmatrix} (p_0 + 1)\chi^m \\ \boldsymbol{\sigma}\cdot\mathbf{p}\,\chi^m \end{pmatrix} - \frac{p p_0^{-1/2}}{2}\begin{pmatrix} \dfrac{\boldsymbol{\sigma}\cdot\mathbf{p}\,\boldsymbol{\sigma}\cdot\hat{\mathbf{p}}}{p_0 + 1}\chi^m \\ \boldsymbol{\sigma}\cdot\hat{\mathbf{p}}\,\chi^m \end{pmatrix}$$

and, since $\boldsymbol{\sigma}\cdot\mathbf{p}\,\boldsymbol{\sigma}\cdot\hat{\mathbf{p}} = p$, the result is

$$\Lambda U = p_0^{-1/2}\begin{pmatrix} \chi^m \\ 0 \end{pmatrix} \tag{3.30}$$

It is obvious that ΛU is not normalized in x-space. But, if we recall that the Lorentz transformation does not change the two coordinates perpendicular to $\hat{\mathbf{p}}$ and stretches the coordinate along $\hat{\mathbf{p}}$ by a factor $\xi = p_0$, it follows that

$$d^3x' = p_0\, d^3x$$

Hence, if

$$\int \psi^* \psi\, d^3x = 1$$

it follows that

$$\int \psi'^* \psi' \, d^3x' = 1$$

as should be expected from the invariance of $\int \rho \, d^3x$. In this sense it may be said that the Lorentz transformation and the S-transformation used at the beginning of this section are equivalent. They differ by an arbitrary unitary transformation.

The Foldy-Wouthuysen Transformation

The diagonal representation discussed above is closely related to an extremely elegant and powerful transformation scheme due to Foldy and Wouthuysen.[10] This will be referred to briefly as the FW transformation, and we shall here discuss only its application to free particles. In section 22 the method will be applied to particles in an electromagnetic field. In general, the method is equivalent to a non-relativistic expansion in which the ratio of the momentum to mc and the ratio of the kinetic and interaction energies to the rest energy mc^2 is a parameter of expansion. For free particles the method gives exact results in closed form.

The purpose of the FW transformation is to find a representation in which the small and large components are decoupled. Thus the electron wave function will be a four-component spinor with the lower two-spinor identically zero, while the positron will be represented by a four-spinor with the upper two-spinor identically zero. The spinors

$$\tfrac{1}{2}(1 \pm \beta)\psi$$

have the property of vanishing small components, but these do not represent states of definite energy in the standard representation.

Instead of working in the plane wave representation, the wave function will be left general and will depend on the coordinates in an unspecified way. The transformation

$$\Psi' = S\Psi = e^{i\mathfrak{U}}\Psi$$

introduces a wave function which fulfills

$$H'\Psi' = i\frac{\partial \Psi'}{\partial t}$$

where

$$H' = e^{i\mathfrak{U}} H e^{-i\mathfrak{U}} - \frac{\partial \mathfrak{U}}{\partial t}$$

We shall be interested in the case $\partial\mathfrak{U}/\partial t = 0$ so

$$H' = e^{i\mathfrak{U}} H e^{-i\mathfrak{U}} \tag{3.31}$$

Other operators transform in exactly the same way. For the hermitian operator $\mathfrak{U}$ the choice†

$$\mathfrak{U} = -\frac{i}{2m}\,\beta\boldsymbol{\alpha}\cdot\mathbf{p}\,\varphi\left(\frac{p}{m}\right) \tag{3.32}$$

is made. Here we are using units with $\hbar = c = 1$, but it is preferable to keep the mass m in evidence so that

$$H = \boldsymbol{\alpha}\cdot\mathbf{p} + \beta m$$

In (3.32) φ is a function of p/m defined in terms of the (Taylor) series expansion of this function. It is to be recognized that $\beta\boldsymbol{\alpha}\cdot\mathbf{p}$ commutes with φ. Since $\mathfrak{U}$ anticommutes with H we can write

$$\begin{aligned} H' = e^{2i\mathfrak{U}}\,H &= [\cos(p\varphi/m) + \beta\boldsymbol{\alpha}\cdot\mathbf{p}p^{-1}\sin(p\varphi/m)]H \\ &= \beta[m\cos(p\varphi/m) + p\sin(p\varphi/m)] \\ &\quad + \boldsymbol{\alpha}\cdot\mathbf{p}p^{-1}[p\cos(p\varphi/m) - m\sin(p\varphi/m)] \end{aligned} \tag{3.33}$$

which follows from the fact that $(\beta\boldsymbol{\alpha}\cdot\mathbf{p})^2 = -\mathbf{p}^2$. It is seen that H' is free of odd operators if

$$\begin{aligned} \varphi(p/m) &= (m/p)\tan^{-1}(p/m) \\ &= \sum_{n=0}^{\infty}\frac{(-)^n(p/m)^{2n}}{2n+1} \end{aligned} \tag{3.34}$$

and with this choice

$$H' = \beta W_p \tag{3.35}$$

where W_p is an *operator*:‡

$$W_p = (m^2 + p^2)^{1/2} \tag{3.35'}$$

which can be expressed by the binomial expansion in ascending powers of $(p/m)^2 = -m^{-2}\nabla^2$.

It follows from (3.35) that Ψ' can be written as a sum of positive and negative energy solutions:

$$\Psi' = \Psi'_+ + \Psi'_- \tag{3.36}$$

† Here and below $\mathbf{p}$ is an operator. The arrow is omitted for simplicity. In φ only $\mathbf{p}^2 = -\nabla^2$ will occur.

‡ For plane waves W_p has the eigenvalue p_0, and the entire discussion reduces to the diagonal representation. The unitary transformation matrix is

$$S = e^{i\mathfrak{U}} = [\tfrac{1}{2}(1 + 1/p_0)]^{1/2} + \beta\,\boldsymbol{\alpha}\cdot\hat{\mathbf{p}}[\tfrac{1}{2}(1 - 1/p_0)]^{1/2}$$

and this is obtained from (3.25) with either

$$M = [2p_0(p_0 - 1)]^{-1/2}\,\boldsymbol{\alpha}\cdot\hat{\mathbf{p}}$$

or

$$M = [2p_0(p_0 + 1)]^{-1/2}\,\beta$$

where

$$\Psi'_{\pm} = \tfrac{1}{2}(1 \pm \beta)\Psi'$$

and for these two solutions the wave equation reads

$$\begin{aligned} W_p\Psi'_{+} &= i\,\partial\Psi'_{+}/\partial t \\ -W_p\Psi'_{-} &= i\,\partial\Psi'_{-}/\partial t \end{aligned} \tag{3.37}$$

To justify these statements the wave function $\Psi(\mathbf{x})$ is written as a Fourier integral:†

$$\Psi(\mathbf{x}) = \int a(\mathbf{p}') \exp(i\mathbf{p}'\cdot\mathbf{x})\, d^3p'$$

and

$$\Psi_{\pm}(\mathbf{x}) = \int \frac{1}{2}\left[1 \pm \frac{H(\mathbf{p}')}{W'_p}\right] a(\mathbf{p}') \exp(i\mathbf{p}'\cdot\mathbf{x})\, d^3p' \tag{3.38}$$

where $H(\mathbf{p}') = \boldsymbol{\alpha}\cdot\mathbf{p}' + \beta m$. Since $\frac{1}{2}[1 \pm H(\mathbf{p}')W_{p'}^{-1}]$ is a positive (upper sign) or negative (lower sign) energy projection operator, Ψ_{+} and Ψ_{-} are positive and negative energy solutions. Since S can be written in the form

$$S = \frac{m + W_p + \beta\boldsymbol{\alpha}\cdot\mathbf{p}}{[2W_p(W_p + m)]^{1/2}}$$

it is readily verified that

$$\begin{aligned} \Psi'_{\pm} &= e^{iU}\Psi_{\pm} \\ &= \tfrac{1}{2}(1 \pm \beta)\int \left[\frac{2W_{p'}}{W_{p'} + m}\right]^{1/2} \frac{1}{2}\left[1 \pm \frac{H(p')}{W_{p'}}\right] a(\mathbf{p}') \exp(i\mathbf{p}'\cdot\mathbf{x})\, d^3p' \end{aligned} \tag{3.39}$$

which, because of the $\frac{1}{2}(1 \pm \beta)$, explicitly shows that the $\Psi'_{\pm}$ have only large components.

An extremely interesting result of the FW transformation is that it leads to a representation in which the operators have a non-local character. To understand this we construct an operator kernel $K(\mathbf{x}, \mathbf{x}')$ which, acting on $\Psi(\mathbf{x}')$, gives $\Psi'(\mathbf{x})$. Thus, with

$$a(\mathbf{p}') = (2\pi)^{-3}\int \psi(\mathbf{x}') \exp(-i\mathbf{p}'\cdot\mathbf{x}')\, d^3x'$$

we obtain

$$\Psi'(\mathbf{x}) = \int K(\mathbf{x}, \mathbf{x}')\, \psi(\mathbf{x}')\, d^3x' \tag{3.40}$$

where

$$K(\mathbf{x}, \mathbf{x}') = (2\pi)^{-3}\int \left[\frac{2W_{p'}}{W_{p'} + m}\right]^{1/2} \frac{1}{2}\left[1 + \frac{\beta H_{p'}}{W_{p'}}\right] \exp[i\mathbf{p}'\cdot(\mathbf{x} - \mathbf{x}')]\, d^3p' \tag{3.41}$$

† Of course, where $\mathbf{p}$ and W_p operate on plane waves they may be replaced by numbers: their plane wave eigenvalues.

It is seen that $K(\mathbf{x}, \mathbf{x}')$ is not a Dirac delta function. In fact, it can be shown that $\Psi'(\mathbf{x})$ is determined from $\Psi'(\mathbf{x}')$ over a finite range of $\mathbf{x}'$ centered around $\mathbf{x}$ and that this range is of the order of the Compton wavelength $\hbar/mc$. To see this we note that K is a displacement kernel depending only on $\mathbf{R} = \mathbf{x} - \mathbf{x}'$. Then

$$\int d^3R K(\mathbf{R}) = \left[\left(\frac{2W_{p'}}{W_{p'} + m}\right)^{1/2} \frac{1}{2}\left(1 + \frac{\beta H_{p'}}{W_{p'}}\right)\right]_{p'=0} = 1$$

The mean square R is

$$\begin{aligned} \langle \mathbf{R}^2 \rangle &= \int d^3R \mathbf{R}^2 K(\mathbf{R}) \\ &= -\left[\nabla_{p'}^2 \left(\frac{2W_{p'}}{W_{p'} + m}\right)^{1/2} \frac{1}{2}\left(1 + \frac{\beta H_{p'}}{W_{p'}}\right)\right]_{p'=0} = \frac{3}{4} \end{aligned}$$

The unit is $(\hbar/mc)^2$, and this result substantiates the statement made above.

The interpretation of this curious result lies in the fact that $\mathbf{x}$ is no longer the position operator. Instead, in the FW representation this is $\mathbf{x}'$ where

$$\mathbf{x}' = e^{i\mathfrak{U}}\mathbf{x}e^{-i\mathfrak{U}} = \mathbf{x} - \frac{i\beta\boldsymbol{\alpha}}{2W_p} + \frac{i\beta\boldsymbol{\alpha}\cdot\mathbf{p}\,\mathbf{p} - (\boldsymbol{\sigma} \times \mathbf{p})p}{2W_p(W_p + m)p}$$

If $\mathbf{X}$ is the operator in the old representation, which in the FW representation becomes just the old $\mathbf{x}$, it is clear that[11]

$$\mathbf{X} = e^{-i\mathfrak{U}}\,\mathbf{x}e^{i\mathfrak{U}} = \mathbf{x} + \frac{i\beta\boldsymbol{\alpha}}{2W_p} - \frac{i\beta\boldsymbol{\alpha}\cdot\mathbf{p}\,\mathbf{p} + (\boldsymbol{\sigma} \times \mathbf{p})\mathbf{p}}{2W_p(W_p + m)p}$$

and its time derivative is

$$\frac{d\mathbf{X}}{dt} = i(H, \mathbf{X}) = \frac{\mathbf{p}}{W_p}\frac{H}{W_p}$$

Thus for positive energy states this is just $\mathbf{p}/W_p$ and for negative energy states $-\mathbf{p}/W_p$, so that $d\mathbf{X}/dt$ is the conventional velocity operator.

In this connection the results of Appendix C should be consulted. It is shown there that the electron executes a complicated motion which is a superposition of an average motion with the expected velocity plus an oscillating motion with a frequency $2mc^2/\hbar$. The latter type of motion is called *Zitterbewegung* or trembling motion.[12] The origin of this trembling motion is seen when one considers a superposition of positive and negative energy states. For instance, a general wave function is

$$\Psi(\mathbf{x}) = \int a_+(\mathbf{p}) \exp\left[i(\mathbf{p}\cdot\mathbf{x} - p_0 t)\right] d^3p + \int a_-(\mathbf{p}) \exp\left[i(\mathbf{p}\cdot\mathbf{x} + p_0 t)\right] d^3p$$

where $a_\pm$ are the positive and negative energy state amplitudes.† The average value of x_k with this wave packet is

$$\begin{aligned}
\langle x_k \rangle &= \int \Psi^* x_k \Psi \, d^3x \\
&= \int d^3x \, d^3p \, d^3p' [a_+^*(\mathbf{p}) \exp[-i(\mathbf{p}\cdot\mathbf{x} - p_0 t)] \\
&\quad + a_-^*(\mathbf{p}) \exp[-i(\mathbf{p}\cdot\mathbf{x} + p_0 t)]] \\
&\quad \times (-i) \left[a_+(\mathbf{p}') e^{-ip_0 t} \left(\frac{\partial}{\partial p_k'} \exp(i\mathbf{p}'\cdot\mathbf{x}) \right) \right. \\
&\quad \left. + a_-(\mathbf{p}') e^{ip_0 t} \left(\frac{\partial}{\partial p_k'} \exp(i\mathbf{p}'\cdot\mathbf{x}) \right) \right] \\
&= (2\pi)^3 \int d^3p (a_+^* e^{ip_0 t} + a_-^* e^{-ip_0 t}) \left(i \frac{\partial}{\partial p_k} \right) (a_+ e^{-ip_0 t} + a_- e^{ip_0 t})
\end{aligned}$$

where the integration over $\mathbf{x}$ has been performed to give $(2\pi)^3 \delta(\mathbf{p} - \mathbf{p}')$, and after the $\mathbf{p}'$ integration is made all arguments of $a_\pm$ are equal to $\mathbf{p}$. If only a_+ or a_- is different from zero, this result for $\langle x_k \rangle$ is linear in t, as is seen when the differentiation with respect to p_k is performed; but with both a_+ and a_- present there are cross terms of the type $a_+^* a_- e^{2ip_0 t}$ and the conjugate term which give rise to an oscillatory time dependence of $\langle x_k \rangle$ with the above-mentioned frequency. An understanding of these effects can be obtained from the requirement of the theory that a probability density exist, implying the possibility of a precise position measurement,[13] and the requirement of energy and momentum conservation, which implies an uncertainty $\Delta x \geqslant \hbar c / p_0 \sim \hbar / mc$. The trembling motion is a consequence of the reconciliation of these two requirements. To avoid this we must redefine the position operator to be $\mathbf{X}$ in the old representation, and not $\mathbf{x}$. This operator $\mathbf{X}$ is appropriately referred to as the *mean position* operator. Its transform in the FW scheme, as indicated, is just $\mathbf{x}$.

The transformation of other operators in the FW scheme is readily carried out. We mention only that the momentum operator, commuting with S, is unchanged. For other cases the original literature may be consulted.[10]

A number of investigations extending the scope of the FW transformation have been published. For example, the extension to two Dirac particles has been studied by Chraplyvy[14] and by Barker and Glover,[15] the extension to an arbitrary number of particles by Pursey,[16] who also discusses the essentially unique character of the transformation. An

† These amplitudes are the unnormalized wave functions in momentum space.

alternative representation in which H' contains only an odd operator ($\boldsymbol{\alpha}\cdot\mathbf{p}\, W_p/p$) can be constructed[17] (see Eq. 3.33), and this is of interest for high energy particles or, alternatively, for massless particles; see also section 40 and Chapter VII. Other methods for decoupling the four Dirac equations into two independent sets of two equations have been described in the literature.[18,19]

19. PROJECTION OPERATORS

General Properties

We have seen that the four-component structure of the wave functions, as well as the existence of four linearly independent plane waves for a given momentum $\mathbf{p}$, is a direct result of the two-valued nature of the spin and of the sign of the energy. This double division of the four states forms a natural basis for the construction of projection operators which play an extremely important role in the theory and its applications.

For convenience the entire set of quantum numbers describing a plane wave state will be designated by η and the corresponding wave functions by $\psi^{(\eta)}(\mathbf{x})$. Only the space part of the wave functions will be needed because the time parts cancel out in the following procedure. In detail, for the representation used above, η will then stand for the three numbers $\mathbf{p}$, the sign of the energy $S_W = W/p_0$, and the eigenvalue, $\lambda(= \pm 1)$, of $\mathcal{O}_z$. Then summation over η has the meaning

$$\sum_{\eta} = (2\pi)^{-3} \int d^3p \sum_{S_W\lambda}$$

since the number of states in the volume element of phase space $d^3p\, d^3x$ is $(2\pi)^{-3}\, d^3p\, d^3x$ and we consider unit volume in configuration space.

Since the $\psi^{(\eta)}$ form a complete orthonormal set, we can expand a four-component function in terms of them:

$$F(\mathbf{x}) = \sum_{\eta} c^{(\eta)}\, \psi^{(\eta)}(\mathbf{x}) = \sum_{\eta} \left[\int d^3x'\, \psi^{(\eta)*}(\mathbf{x}')\, F(\mathbf{x}') \right] \psi^{(\eta)}(\mathbf{x})$$

Here $\mathbf{x}'$ is used to distinguish the integration variable from $\mathbf{x}$. In spinor index notation the above reads

$$\begin{aligned} F_\rho(\mathbf{x}) &= \sum_{\eta} \left[\int d^3x'\, \psi_\sigma^{(\eta)\times}(\mathbf{x}')\, F_\sigma(\mathbf{x}') \right] \psi_\rho^{(\eta)}(\mathbf{x}) \\ &= \delta_{\sigma\rho} \int d^3x'\, F_\sigma(\mathbf{x}')\delta(\mathbf{x} - \mathbf{x}') \end{aligned}$$

so that we obtain the completeness relation

$$\sum_{\eta} \psi_\sigma^{(\eta)\times}(\mathbf{x}')\, \psi_\rho^{(\eta)}(\mathbf{x}) = \delta_{\sigma\rho}\delta(\mathbf{x} - \mathbf{x}') \tag{3.42}$$

This relation would be valid for any complete orthonormal set. For the plane wave case we use

$$\psi^{(\eta)}(\mathbf{x}) = a^{(\eta)}(\mathbf{p}) \exp(i\mathbf{p}\cdot\mathbf{x})$$

and (3.42) becomes

$$(2\pi)^{-3}\int \sum_{S_W\lambda} d^3p\, a_\sigma^{(\eta)\times}(\mathbf{p})\, a_\rho^{(\eta)}(\mathbf{p}) \exp[i\mathbf{p}\cdot(\mathbf{x} - \mathbf{x}')]$$
$$= \delta_{\sigma\rho}\delta(\mathbf{x} - \mathbf{x}') = (2\pi)^{-3}\delta_{\sigma\rho}\int d^3p \exp[i\mathbf{p}\cdot(\mathbf{x} - \mathbf{x}')]$$

by the Fourier expansion of the delta function. Hence

$$\sum_{S_W\lambda} a_\rho^{(\eta)}(\mathbf{p})\, a_\sigma^{(\eta)\times}(\mathbf{p}) = \delta_{\rho\sigma} \tag{3.43}$$

In previous sections the notation was $a(\mathbf{p}) = U(\mathbf{p})$ for $W = p_0$ and $a = V(-\mathbf{p})$ for $W = -p_0$. In (3.43) the label η should be interpreted only as an abbreviation for the set of two numbers S_W and λ. For definiteness we label the four by $\eta = 1, 2, 3, 4$ according to the following scheme:

η	1	2	3	4
S_W	1	1	−1	−1
λ	1	−1	1	−1

(3.44)

Thus $\eta = 1$ and 2 are positive energy states, $\eta = 3$ and 4 are negative energy states. For $\eta = 1$ and 3 the spin component ($\langle \mathcal{O}_z \rangle$) along z is positive; for $\eta = 2$ and 4 it is negative. The notation

$$P_{\rho\sigma}^{(\eta)} = a_\rho^{(\eta)}(\mathbf{p})\, a_\sigma^{(\eta)\times}(\mathbf{p})$$

then refers to the elements of a matrix $P^{(\eta)}$. Since

$$(a^{(\eta)}, a^{(\eta')}) = \delta_{\eta\eta'} = \delta_{S_W S_{W'}}\delta_{\lambda\lambda'}$$

the following properties are seen to hold:

$$(P^{(\eta)} P^{(\eta')})_{\rho\sigma} = P_{\rho\tau}^{(\eta)} P_{\tau\sigma}^{(\eta')} = a_\rho^{(\eta)}\, a_\tau^{(\eta)\times}\, a_\tau^{(\eta')}\, a_\sigma^{(\eta')\times}$$
$$= \delta_{\eta\eta'} a_\rho^{(\eta)} a_\sigma^{(\eta')\times} = \delta_{\eta\eta'} P_{\rho\sigma}^{(\eta)}$$

Hence

$$P^{(\eta)} P^{(\eta')} = 0 \qquad \text{if } \eta \neq \eta' \tag{3.45a}$$

and†

$$[P^{(\eta)}]^2 = P^{(\eta)} \tag{3.45b}$$

† Since $P^{(\eta)}$ is not a unit matrix, it follows that $\det P^{(\eta)} = 0$, as it must for all projection operators.

Finally,

$$\sum_{\eta=1}^{4} P^{(\eta)} = 1 \tag{3.46}$$

These results show that each $P^{(\eta)}$ is a projection operator: Eq. (3.45a) is the mutually exclusive property, (3.45b) the idempotent property, and (3.46) the exhaustive property.

If $\eta \neq \eta'$ the matrix $P^{(\eta)} + P^{(\eta')}$ is also a projection operator. Thus, for

$$P(12) = P^{(1)} + P^{(2)}$$

we have, from (3.45),

$$[P(12)]^2 = [P^{(1)}]^2 + [P^{(2)}]^2 = P^{(1)} + P^{(2)} = P(12)$$

Also

$$P(34)\,P(12) = P(12)\,P(34) = 0$$

by (3.45a) and

$$P(12) + P(34) = 1$$

by (3.46).

The projection of greatest physical interest are the four $P^{(\eta)}$ and those for positive and negative energy as well as positive and negative spin projection. The energy projection operators are

$$\begin{aligned} P(p_0) &\equiv P^{(1)} + P^{(2)} \\ P(-p_0) &\equiv P^{(3)} + P^{(4)} \end{aligned} \tag{3.48}$$

and the spin projection operators are

$$\begin{aligned} P(1) &\equiv P^{(1)} + P^{(3)} \\ P(-1) &\equiv P^{(2)} + P^{(4)} \end{aligned} \tag{3.48}$$

Energy Projection Operators

We first consider the positive energy projection operator. We write

$$P(p_0) = \sum_{A=1}^{16} c_A \gamma_A$$

and it follows that

$$\begin{aligned} 4c_A \equiv 4c(\gamma_A) &= \operatorname{Tr} \gamma_A P(p_0) \\ &= (\gamma_A)_{\lambda\rho} \sum_{\eta=1,2} a_\rho^{(\eta)} a_\lambda^{(\eta)\times} \\ &= \sum_{\eta=1,2} a_\lambda^{(\eta)\times} (\gamma_A)_{\lambda\rho}\, a_\rho^{(\eta)} \\ &= \sum_{\eta=1,2} (a^{(\eta)}, \gamma_A a^{(\eta)}) \end{aligned}$$

Whereas the trace is independent of the representation, the explicit γ_A are not. We use the standard representation. With $a^{(1)} = U_+$ and $a^{(2)} = U_-$ we obtain

$$4c(1) = \sum_\eta (a^{(\eta)}, a^{(\eta)}) = 2$$
$$4c(\beta) = 2/p_0$$
$$4c(\alpha_i) = 2p_i/p_0$$

and all other $c(\gamma_A) = 0$. These results are obtained easily by recognizing that γ_A has one of two forms: either γ_A is even:

$$\gamma_A = \begin{pmatrix} a & 0 \\ 0 & b \end{pmatrix}$$

with $a = \pm b$, or γ_A is odd:

$$\gamma_A = \begin{pmatrix} 0 & a \\ b & 0 \end{pmatrix}$$

with $a^* = b$ and, since a (and therefore b) is either hermitian or anti-hermitian, $a = \pm b$. Then, for even γ_A,

$$\sum_\eta (a^{(\eta)}, \gamma_A a^{(\eta)}) = \frac{p_0 + 1}{2p_0} \sum_m \left(\chi^m, \left(a \pm \frac{p_0 - 1}{p_0 + 1} \boldsymbol{\sigma}\cdot\hat{\mathbf{p}}\; a\boldsymbol{\sigma}\cdot\hat{\mathbf{p}}\right) \chi^m\right)$$

for $a = \pm b$, and, for γ_A odd,

$$\sum_\eta (a^{(\eta)}, \gamma_A a^{(\eta)}) = \frac{p}{2p_0} \sum_m (\chi^m, (a, \boldsymbol{\sigma}\cdot\hat{\mathbf{p}})_\pm\, \chi^m)$$

where the anticommutator is used for $a = b$ and the commutator, $(a, \boldsymbol{\sigma}\cdot\hat{\mathbf{p}})_-$, for $a = -b$. The result is then

$$P(p_0) = P_+ = \frac{1}{2}\left(1 + \frac{\boldsymbol{\alpha}\cdot\mathbf{p} + \beta}{p_0}\right)$$
$$= \frac{1}{2}\left(1 + \frac{h}{p_0}\right) \tag{3.49}$$

just as was to be expected. From (3.49) the idempotent property is obvious since $h^2/p_0^2 = 1$.

For the negative energy states, $a^{(3)} = V_+(-\mathbf{p})$, $a^{(4)} = V_-(-\mathbf{p})$, and

$$P(-p_0) = P_- = \frac{1}{4} \sum_A \sum_{\eta=3,4} (a^{(\eta)}, \gamma_A a^{(\eta)})\gamma_A$$

Interchanging small and large components and changing the sign of $\mathbf{p}$ in the positive energy case, we have

$$\sum_\eta (a^{(\eta)}, \gamma_A a^{(\eta)}) = \frac{p_0 + 1}{2p_0} \sum_m \left[\chi^m, \left(\frac{p_0 - 1}{p_0 + 1} \boldsymbol{\sigma}\cdot\hat{\mathbf{p}}a\, \boldsymbol{\sigma}\cdot\hat{\mathbf{p}} \pm a\right) \chi^m\right]$$

for even γ_A and $a = \pm b$, and also

$$\sum_{\eta} (a^{(\eta)}, \gamma_A a^{(\eta)}) = -\frac{p}{2p_0} \sum_{m} (\chi^m, (\boldsymbol{\sigma}\cdot\hat{\mathbf{p}}, a)_{\pm}\, \chi^m)$$

for γ_A odd and $a = \pm b$. Hence c_A changes sign for γ_A odd and for γ_A even with $a = -b$, while c_A remains the same for γ_A even and $a = b$. Thus we find

$$P_- = \frac{1}{2}\left(1 - \frac{\boldsymbol{\alpha}\cdot\mathbf{p} + \beta}{p_0}\right) = \frac{1}{2}\left(1 - \frac{h}{p_0}\right) \tag{3.50}$$

Again $P_-^2 = P_-$ is obvious and

$$P_+P_- = P_-P_+ = 0, \qquad P_+ + P_- = 1$$

is readily checked.

In general, if ψ is a linear combination of positive and negative energy states

$$\psi = \psi_+ + \psi_-$$

in an obvious notation,

$$P_+\psi = \psi_+$$

$$P_-\psi = \psi_-$$

since $P_+\psi_- = P_-\psi_+ = 0$. The result $P_+^n\psi = \psi_+$ and $P_-^n\psi = \psi_-$ for any integer n is then also obvious.

For the positron states the momentum is the negative of that for negative energy states. Retaining the symbol $\mathbf{p}$ for the observed momentum gives the operator

$$P_{\text{pos}} = \frac{1}{2}\left(1 + \frac{\boldsymbol{\alpha}\cdot\mathbf{p} - \beta}{p_0}\right) = P_+^c = CP_+^{\times}C^{-1} \tag{3.51}$$

This is a projection operator in the sense that $P_{\text{pos}}^2 = P_{\text{pos}}$, but clearly the complete set of projection operators of which P_{pos} is a member contains $P_+(-\mathbf{p}) = \frac{1}{2}p_0^{-1}(p_0 - \boldsymbol{\alpha}\cdot\mathbf{p} + \beta)$, as the other member.

The New Representation

Instead of using $P(\pm 1)$ or $P^{(\eta)}$ defined above, it is more useful to define the spin projection operators in terms of eigenfunctions of $\mathcal{O}\cdot\hat{\mathbf{n}}$ and $\mathcal{O}^c\cdot\hat{\mathbf{n}}$ where, as before,

$$\mathcal{O} = \boldsymbol{\sigma}\cdot\hat{\mathbf{p}}\,\hat{\mathbf{p}} + \sum_i \beta\boldsymbol{\sigma}\cdot\hat{\mathbf{e}}_i\,\hat{\mathbf{e}}_i$$

$$\mathcal{O}^c = -\boldsymbol{\sigma}\cdot\hat{\mathbf{p}}\,\hat{\mathbf{p}} + \sum_i \beta\boldsymbol{\sigma}\cdot\hat{\mathbf{e}}_i\,\hat{\mathbf{e}}_i$$

Since

$$\sum_i \boldsymbol{\sigma}\cdot\hat{\mathbf{e}}_i\,\hat{\mathbf{e}}_i = \boldsymbol{\sigma} - \boldsymbol{\sigma}\cdot\hat{\mathbf{p}}\,\hat{\mathbf{p}} = \hat{\mathbf{p}} \times (\boldsymbol{\sigma} \times \hat{\mathbf{p}}) = \boldsymbol{\sigma}_\perp$$

these can also be written in the form

$$\left.\begin{matrix}\mathcal{O}\\ \mathcal{O}^c\end{matrix}\right\} = \pm\boldsymbol{\sigma}\cdot\hat{\mathbf{p}}\,\hat{\mathbf{p}} + \beta\boldsymbol{\sigma}_\perp$$

Clearly $\boldsymbol{\sigma}_\perp$ and $\boldsymbol{\sigma}\cdot\hat{\mathbf{p}}\,\hat{\mathbf{p}}$ anticommute since they are obtained from σ_x, σ_y, and σ_z by a rotation of the z-axis to the direction $\hat{\mathbf{n}}$. We note that

$$\mathcal{O} = \beta\boldsymbol{\sigma} + (1 - \beta)\,\boldsymbol{\sigma}\cdot\hat{\mathbf{p}}\,\hat{\mathbf{p}}$$

$$\mathcal{O}^c = \beta\boldsymbol{\sigma} - (1 + \beta)\,\boldsymbol{\sigma}\cdot\hat{\mathbf{p}}\,\hat{\mathbf{p}}$$

so that in the non-relativistic limit $\beta \to 1$, $\mathcal{O} \to \boldsymbol{\sigma}$ and $\beta \to -1$, $\mathcal{O}^c \to -\boldsymbol{\sigma}$ as expected.

The eigenvalue problem

$$\mathcal{O}\cdot\hat{\mathbf{n}}\,\Psi = \lambda\Psi$$

must give eigenvalues $\lambda = \pm 1$ since

$$(\mathcal{O}\cdot\hat{\mathbf{n}})^2 = 1$$

The same is true for $\mathcal{O}^c\cdot\hat{\mathbf{n}}$. We write, for the electron,

$$\Psi = b_+\psi_+ + b_-\psi_- = A\exp(i\mathbf{p}\cdot\mathbf{x})$$

where

$$\psi_\pm = U_\pm(\mathbf{p})\exp(i\mathbf{p}\cdot\mathbf{x})$$

since Ψ is also an eigenfunction of $\vec{\mathbf{p}}$ with eigenvalue $\mathbf{p}$. Then the exponential factors cancel. The eigenvalue problem is then

$$\mathcal{O}\cdot\hat{\mathbf{n}}A = \mathcal{O}\cdot\hat{\mathbf{n}}(b_+U_+ + b_-U_-) = \lambda(b_+U_+ + b_-U_-) \tag{3.52}$$

But

$$\mathcal{O}\cdot\hat{\mathbf{n}}U_\pm = \left(\frac{p_0 + 1}{2p_0}\right)^{1/2}\begin{pmatrix}(\boldsymbol{\sigma}\cdot\hat{\mathbf{p}}\,\hat{\mathbf{p}} + \boldsymbol{\sigma}_\perp)\,\chi^m \\ (\boldsymbol{\sigma}\cdot\hat{\mathbf{p}}\,\hat{\mathbf{p}} - \boldsymbol{\sigma}_\perp)\,\dfrac{\boldsymbol{\sigma}\cdot\mathbf{p}}{p_0 + 1}\,\chi^m\end{pmatrix}\cdot\hat{\mathbf{n}}$$

We observe that $\boldsymbol{\sigma}_\perp\cdot\hat{\mathbf{n}}$ and $\boldsymbol{\sigma}\cdot\hat{\mathbf{p}}$ anticommute, and (3.52) becomes

$$\sum_m b_m(\boldsymbol{\sigma}\cdot\hat{\mathbf{p}}\,\hat{\mathbf{p}}\cdot\hat{\mathbf{n}} + \boldsymbol{\sigma}_\perp\cdot\hat{\mathbf{n}})\,\chi^m = \lambda\sum_m b_m\,\chi^m$$

from the upper components and

$$\sum_m b_m(\hat{\mathbf{p}}\cdot\hat{\mathbf{n}} + \boldsymbol{\sigma}\cdot\hat{\mathbf{p}}\,\boldsymbol{\sigma}_\perp\cdot\hat{\mathbf{n}})\,\chi^m = \lambda\sum_m b_m\boldsymbol{\sigma}\cdot\hat{\mathbf{p}}\,\chi^m$$

from the lower components. By operating on the left with $\boldsymbol{\sigma}\cdot\hat{\mathbf{p}}$ in the second equation, this equation becomes identical with the first and the problem is reduced to the transformation of the upper components only, that is, of the Pauli spin functions. Moreover, $\boldsymbol{\sigma}\cdot\hat{\mathbf{p}}\,\hat{\mathbf{p}}\cdot\hat{\mathbf{n}} + \boldsymbol{\sigma}_\perp\cdot\hat{\mathbf{n}} = \boldsymbol{\sigma}\cdot\hat{\mathbf{n}}$ and the transformation in question is one that diagonalizes $\boldsymbol{\sigma}\cdot\hat{\mathbf{n}}$ in the χ^m representation. This transformation has already been carried out in section 5, and those results can be taken over at once. Thus the coefficients $b_\pm$ are identical with the a_m used there. The result is then

$$A = A_+ = e^{-i\varphi/2}\cos\frac{\vartheta}{2}\,U_+ + e^{i\varphi/2}\sin\frac{\vartheta}{2}\,U_- \tag{3.53a}$$

for $\lambda = 1$ and

$$A = A_- = -e^{-i\varphi/2}\sin\frac{\vartheta}{2}\,U_+ + e^{i\varphi/2}\cos\frac{\vartheta}{2}\,U_- \tag{3.53b}$$

for $\lambda = -1$. Here ϑ and φ are the polar and azimuth angles of $\hat{\mathbf{n}}$ as before. For $\varphi = 0$, $\vartheta = 0$ these reduce to $A_\pm = U_\pm$ as they should. Note that, for $\vartheta = 0$, the factor $\exp(\pm i\varphi/2)$ enters as a trivial phase corresponding to the fact that, if $\hat{\mathbf{n}}$ is along the z-axis, the positions of the x- and y-axes are not specified.

Just as in section 15 we can show that

$$(\Psi_\pm, \mathcal{O}\Psi_\pm) = (A_\pm, \mathcal{O}A_\pm) = \pm\hat{\mathbf{n}} \tag{3.54}$$

This would be expected from the general principle of covariance. However, as a check the result (3.54) will be worked out for Ψ_+. From (3.53),

$$(\Psi_+, \mathcal{O}\Psi_+) = \cos^2\frac{\vartheta}{2}\,(U_+|\mathcal{O}|U_+) + \sin^2\frac{\vartheta}{2}\,(U_-\,\mathcal{O}|U_-)$$
$$+ \tfrac{1}{2}e^{i\varphi}\sin\vartheta(U_+|\mathcal{O}|U_-) + \tfrac{1}{2}e^{-i\varphi}\sin\vartheta(U_-|\mathcal{O}|U_+)$$

Since $\mathcal{O}$ is hermitian the last term is the complex conjugate of the third. It is also seen that

$$(U_m|\boldsymbol{\sigma}\cdot\hat{\mathbf{p}}\,\hat{\mathbf{p}}|U_{m'}) = \hat{\mathbf{p}}\,\frac{p_0+1}{2p_0}\left[1 + \frac{p^2}{(p_0+1)^2}\right](\chi^m, \boldsymbol{\sigma}\cdot\hat{\mathbf{p}}\,\chi^{m'})$$
$$= \hat{\mathbf{p}}(\chi^m, \boldsymbol{\sigma}\cdot\hat{\mathbf{p}}\,\chi^{m'})$$

and

$$(U_m|\beta\boldsymbol{\sigma}\cdot\hat{\mathbf{e}}_i\,\hat{\mathbf{e}}_i|U_{m'}) = \hat{\mathbf{e}}_i(\chi^m, \boldsymbol{\sigma}\cdot\hat{\mathbf{e}}_i\,\chi^{m'}); \qquad i = 1, 2$$

where again U_m is written for $U_\pm$. Then since

$$\begin{aligned}(\chi^m, \boldsymbol{\sigma}\cdot\mathbf{V}\,\chi^{m'}) &= V_z && \text{for } m = m' = \tfrac{1}{2}\\ &= -V_z && \text{for } m = m' = -\tfrac{1}{2}\\ &= V_x - iV_y && \text{for } m = -m' = \tfrac{1}{2}\\ &= V_x + iV_y && \text{for } m = -m' = -\tfrac{1}{2}\end{aligned} \tag{3.55}$$

we obtain

$$\left(\Upsilon_+, \mathcal{O}\Upsilon_+\right) = \cos\vartheta\left(\hat{\mathbf{p}}\,\hat{p}_z + \sum_j \hat{\mathbf{e}}_j\hat{e}_{jz}\right)$$

$$+ \tfrac{1}{2}\sin\vartheta\left\{e^{i\varphi}\left[\hat{\mathbf{p}}(\hat{p}_x - i\hat{p}_y) + \sum_j \hat{\mathbf{e}}_j(\hat{e}_{jx} - i\hat{e}_{jy})\right] + \text{complex conjugate}\right\}$$

Since $\hat{n}_z = \cos\vartheta$ and $\hat{n}_x \pm i\hat{n}_y = \sin\vartheta e^{\pm i\varphi}$, this becomes

$$(\Upsilon_+, \mathcal{O}\Upsilon_+) = \hat{n}_z\hat{\mathbf{e}}_z + \tfrac{1}{2}(\hat{n}_x + i\hat{n}_y)(\hat{\mathbf{e}}_x - i\hat{\mathbf{e}}_y) + \tfrac{1}{2}(\hat{n}_x - i\hat{n}_y)(\hat{\mathbf{e}}_x + i\hat{\mathbf{e}}_y)$$

$$= \hat{\mathbf{n}} \tag{3.56}$$

In a similar way we find

$$(\Upsilon_-, \mathcal{O}\Upsilon_-) = -\hat{\mathbf{n}} \tag{3.56'}$$

since the vector $\hat{\mathbf{n}}$ occurs only in the coefficients b_m and, under the transformation $\vartheta \to \pi - \vartheta$, $\varphi \to \pi + \varphi$, the coefficients b_m for $\lambda = 1$ go over into i times the coefficients b_m for $\lambda = -1$. The factor i, of course, does not enter into the expectation value.

The two states $\Upsilon_\pm$ completely span the two-dimensional spin space for positive energy states, just as was the case for $\psi_\pm$. For the positron states the results are obtained most simply by charge conjugation. Thus

$$\Upsilon^c_\pm = C\Upsilon^\times_\mp$$

so

$$A^c_+ = -e^{i\varphi/2}\sin\frac{\vartheta}{2}\,U^c_+ + e^{-i\varphi/2}\cos\frac{\vartheta}{2}\,U^c_-$$

$$= e^{-i\varphi/2}\cos\frac{\vartheta}{2}\,V_+ - e^{i\varphi/2}\sin\frac{\vartheta}{2}\,V_-$$

and

$$A^c_- = e^{i\varphi/2}\cos\frac{\vartheta}{2}\,U^c_+ + e^{-i\varphi/2}\sin\frac{\vartheta}{2}\,U^c_-$$

$$= e^{i\varphi/2}\cos\frac{\vartheta}{2}\,V_- + e^{-i\varphi/2}\sin\frac{\vartheta}{2}\,V_+$$

which should be compared with (3.53a, b). The eigenvalue equations for the spin now read

$$\mathcal{O}^c\cdot\hat{\mathbf{n}}\,\Upsilon^c_\pm = \mp\Upsilon^c_\pm$$

and, in addition,

$$(\Upsilon^c_\pm, \mathcal{O}^c\Upsilon^c_\pm) = (C\Upsilon^\times_\mp, C\mathcal{O}^\times C^{-1}C\Upsilon^\times_\mp)$$

$$= (\Upsilon_\mp, \mathcal{O}\Upsilon_\mp)^\times = \mp\hat{\mathbf{n}}$$

The interpretation of $\Psi^{c}_{\pm}$, for a given vector $\hat{\mathbf{n}}$, is then in one-to-one correspondence with the interpretation of $\Psi_{\mp}$. Alternatively, the vector $\hat{\mathbf{n}}$ is replaced by $-\hat{\mathbf{n}}$ upon charge conjugation. This is in agreement with the result that the $V_{\pm}$ are eigenfunctions of $\mathcal{O}^{c}_{z}$ with eigenvalues ∓ 1.

The Spin Projection Operators

With the wave functions $\Psi_{\pm}$ and $\Psi^{c}_{\pm}$ we construct the spin projection operators, that is, the matrices with elements

$$P_{\rho\sigma}(\pm\hat{\mathbf{n}}) = (\Psi_{\pm})_{\rho}(\Psi_{\pm})^{\times}_{\sigma} = (A_{\pm})_{\rho}(A_{\pm})^{\times}_{\sigma} \tag{3.57}$$

Only $P(\hat{\mathbf{n}})$ need be calculated since $P(-\hat{\mathbf{n}})$ is obtained by changing the sign of $\hat{\mathbf{n}}$. As before,

$$P(n) = \tfrac{1}{4}\sum_{A}(A_{+}, \gamma_{A}A_{+})\gamma_{A} \tag{3.57'}$$

Separating the various possible γ_A into even and odd Dirac matrices facilitates the calculation of the expectation values. For even Dirac matrices we find

γ_A	$(A_{+}, \gamma_A A_{+})$
1	1
β	p_0^{-1}
$\boldsymbol{\sigma}$	$p_0^{-1}[\mathbf{V} + (p_0 - 1)\hat{\mathbf{p}}\cdot\mathbf{V}\,\hat{\mathbf{p}}]$
$\beta\boldsymbol{\sigma}$	$\mathbf{V} - p_0^{-1}(p_0 - 1)\hat{\mathbf{p}}\cdot\mathbf{V}\,\hat{\mathbf{p}}$

where

$$\mathbf{V} = \sum_{mm'} b^{\times}_{m} b_{m'}(\chi^{m}, \boldsymbol{\sigma}\chi^{m'})$$

For the odd γ_A the results are

γ_A	$(A_{+}, \gamma_A A_{+})$
γ_5	$-p_0^{-1}\mathbf{p}\cdot\mathbf{V}$
$\boldsymbol{\alpha}$	$\mathbf{p}/p_0$
$i\beta\boldsymbol{\alpha}$	$-p_0^{-1}(\mathbf{p}\times\mathbf{V})$
$i\beta\gamma_5$	0

The vector $\mathbf{V}$ is readily obtained from (3.53a) and the result is

$$\mathbf{V} = \hat{\mathbf{n}}$$

Consequently,

$$\begin{aligned} P(\hat{\mathbf{n}}) = \tfrac{1}{4}\{1 &+ p_0^{-1}(\beta + \boldsymbol{\alpha}\cdot\mathbf{p}) + p_0^{-1}\boldsymbol{\sigma}\cdot[\hat{\mathbf{n}} + (p_0 - 1)\hat{\mathbf{n}}\cdot\hat{\mathbf{p}}\,\hat{\mathbf{p}}] \\ &+ \beta\boldsymbol{\sigma}\cdot[\hat{\mathbf{n}} - p_0^{-1}(p_0 - 1)\hat{\mathbf{n}}\cdot\hat{\mathbf{p}}\,\hat{\mathbf{p}}] \\ &- ip_0^{-1}\beta\boldsymbol{\alpha}\cdot(\mathbf{p}\times\hat{\mathbf{n}}) - p_0^{-1}\gamma_5\hat{\mathbf{n}}\cdot\mathbf{p}\} \end{aligned} \tag{3.58}$$

We observe that

$$P(\mathbf{n}) + P(-\mathbf{n}) = \tfrac{1}{2}(1 + h/p_0) = P_+$$

That is, the positive energy projection operator is obtained by summing over the two spin states in either basis, as expected.

For the positron the projection operator is readily obtained by charge conjugation. This gives

$$\begin{aligned} P^c(\hat{\mathbf{n}}) = \tfrac{1}{4}\{1 &+ p_0^{-1}(-\beta + \boldsymbol{\alpha}\cdot\mathbf{p}) - p_0^{-1}\boldsymbol{\sigma}\cdot[\hat{\mathbf{n}} + (p_0 - 1)\hat{\mathbf{n}}\cdot\hat{\mathbf{p}}\,\hat{\mathbf{p}}] \\ &+ \beta\boldsymbol{\sigma}\cdot[\hat{\mathbf{n}} - p_0^{-1}(p_0 - 1)\hat{\mathbf{n}}\cdot\hat{\mathbf{p}}\,\hat{\mathbf{p}}] \\ &- ip_0^{-1}\beta\boldsymbol{\alpha}\cdot(\mathbf{p} \times \hat{\mathbf{n}}) + p_0^{-1}\gamma_5\hat{\mathbf{n}}\cdot\mathbf{p}\} \end{aligned} \tag{3.59}$$

In the rest system, $p \to 0$, $p_0 \to 1$, and

$$P(\hat{\mathbf{n}}) \to \tfrac{1}{2}(1 + \boldsymbol{\sigma}\cdot\hat{\mathbf{n}})\tfrac{1}{2}(1 + \beta) = P_0(\hat{\mathbf{n}}) \tag{3.60a}$$

$$P^c(n) \to \tfrac{1}{2}(1 - \boldsymbol{\sigma}\cdot\hat{\mathbf{n}})\tfrac{1}{2}(1 - \beta) = P_0^c(\hat{\mathbf{n}}) \tag{3.60b}$$

These are just the products of the non-relativistic spin projection operator and the positive and negative energy projection operators in the rest system. The projection operators $P(\hat{\mathbf{n}})$ and $P^c(\hat{\mathbf{n}})$ can be written more compactly in terms of these rest system operators. For this purpose we define

$$\Psi(0) = \sum_m b_m \begin{pmatrix} \chi^m \\ 0 \end{pmatrix}$$

which is the limit as $p \to 0$ of the actual wave functions. Then, for positive energy,

$$\begin{aligned} P_+\Psi(0) &= \frac{1}{2}\left[1 + \frac{\boldsymbol{\alpha}\cdot\mathbf{p} + \beta}{p_0}\right]\sum b_m \begin{pmatrix} \chi^m \\ 0 \end{pmatrix} \\ &= \sum_m b_m \frac{p_0 + 1}{2p_0}\begin{pmatrix} \chi^m \\ \dfrac{\boldsymbol{\sigma}\cdot\mathbf{p}}{p_0 + 1}\chi^m \end{pmatrix} = \left(\frac{p_0 + 1}{2p_0}\right)^{\frac{1}{2}} A_+ \end{aligned}$$

Then

$$\begin{aligned} P_{\sigma\rho}(\hat{\mathbf{n}}) = \Psi_\sigma\Psi_\rho^\times &= \frac{2p_0}{p_0 + 1}(P_+)_{\sigma\mu}\Psi_\mu(0)\Psi_\tau^\times(0)(P_+)_{\tau\rho} \\ &= \frac{2p_0}{p_0 + 1}(P_+P_0P_+)_{\sigma\rho} \end{aligned}$$

Therefore

$$P(\hat{\mathbf{n}}) = \frac{2p_0}{p_0 + 1}P_+\frac{(1 + \boldsymbol{\sigma}\cdot n)(1 + \beta)}{4}P_+ \tag{3.61}$$

Similarly,

$$P^c(\hat{\mathbf{n}}) = \frac{2p_0}{p_0 + 1} P_+^c P_0^c P_+^c$$

$$= \frac{2p_0}{p_0 + 1} P_{\text{pos}} \frac{(1 - \boldsymbol{\sigma}\cdot\hat{\mathbf{n}})(1 - \beta)}{4} P_{\text{pos}} \tag{3.62}$$

The projection operators in this form will play an important role in the theory of scattering as given in section 33 and the discussion of Compton scattering, section 37.

20. COVARIANT DESCRIPTION OF SPIN[20,21]

The spin projection operator obtained in the preceding section is readily understood in terms of a covariant description of the spin.

We consider two reference systems: the rest system and the laboratory system in which the electron or positron has momentum **p**. We use bars to refer to the rest system and write the four-vector momentum:

$$\bar{p}_\mu = (0, i) \tag{3.63}$$

where the first entry in the parentheses gives the space part of the vector. The spin vector will be

$$\bar{n}_\mu = (\hat{\mathbf{n}}_0, 0) \tag{3.64}$$

where $\hat{\mathbf{n}}_0$ is the unit vector previously written $\hat{\mathbf{n}}$. Obviously

$$\bar{n}_\mu \bar{p}_\mu = 0$$

and therefore, in all reference systems,

$$n_\mu p_\mu = 0 \tag{3.65}$$

where n_μ and p_μ are the components of the four-vector into which $\bar{n}_\mu$ and $\bar{p}_\mu$ transform under the Lorentz transformation. Similarly,

$$n_\mu n_\mu = 1 = \mathbf{n}^2 + n_4^2 \tag{3.66}$$

where $n_\mu = (\mathbf{n}, n_4)$ and

$$p_\mu p_\mu = -1 = \mathbf{p}^2 - p_0^2$$

since $p_\mu = (\mathbf{p}, p_4 = ip_0)$.

Under a Lorentz transformation of the rest system with velocity $-\mathbf{v} = -\mathbf{p}/\xi$ the particle acquires a velocity $\mathbf{v}$. Then, since $\bar{n}_\mu$ transforms like a polar four-vector under the continuous Lorentz transformation, we can use (B.6) and (B.7) of Appendix B with $\mathbf{v}$ replaced by $-\mathbf{p}/p_0$, $\xi = p^0$ and obtain

$$\begin{aligned} \mathbf{n} &= \hat{\mathbf{n}}_0 + (p_0 - 1)\hat{\mathbf{n}}_0\cdot\hat{\mathbf{p}}\,\hat{\mathbf{p}} \\ n_4 &= i\hat{\mathbf{n}}_0\cdot\mathbf{p} \end{aligned} \tag{3.67}$$

From (3.65) we obtain

$$n_4 = i\mathbf{n}\cdot\mathbf{p}/p_0 \tag{3.67a}$$

From (3.66) we obtain

$$\mathbf{n}^2 = 1 + (\mathbf{n}_0\cdot\mathbf{p})^2 \geqslant 1 \tag{3.68}$$

Of course, (3.67) substituted into (3.67a) gives an identity.

For $\hat{\mathbf{n}}_0\cdot\mathbf{p} = 0$, the vector $\mathbf{n}$ is a unit vector $= \hat{\mathbf{n}}_0$. For $\hat{\mathbf{n}}_0 \times \mathbf{p} = 0$, so that $(\hat{\mathbf{n}}_0\cdot\mathbf{p})^2 = \mathbf{p}^2$, $\mathbf{n}$ has the magnitude p_0 and is again in the direction of $\hat{\mathbf{n}}_0$. For other cases these two vectors are not parallel.

The spin is described in a covariant manner by introducing the operator

$$Q(n) = i\gamma_5\gamma_\mu n_\mu \tag{3.69}$$

Clearly $\bar{\psi}Q(n)\psi$ transforms like a pseudoscalar under Lorentz transformation just as $\boldsymbol{\sigma}\cdot\hat{\mathbf{n}}_0$ transforms under the extended group of three-dimensional space rotations and reflections. The operators

$$\tfrac{1}{2}[1 \pm Q(n)]$$

are, moreover, projection operators since

$$\begin{aligned} Q^2(n) &= -\gamma_5\gamma_\mu n_\mu \gamma_5\gamma_\nu n_\nu \\ &= n_\mu n_\nu \tfrac{1}{2}(\gamma_\mu\gamma_\nu + \gamma_\nu\gamma_\mu) \\ &= n_\mu n_\mu = 1 \end{aligned}$$

For the rest system

$$\tfrac{1}{2}[1 \pm Q(n)] \to \tfrac{1}{2}(1 \pm \beta\boldsymbol{\sigma}\cdot\mathbf{n}) = \tfrac{1}{2}(1 \pm \beta\boldsymbol{\sigma}\cdot\hat{\mathbf{n}}_0)$$

and for both electrons ($\beta \to 1$) and positrons ($\beta \to -1$) this gives the expected results. We may also observe that the charge conjugated operator is

$$Q^c(n) = Q(n) \tag{3.69'}$$

We now show that $Q(n)$ is completely equivalent to $\mathcal{O}\cdot\hat{\mathbf{n}}_0$ for the electron and to $\mathcal{O}^c\cdot\hat{\mathbf{n}}_0$ for the positron. It is first observed that

$$\begin{aligned} Q &= \gamma_5\beta\boldsymbol{\alpha}\cdot\mathbf{n} + i\gamma_5\beta n_4 \\ &= \beta\boldsymbol{\sigma}\cdot\mathbf{n} + \beta\gamma_5\mathbf{n}\cdot\mathbf{p}/p_0 \end{aligned}$$

With

$$\mathcal{O}\cdot\hat{\mathbf{n}}_0 = \boldsymbol{\sigma}\cdot\hat{\mathbf{p}}\,\hat{\mathbf{p}}\cdot\hat{\mathbf{n}}_0 + \beta\boldsymbol{\sigma}\cdot\hat{\mathbf{n}}_0 - \beta\boldsymbol{\sigma}\cdot\hat{\mathbf{p}}\,\hat{\mathbf{p}}\cdot\hat{\mathbf{n}}_0$$

we obtain from (3.67) and (3.69)

$$\begin{aligned} Q(n) - \mathcal{O}\cdot\hat{\mathbf{n}}_0 &= \hat{\mathbf{n}}_0\cdot\hat{\mathbf{p}}[(p_0 - 1)\beta\boldsymbol{\sigma}\cdot\hat{\mathbf{p}} + p\beta\gamma_5/p_0 + \beta\gamma_5(p_0 - 1)p/p_0 \\ &\qquad - \boldsymbol{\sigma}\cdot\hat{\mathbf{p}} + \beta\boldsymbol{\sigma}\cdot\hat{\mathbf{p}}] \\ &= \mathbf{n}_0\cdot\hat{\mathbf{p}}[p_0\beta\boldsymbol{\sigma}\cdot\hat{\mathbf{p}} + \beta\gamma_5 p - \boldsymbol{\sigma}\cdot\hat{\mathbf{p}}] \\ &= \hat{\mathbf{n}}_0\cdot\hat{\mathbf{p}}\,\boldsymbol{\sigma}\cdot\hat{\mathbf{p}}[p_0\beta + \boldsymbol{\sigma}\cdot\hat{\mathbf{p}}\beta\gamma_5 p - 1] \\ &= \hat{\mathbf{n}}_0\cdot\hat{\mathbf{p}}\,\boldsymbol{\sigma}\cdot\hat{\mathbf{p}}[p_0\beta - \beta\boldsymbol{\alpha}\cdot\mathbf{p} - 1] \\ &= \hat{\mathbf{n}}_0\cdot\hat{\mathbf{p}}\,\boldsymbol{\sigma}\cdot\hat{\mathbf{p}}\beta(p_0 - \boldsymbol{\alpha}\cdot\mathbf{p} - \beta) \\ &= 2p_0\hat{\mathbf{n}}_0\cdot\hat{\mathbf{p}}\,\boldsymbol{\sigma}\cdot\hat{\mathbf{p}}\beta P_- \end{aligned} \tag{3.70}$$

Consequently, for a positive energy state ψ for which $\psi = P_+\psi$, it follows that

$$[Q(n) - \mathcal{O}\cdot\hat{\mathbf{n}}_0]\psi = 0 \tag{3.71}$$

In other words, the operator $Q(n) - \mathcal{O}\cdot\hat{\mathbf{n}}_0$ is a null operator for positive energy states only. We observe that, in contrast to $\mathcal{O}\cdot\hat{\mathbf{n}}_0$, $Q(n)$ does not commute with the free particle Hamiltonian. In fact,

$$[Q(n), h] = 2\gamma_5\gamma_4[n_\mu p_\mu + i(h - p_0)n_4] \neq 0$$

However, since $n_\mu p_\mu = 0$ we see that

$$[Q(n), h] = -4in_4\gamma_5\gamma_4 p_0 P_-$$

and, again, this gives zero when applied to a positive energy state. We see, then, that every positive energy eigenstate of $\mathcal{O}\cdot\hat{\mathbf{n}}_0$ is an eigenstate of $Q(n)$ with the same eigenvalue (± 1) and vice versa. This clarifies the observation that $\frac{1}{2}[1 \pm Q(n)]$ are projection operators. The same, of course, is true of $\frac{1}{2}(1 \pm \mathcal{O}\cdot\hat{\mathbf{n}}_0)$, and these projection operators select the spin eigenstates in the sense that these have been defined above.

For the spin operator $\mathcal{O}^c$ only the sign of the term without β must be changed. The steps given in (3.70) yield the result

$$Q(n) - \mathcal{O}^c\cdot\mathbf{n}_0 = 2p_0\hat{\mathbf{n}}_0\cdot\hat{\mathbf{p}}\,\boldsymbol{\sigma}\cdot\hat{\mathbf{p}}\beta(1 - P_{\text{pos}})$$

where P_{pos} is the positron energy projection operator introduced in (3.51). Therefore, for positrons as well, the operator $Q(n)$ is fully equivalent to $\mathcal{O}^c\cdot\hat{\mathbf{n}}_0$—a result to be anticipated in view of (3.69′).

The spin projection operator given in (3.58) or (3.61) is related to the spin operator $\mathcal{O}$ by

$$P(n_0) = P_+\tfrac{1}{2}(1 + \mathcal{O}\cdot\hat{\mathbf{n}}_0) \tag{3.72}$$

and the corresponding charge conjugate equation also holds, of course. This is the relation analogous to (3.60). Transformations to other coordinate systems are facilitated by using the covariant form of the projection operator. However, $P(\hat{\mathbf{n}}_0)$, as (3.72) shows, is not in such a form since P_+ is not. In fact, the covariant energy projection operators are

$$\tfrac{1}{2}(1 \mp i\gamma_\mu p_\mu) = p_0 \begin{Bmatrix} P_+\beta \\ -P^c_+\beta \end{Bmatrix} \tag{3.73}$$

where $P^c_+ = P_{\text{pos}}$. Since the spin-independent terms in $P(\hat{\mathbf{n}}_0)$ constitute the operator $\frac{1}{2}P_+$ the covariant form must be $p_0 P(\hat{\mathbf{n}}_0)\beta$. Direct calculation yields the result

$$4p_0 P(\hat{\mathbf{n}}_0)\beta = 1 - i\gamma_\mu p_\mu + i\gamma_5\gamma_\mu n_\mu + \gamma_\mu\gamma_\nu T_{\mu\nu} \tag{3.74}$$

Here n_μ is given by (3.67) and $T_{\mu\nu}$ is an antisymmetric four-tensor whose space-space components are

$$T_{jk} = -\frac{i}{2}\epsilon_{jkl}[p_0(\hat{n}_0)_l - (p_0 - 1)\hat{\mathbf{n}}_0\cdot\hat{\mathbf{p}}\,\hat{p}_l] \tag{3.74$'$}$$

and space-time components are

$$T_{j4} = \tfrac{1}{2}\epsilon_{jkl}p_k(\hat{n}_0)_l \tag{3.74$''$}$$

The stated transformation properties of $T_{\mu\nu}$ are readily verified by the methods of Appendix B. Each term in (3.74) is evidently covariant; thus $p_0\bar{\psi}P(\hat{\mathbf{n}}_0)\beta\psi$ is an invariant. The appearance of $Q(n)$ in (3.74) is to be noted. The last term in (3.74) indicates that an alternative and equivalent covariant description of spin is possible in terms of an antisymmetric four-tensor. In the rest system, for example, T_{jk} reduces to a multiple of $\hat{\mathbf{n}}_0$.

21. APPLICATION TO NUCLEAR BETA DECAY[22]

The extensive literature of nuclear beta decay and weak interactions in general bears testimony to the numerous phenomena involved. A comprehensive discussion of these phenomena is not our purpose, and our attention is restricted to a brief outline of the foundations of the theory and some applications.

A convenient starting point is that of the Lagrangian density $\mathscr{L}$ of the Dirac field. The Dirac equations themselves can be derived from a variation principle[23]

$$\delta\int \mathscr{L}(x)\, d^4x = 0$$

where, for free particles,

$$\mathscr{L}(x) = \psi^*\left(i\frac{\partial\psi}{\partial t} - \boldsymbol{\alpha}\cdot\vec{\mathbf{p}}\psi - \beta\psi\right) \tag{3.75}$$

$\mathscr{L}$ is a function of the four components of ψ^*, those of ψ and the derivatives thereof. Variation with respect to ψ_ρ gives the ρ-component of the wave equation for ψ^* and similarly for ψ.

For the interaction of four fermions which are taken to be Dirac particles the total Lagrangian density must then be a sum of four terms like (3.75), one for each particle, and an interaction term. The interaction term must be Lorentz invariant at least for the continuous transformations, and it will be assumed, in agreement with observations, that this interaction contains each of the four particles linearly with no derivatives of the fields occurring. Thus in the process

$$n \to p + e^- + \bar{\nu}$$

where, by definition the light neutral particle is an antineutrino, the interaction density in the Lagrangian is

$$\mathscr{L}_{\text{int}}(x) = -g\int d^3y(\bar{\psi}^p(\mathbf{x})\,\Gamma_{\mu..}\,\psi^n(\mathbf{x}))(\bar{\psi}^e(\mathbf{y})\,\Gamma_{\mu..}\,\psi^\nu(\mathbf{y}))\delta(\mathbf{x}-\mathbf{y})$$
$$+ \text{ hermitian conjugate} \qquad (3.76)$$

The δ-function implies a local interaction as in electromagnetic theory. It does not seem possible, within the present framework, to construct a consistent relativistic theory with any other kernel corresponding to a non-local theory. In (3.76) the $\Gamma_{\mu..}$ may be one of the five groups of γ_A matrices discussed in section 14. More generally, it is a linear combination of them. Thereby the relativistic invariance is assured. The constant g is determined empirically by the observed beta half-lives. The structure of the first term of (3.76) corresponds to creation of a proton and a positive energy electron and annihilation of a neutron and a negative energy neutrino. The hermitian conjugate term corresponds to the process

$$p \to n + e^+ + \nu$$

with a positive energy neutrino emitted with the positron. The ν and $\bar{\nu}$ are taken to be Dirac particles with zero rest mass.†

The Hamiltonian density is obtained from $\mathscr{L}$ in the usual way:

$$\mathscr{H} = \sum_\sigma \frac{\partial \mathscr{L}}{\partial \dot{\psi}_\sigma}\,\dot{\psi}_\sigma - \mathscr{L}$$

where σ runs over all fields and their conjugates. Since $\mathscr{L}_{\text{int}}$ contains no derivatives, the corresponding term in $\mathscr{H}$, that is, $\mathscr{H}_{\text{int}}$ will be just $-\mathscr{L}_{\text{int}}$.

† Experimentally, the neutrino mass is known to be less than 10^{-3} times the electron mass; see section 41. No experiment yet devised is sufficiently accurate to distinguish between zero mass and a mass of, say, $10^{-4}\,m$.[22]

The beta interaction obtained by the foregoing prescription would have the form

$$\mathscr{H}_{\text{int}} = g \sum_x C_x \mathscr{H}_x + \text{h.c.} \tag{3.77a}$$

where $x = S, V, T, A$, and P and, from (2.79),

$$\begin{aligned}
\mathscr{H}_S &= (\psi^{p*}\beta\psi^n)(\psi^{e*}\beta\psi^\nu) \\
\mathscr{H}_V &= (\psi^{p*}\psi^n)(\psi^{e}\ \psi^\nu) - (\psi^{p*}\boldsymbol{\alpha}\psi^n)\cdot(\psi^{e*}\boldsymbol{\alpha}\psi^\nu) \\
\mathscr{H}_T &= (\psi^{p*}\beta\boldsymbol{\sigma}\psi^n)\cdot(\psi^{e*}\beta\boldsymbol{\sigma}\psi^\nu) + (\psi^{p*}\beta\boldsymbol{\alpha}\psi^n)\cdot(\psi^{e*}\beta\boldsymbol{\alpha}\psi^\nu) \\
\mathscr{H}_A &= (\psi^{p*}\boldsymbol{\sigma}\psi^n)\cdot(\psi^{e*}\boldsymbol{\sigma}\psi^\nu) - (\psi^{p*}\gamma_5\psi^n)(\psi^{e*}\gamma_5\psi^\nu) \\
\mathscr{H}_P &= (\psi^{p*}\beta\gamma_5\psi^n)(\psi^{e*}\beta\gamma_5\psi^\nu)
\end{aligned} \tag{3.77b}$$

Therefore there would be ten coupling constants since the C_x are, in general, complex. There are, however, two important results which bear on the interaction $\mathscr{H}_{\text{int}}$. The first is the well-known fact that the interaction is *not* parity conserving as the scalar character of (3.77a) would indicate.[24,25] Actually, the assumption that $\mathscr{L}_{\text{int}}$ and therefore $\mathscr{H}_{\text{int}}$ must be a scalar is not based on experimental fact but was initially made as a natural assumption which is not only the simplest but is in complete parallel with other interactions, notably those of electromagnetic type. The observation, for example, that beta particles which are emitted from nuclei are polarized[26] is a sufficient datum to cause the conventional theory to be scrapped.

With this in mind, $\mathscr{H}_{\text{int}}$ must be a combination of scalar and pseudo-scalar terms since either one alone would give parity conservation.† Therefore, one writes

$$\mathscr{H}_{\text{int}} = g \sum_x (C_x \mathscr{H}_x + C'_x \mathscr{H}'_x) + \text{h.c.} \tag{3.78}$$

where C'_x are ten new constants and $\mathscr{H}'_x$ differs from $\mathscr{H}_x$ in that each lepton covariant is replaced by its pseudo-form $S \leftrightarrow P$, $V \leftrightarrow A$, $T \leftrightarrow T$. This means that each ψ^ν in (3.77b) is replaced by $\gamma_5\psi^\nu$ in $\mathscr{H}'_x$.

Thus far it would appear that ten constants have been replaced by twenty. The additional complication in the theory is more than compensated by the added variety of experiments which can be performed.[22] As a result of these the following values of the constants can be given with reasonably good accuracy:

$$\begin{aligned}
&C_S = C'_S = C_T = C'_T = 0 \\
&C_V \cong C'_V, \qquad C_A \cong C'_A = -\lambda C_V
\end{aligned} \tag{3.79}$$

† We recall that transition probabilities depend on absolute squares of matrix elements of $\mathscr{H}_{\text{int}}$.

where $\lambda \approx 1.2$; also $g'^2 = 2g^2(C_V^2 + C_A^2) \approx 2.1 \times 10^{-23}$ in rational relativistic units.† An overall phase is irrelevant.‡ Also, as will be evident, the equality of the so-called even and odd coupling constants (C_x and C_x') means that parity breakdown effects are as large as possible. Although this equality of C_x and C_x' is fairly well established, it is useful to write $C_x' = \epsilon C_x$ in order to study the effects of deviations from the condition of equality. The significance of the equality will become much more apparent in light of the discussion of the two-component neutrino theory; see Chapter VII.

The choice of coupling constants given in (3.79) leads to the so-called $V - \lambda A$ theory which, at present, seems to give good agreement with all observations. With this choice we can write the part of $\mathscr{H}_{\text{int}}$ leading to e^- emission in the form

$$g^{-1}\mathscr{H}_{\text{int}}^- = (\bar{\psi}^p\gamma_\mu(1 + \lambda\gamma_5)\,\psi^n)(\bar{\psi}^e\gamma_\mu(1 + \gamma_5)\,\psi^\nu)$$
$$= (\psi^{p*}\gamma_4\gamma_\mu(1 + \lambda\gamma_5)\,\psi^n)(\psi^{e*}\gamma_4\gamma_\mu(1 + \gamma_5)\,\psi^\nu)$$

for $C_x = C_x'$. For $C_x = \epsilon C_x'$ the factor $1 + \gamma_5$ in the λ-independent term is replaced by $1 + \epsilon\gamma_5$ and in the λ terms by $\epsilon + \gamma_5 = \gamma_5(1 + \epsilon\gamma_5)$. To introduce the ϵ we designate this matrix by $a + b\gamma_5$ so that a and b interchange their roles in going from V to A interactions.§

When the interaction is used in a perturbation calculation of the transition probability the following result is obtained. For the number of transitions in which the electron has momentum between $\mathbf{p}$ and $\mathbf{p} + d\mathbf{p}$, the antineutrino momentum is between $\mathbf{q}$ and $\mathbf{q} + d\mathbf{q}$, and the electron spin state is specified, say by the unit vector $\hat{\mathbf{n}}_0$ in the rest system, the result is

$$w\,d\mathbf{p}\,d\mathbf{q} = (2\pi)^{-5}g^2C_V^2\,d\mathbf{p}\,d\mathbf{q}|\mathscr{H}_{fi}|^2 \tag{3.80}$$

A sum over neutrino spin states is implied since it will be assumed that this observation is not made. The transition probability w is in units $mc^2/\hbar$. In (3.80) the matrix element is between final (f) and initial (i) nuclear states (Ψ_f and Ψ_i)

$$\mathscr{H}_{fi} = \int d\mathbf{x}_N\,\Psi_f^*\gamma_4\gamma_\mu(1 + \lambda\gamma_5)\,\Psi_i[\psi^{e*}\gamma_4\gamma_\mu(a + b\gamma_5)\,\psi^\nu]$$

The factor in square brackets is evaluated at the position of nucleon number k, and we have suppressed the explicit appearance in front of Ψ_i

† The dimensions of g are energy times volume, so that g' in ordinary units is obtained by multiplying by $\hbar^3/m^2c$. Thus $g' \approx 2.2 \times 10^{-49}$ erg cm³.

‡ This means that for all purposes the constants may be assumed real and also that $\mathscr{H}_{\text{int}}$ is time reversal invariant; see section 25.

§ For $\epsilon = 1$ the interaction is equivalent to that of the two-component neutrino theory of Chapter VII.

of an operator which changes the kth nucleon from a neutron to a proton if it is a neutron and gives zero otherwise. This detail and, all effects arising from the fact that nucleons are not actually bare Dirac particles, will affect only the nuclear matrix elements which enter as described in the next paragraph. A sum over all nucleons is also implied in $\mathscr{H}_{fi}$.

For ψ^e and ψ^ν plane waves are assumed. Corrections due to Coulomb fields will alter only the total intensity of beta particles. This assumption of plane waves gives a factor $\exp[-i(\mathbf{p} + \mathbf{q})\cdot\mathbf{x}_N]$, where $\mathbf{x}_N$ is the position of a nucleon. Since $x_N \leqslant R$, the nuclear radius, and R in our units is $0.4\alpha A^{1/3}$ (A is the mass number), it follows that for typical beta spectra, in which p and q are of order 1, that $(\mathbf{p} + \mathbf{q})\cdot\mathbf{x}_N \ll 1$. The exponential will therefore be replaced by unity for the transitions of greatest probability, and then ψ^e in the above is given by (3.53a). For these ("allowed") transitions only the even parts of the nuclear Dirac matrices should be retained. Therefore $\mathscr{H}_{fi}$ becomes

$$\mathscr{H}_{fi} = (U^e, (1 + \epsilon\gamma_5)U^\nu)M(1) - \lambda(U^e, \boldsymbol{\sigma}(1 + \epsilon\gamma_5)U^\nu)\cdot\mathbf{M}(\sigma) \quad (3.81)$$

where $M(1)$ and $\mathbf{M}(\sigma)$ are nuclear matrix elements:

$$M(1) = \int d\mathbf{x}_N\, \Psi_f^*\Psi_i$$

$$\mathbf{M}(\sigma) = \int d\mathbf{x}_N\, \Psi_f^*\boldsymbol{\sigma}\Psi_i$$

It is evident that allowed transitions should then be characterized by no nuclear parity change. This is indeed what is observed.

It is customary to observe only the electron, and the usual result of interest is obtained by writing an expression for the energy distribution. Therefore we write, for the transition probability for electrons with energy in the interval p_0 to $p_0 + dp_0$, direction $\hat{\mathbf{p}}$ in the solid angle range $d\Omega_{\hat{\mathbf{p}}}$ and neutrinos with momentum† $\mathbf{q}$ in the solid angle range $d\Omega_{\hat{\mathbf{q}}}$, and "spin direction" $\hat{\mathbf{n}}_0$ for the electrons,

$$w\, dp_0\, d\Omega_{\hat{\mathbf{p}}}\, d\Omega_{\hat{\mathbf{q}}} = \frac{g^2C_V^2}{(2\pi)^5}\, dp_0\, d\Omega_{\hat{\mathbf{p}}}\, d\Omega_{\hat{\mathbf{q}}} S(p_0)|\mathscr{H}_{fi}|^2 \quad (3.82)$$

where, using the conservation of energy,

$$S(p_0) = \frac{dp}{dp_0}\, p^2 \int dq\, \delta(q - W_0 + p_0)q^2 = pp_0(W_0 - p_0)^2$$

† $q = W_0 - p_0$, where W_0 is the total energy release: maximum kinetic energy of the beta particle plus its rest energy.

$S(p_0)$ is a statistical factor arising from the volume in momentum space available to the two light particles. The nucleus, which is very accurately treated as infinitely heavy, will take up recoil momentum but negligible recoil energy.

For simplicity we shall consider separately those nuclear transitions for which $\mathbf{M}(\sigma) = 0$ and those for which $M(1) = 0$. The former case arises when[22]

$$J_f = J_i = 0$$

and these are called pure Fermi transitions. The latter arises when

$$J_f - J_i = \pm 1$$

and these are called pure Gamow-Teller transitions. For $J_i = J_f \neq 0$ both matrix elements would contribute in general.

For pure Fermi transitions we need to calculate

$$|\mathscr{H}_{fi}|^2 = |M(1)|^2 \sum_{s_\nu} |U^e, (1 + \epsilon\gamma_5)U^\nu|^2$$

and the sum is over $\bar{\nu}$ spin states. Then

$$\begin{aligned} |U^e, (1 + \epsilon\gamma_5)U^\nu|^2 &= U_\rho^{e\times}(1 + \epsilon\gamma_5)_{\rho\sigma}\, U_\sigma^\nu\, U_{\rho'}^e(1 + \epsilon\gamma_5)_{\rho'\sigma'}^\times\, U_{\sigma'}^{\nu\times} \\ &= P_{\rho'\rho}(\hat{\mathbf{n}}_0)(1 + \epsilon\gamma_5)_{\rho\sigma}\, P_{\sigma\sigma'}^\nu(1 + \epsilon\gamma_5)_{\sigma'\rho'}^* \end{aligned}$$

where $P(\hat{\mathbf{n}}_0)$ is the spin projection operator of section 19 and P^ν is a similar operator defined for the neutrino. When the sum over neutrino spins is made, P^ν becomes the energy projection operator for the neutrino. For zero rest mass and physical momentum $\mathbf{q}$ this is

$$\sum_{s_\nu} P^\nu = P(\nu) = \tfrac{1}{2}(1 + \boldsymbol{\alpha}\cdot\hat{\mathbf{q}}) \tag{3.83}$$

since $|\mathbf{q}| = q$. Then we obtain

$$\begin{aligned} |\mathscr{H}_{fi}|^2 &= |M(1)|^2 \operatorname{Tr} P(\hat{\mathbf{n}}_0)(1 + \epsilon\gamma_5)\, P(\nu)(1 + \epsilon\gamma_5) \\ &= |M(1)|^2 \operatorname{Tr} P(\hat{\mathbf{n}}_0)[1 + \epsilon^2 + 2\epsilon\gamma_5]\, P(\nu) \end{aligned} \tag{3.84}$$

since $P(\nu)$ commutes with $1 + \epsilon\gamma_5$. A parity conserving theory in which $\epsilon = 0$ gives 1 for the square bracket. Similarly, if only the $\epsilon\gamma_5$ term were present instead of $1 + \epsilon\gamma_5$, the square bracket would be ϵ^2. Therefore the parity non-conserving effects must arise from the $2\epsilon\gamma_5$ cross term, and the relative order of parity non-conserving terms to parity conserving terms is

$$f = \frac{2\epsilon}{1 + \epsilon^2} \tag{3.85}$$

For $\epsilon = 1$, f has its maximum value, namely 1, and for $\epsilon = 1 + \delta$ with $\delta \ll 1$ this factor f is $1 - \delta^2/2$.

The trace in (3.84) is easily evaluated, and for the transition probability one obtains[27]

$$w = \frac{g_V^2}{(2\pi)^5} S(p_0)|M(1)|^2 I_F \tag{3.86}$$

where

$$g_V^2 = \tfrac{1}{2}g^2C_V^2(1 + \epsilon^2)$$

and

$$I_F = (1 + \mathbf{p}\cdot\hat{\mathbf{q}}/p_0)(1 + \mathscr{P}\cdot\hat{\mathbf{n}}_0) \tag{3.86'}$$

The beta particle polarization is

$$\mathscr{P} = -f\frac{\hat{\mathbf{q}} + \mathbf{p} + (p_0 - 1)\hat{\mathbf{p}}\cdot\hat{\mathbf{q}}\,\hat{\mathbf{p}}}{p_0 + \mathbf{p}\cdot\hat{\mathbf{q}}} \tag{3.87}$$

for electrons. For positrons the same result applies with the exception that the sign of $\mathscr{P}$ is changed.

If the electron polarization is not measured, I_F is replaced by

$$\sum_{s_e} I_F = 2(1 + \mathbf{p}\cdot\hat{\mathbf{q}}/p_0)$$

and this gives the well-known electron-neutrino correlation, $1 + (v/c)\cos\vartheta$, where ϑ is the angle between $\mathbf{p}$ and $\mathbf{q}$. If the neutrino direction is not observed, $P(\nu)$ will be replaced by $\frac{1}{2}$ and a factor 4π from integrating over $d\Omega_{\hat{\mathbf{q}}}$ is introduced in w. Then

$$\mathscr{P} = -\mathbf{p}/p_0$$

Thus the polarization is longitudinal and the helicity is negative for electrons, positive for positrons. In the general case $\mathscr{P}$ can have any direction in the $\mathbf{p}$–$\mathbf{q}$ plane, even transverse to $\mathbf{p}$.[28] It is seen that when $f = 1$ the magnitude of $\mathscr{P}$ is unity; this implies that for $\hat{\mathbf{n}}_0 = -\mathscr{P}$ no beta particles are emitted. Hence in pure Fermi transitions only one of two spin states is formed, provided the spin basis, or selection of spin states, is made in terms of the vector $\mathscr{P}$ defined by (3.87). When $f < 1$ the polarization is not complete and both spin states are formed, though not equally. It will be seen in Chapter VII that the explanation lies in the fact that for $f = 1$, $\epsilon = 1$ only one neutrino spin state is possible. Hence the averaging over neutrino spin states is superfluous in that case. For $f < 1$ there are two neutrino spin states and the averaging process reduces $\mathscr{P}$ to a value less than unity.

For the pure Gamow-Teller case we calculate

$$|\mathscr{H}_{fi}|^2 = \lambda^2 \sum_{s_\nu} U_\rho^{e\times}(\boldsymbol{\sigma}\cdot\mathbf{M}(\sigma)(1+\epsilon\gamma_5))_{\rho\mu} U_\mu^\nu U_{\rho'}^e(\boldsymbol{\sigma}\cdot\mathbf{M}(\sigma)(1+\epsilon\gamma_5))^\times_{\rho'\mu'} U_{\mu'}^{\nu\times}$$

$$= \lambda^2 \operatorname{Tr} P(\hat{\mathbf{n}}_0)\, \boldsymbol{\sigma}\cdot\mathbf{M}(\sigma)(1+\epsilon\gamma_5)\, P(\nu)\, \boldsymbol{\sigma}\cdot\mathbf{M}^\times(\sigma)(1+\epsilon\gamma_5)$$

$$= \lambda^2 \operatorname{Tr} P(\hat{\mathbf{n}}_0)\, \boldsymbol{\sigma}\cdot\mathbf{M}(\sigma)(1+\epsilon^2+2\epsilon\gamma_5)\, P(\nu)\, \boldsymbol{\sigma}\cdot\mathbf{M}^\times(\sigma)$$

The transition probability is now given[27] in terms of

$$w = \frac{g_A^2}{(2\pi)^5} S(p_0) I_{\mathrm{GT}} \tag{3.88}$$

where

$$g_A^2 = \tfrac{1}{2} g^2 C_A^2 (1+\epsilon^2)$$

and

$$I_{\mathrm{GT}} = \left(B_1 - \frac{\mathbf{p}\cdot\mathbf{A}_1}{p_0}\right)(1 + \mathscr{P}\cdot\hat{\mathbf{n}}_0) \tag{3.89}$$

Here the polarization[28] is

$$\mathscr{P} = \pm \frac{\mathbf{A}_0 - B_0\mathbf{p} + (p_0 - 1)\hat{\mathbf{p}}\cdot\mathbf{A}_0\,\hat{\mathbf{p}}}{p_0 B_1 - \mathbf{p}\cdot\mathbf{A}_1} \tag{3.90}$$

and

$$\mathbf{A}_m = \pm i f^m \mathbf{M}\times\mathbf{M}^\times + f^{1-m}[\mathbf{M}\cdot\mathbf{M}^\times\,\hat{\mathbf{q}} - \hat{\mathbf{q}}\cdot\mathbf{M}\, M^\times - \hat{\mathbf{q}}\cdot\mathbf{M}^\times\,\mathbf{M}]$$

$$B_m = f^{1-m}\mathbf{M}\cdot\mathbf{M}^\times \pm i f^m \hat{\mathbf{q}}\cdot\mathbf{M}\times\mathbf{M}^\times \geqslant 0$$

The upper sign refers to electrons, the lower to positrons. Now the matrix elements $\mathbf{M}$ and $\mathbf{M}^\times$ depend on the nuclear orientation. If all substates in the initial and final nucleus are uniformly populated and the nuclei are not oriented, we find

$$\langle\mathbf{M}\cdot\mathbf{M}^\times\rangle = |\mathbf{M}_\sigma|^2 \equiv \mathbf{M}(\sigma)\cdot\mathbf{M}^\times(\sigma); \qquad \operatorname{Re}\langle\hat{\mathbf{q}}\cdot\mathbf{M}\,\mathbf{M}^\times\rangle = \tfrac{1}{3}\hat{\mathbf{q}}|\mathbf{M}_\sigma|^2$$

$$i\langle\mathbf{M}\times\mathbf{M}^\times\rangle = 0$$

where the angular brackets now indicate an average over nuclear substates. Then, for $f = 1$,

$$\mathscr{P} = \pm \frac{\tfrac{1}{3}\hat{\mathbf{q}} - \mathbf{p} + \tfrac{1}{3}(p_0 - 1)\hat{\mathbf{p}}\cdot\hat{\mathbf{q}}\,\hat{\mathbf{p}}}{p_0 - \tfrac{1}{3}\mathbf{p}\cdot\hat{\mathbf{q}}} \tag{3.91}$$

Now $|\mathscr{P}| < 1$ even though $f = 1$. This result might have been expected in view of the averaging over nuclear states. For no observation of the electron polarization the usual electron-neutrino correlation is observed. For unoriented nuclei this is

$$I_{\mathrm{GT}} = 2|\mathbf{M}_\sigma|^2(1 - \tfrac{1}{3}\mathbf{p}\cdot\hat{\mathbf{q}}/p_0)$$

If the direction of the neutrino is not observed and no polarization measurement of the electrons is made there is, from the $\mathbf{p}\cdot\mathbf{A}_1$ term in the first factor of I_{GT}, a correlation[25] between the direction of the electron momentum and the nuclear polarization $i\langle \mathbf{M} \times \mathbf{M}^{\times} \rangle$ which is now not zero. This vector is

$$i\langle \mathbf{M} \times \mathbf{M}^{\times} \rangle = N\left\langle \frac{\mathbf{J}_i}{J_i} \right\rangle |\mathbf{M}_\sigma|^2$$

where $\langle \mathbf{J}_i/J_i \rangle$ is the polarization of the initial nuclear state and[28]

$$\begin{aligned} N &= 1 && \text{for } J_i = J_f + 1 \\ &= (J_i + 1)^{-1} && \text{for } J_i = J_f \\ &= -J_i/(J_i + 1) && \text{for } J_i = J_f - 1 \end{aligned}$$

PROBLEMS

1. Explain, from a consideration of the momentum spectrum resulting from a precise position measurement, the fact that the instantaneous velocity of a relativistic electron must have the value $\pm c$.

2. Show that each column of the 4 by 4 matrix $h + p_0$ where

$$h = \boldsymbol{\alpha}\cdot\mathbf{p} + \beta$$

is a solution of the amplitude equation (3.4). Are these four solutions linearly independent? Answer the same questions for the columns of the matrix $(h + p_0)A$ where A is an arbitrary 4 by 4 matrix.

3. Obtain the electron and positron wave functions in the representation

$$\boldsymbol{\alpha} = \rho_3\boldsymbol{\sigma}, \qquad \beta = \rho_1$$

where ρ_3 and ρ_1 are given in (2.38b). Find S where

$$S\rho_1\boldsymbol{\sigma}S^{-1} = \rho_3\boldsymbol{\sigma}, \qquad S\rho_3S^{-1} = \rho_1$$

Compare the non-relativistic limit of the wave functions in this representation with those obtained in the standard representation.

4. Using anticommutator relations, show that the expectation value of β for positive energy states is

$$\langle \beta \rangle = 1/p_0$$

independent of the representation. In a similar way show that

$$\langle \boldsymbol{\alpha} \rangle = \mathbf{p}/p_0$$

in all representations.

5. Let A be an arbitrary four-component spinor. Show that $P_+A = \psi_+$, where ψ_+ is an eigenfunction of $P_+ = \frac{1}{2}(1 + h/p_0)$. Thus a positive energy amplitude can be generated by P_+ operating on any four-component spinor.

6. Show that the spin operator $\mathcal{O}$ can be obtained from $\boldsymbol{\sigma}$ by a unitary transformation; that is

$$S\boldsymbol{\sigma}S^{-1} = \mathcal{O}$$

Find S subject to $S^* = S^{-1}$. Obtain the corresponding result for the positron.

7. For two vectors **A** and **B**, whose components commute with the components of $\mathcal{O}$, show that

$$\mathcal{O}\cdot\mathbf{A}\,\mathcal{O}\cdot\mathbf{B} = \mathbf{A}\cdot\mathbf{B} + i\mathcal{O}\cdot\mathbf{A}\times\mathbf{B}$$

Write the corresponding result for the positron.

8. Show that the product of two projection operators A and B is again a projection operator if A and B commute. Is the converse theorem true?

9. The pair of operators A and B fulfill two of the following:

(a) $$A^2 = A, \qquad B^2 = B$$
(b) $$AB = BA = 0$$
(c) $$A + B = 1$$

Show that if (c) and (a) or (b) are true then (b) or (a) must be valid, but if (a) and (b) hold then (c) is not necessarily valid. What is the relation between these results and the existence of a complete set of eigenfunctions of a set of commuting operators?

10. Verify Eqs. (3.61) and (3.62).

11. What interpretation should be given to the projection operator $P(13) = P^{(1)} + P^{(3)}$? Compare the operator $P(\hat{\mathbf{n}})$ with $P_+P(13)$. Under what circumstances are they equal?

12. Show that $\beta^c(Q^c(n) - \mathcal{O}^c\cdot\hat{\mathbf{n}}_0)$ is a null operator for positron energy states.

13. Considering plane wave states of given momentum, show that in any representation the Dirac current for positive and negative energy states with the same physical momentum must always have the same magnitude and sign.

14. Show that for $\hat{\mathbf{n}}_0$ parallel or antiparallel to the momentum $\mathbf{p}$ the spin operator projected on $\hat{\mathbf{n}}_0$, that is, $\mathcal{O}\cdot\hat{\mathbf{n}}_0$, is equal to the helicity operator $\boldsymbol{\sigma}\cdot\hat{\mathbf{p}}$ while for $\hat{\mathbf{n}}_0$ perpendicular to $\mathbf{p}$ it is $\beta\boldsymbol{\sigma}\cdot\hat{\mathbf{n}}_0$.

15. Verify that T_{jk} and T_{j4} defined by Eqs. (3.74′) and (3.74″) do in fact transform like a four-tensor.

16. Evaluate the position operator $\mathbf{x}'$ in the Foldy-Wouthuysen scheme to obtain the result given in the text. Evaluate the FW transform of the spin operator $\boldsymbol{\sigma}$ and of the orbital angular momentum $\mathbf{l} = \mathbf{r}\times\mathbf{p}$. Should $\mathbf{l}' + \frac{1}{2}\boldsymbol{\sigma}'$ commute with H', the (new) FW Hamiltonian?

17. For a general wave packet consisting of a superposition of positive and negative energy states show that the current density has oscillatory terms corresponding to the *Zitterbewegung*. Is this also true of the average momentum?

18. If in the beta decay formulas (3.86′) and (3.89) the vector $\hat{\mathbf{n}}_0$ is replaced by the Pauli spin matrix $\boldsymbol{\sigma}$, the polarization is

$$\mathcal{P} = \frac{\mathrm{Tr}\,\boldsymbol{\sigma}I}{\mathrm{Tr}\,I}$$

How should this fact be interpreted?

19. From the result

$$\mathcal{O}_j\mathcal{O}_k = \delta_{jk} + i\epsilon_{jkm}\mathcal{O}_m$$

evaluate the anticommutator of $\mathcal{O}\cdot\hat{\mathbf{n}}$ and $\mathcal{O}_j$, and show from this that the expectation value of $\mathcal{O}$ is $\pm\hat{\mathbf{n}}$. Note that this proof does not require the use of a specific representation.

REFERENCES

1. P. A. M. Dirac, *Proc. Roy. Soc. (London)* A **126,** 360 (1930). See also P. A. M. Dirac, *Proc. Cambridge Phil. Soc.* **30,** 150 (1934); W. Heisenberg, *Z. Physik* **90,** 209 (1934); V. Weisskopf, *Proc. Danish Acad. Sci.* 24, No. 6 (1936).
2. C. D. Anderson, *Phys. Rev.* **43,** 491 (1933).
3. J. Schwinger, *Phys. Rev.* **74,** 1439 (1948); **75,** 651 (1949).
4. S. Tomonaga, *Prog. Theoret. Phys. (Kyoto)* **1,** 27 (1946).
5. See, for example, J. M. Jauch and F. Rohrlich, *The Theory of Photons and Electrons*, Addison-Wesley Publishing Co., Cambridge, Mass., 1955, p. 342.
6. S. Koenig, A. G. Pradell, and P. Kusch, *Phys. Rev.* **88,** 191 (1952).
7. An excellent summary of the data as of April 1958 appears in the article by E. Segrè, *Ann. Rev. Nuclear Sci.* **8,** 127 (1958).
8. R. L. Garwin, D. P. Hutchison, S. Penman, and G. Shapiro, *Nevis Rept.* 79 (1959).
9. J. Rainwater, *Ann. Rev. Nuclear Sci.*, **7,** 1 (1957).
10. L. Foldy and S. A. Wouthuysen, *Phys. Rev.* **78,** 29 (1950). See also S. Tani, *Progr. Theoret. Phys.* **6,** 267 (1957).
11. M. H. L. Pryce, *Proc. Roy. Soc. (London)* A **150,** 166 (1935); A **195,** 62 (1948).
12. E. Schrödinger, *Berlin Ber.* 419 (1930); 63 (1931).
13. T. D. Newton and E. P. Wigner, *Revs. Mod. Phys.* **21,** 400 (1949).
14. Z. V. Chraplyvy, *Phys. Rev.* **91,** 388 (1953); **92,** 1310 (1953).
15. W. A. Barker and F. N. Glover, *Phys. Rev.* **99,** 317 (1955).
16. D. L. Pursey, *Nuclear Phys.* **8,** 595 (1958).
17. M. Cini and B. Touschek, *Nuovo cimento* **7,** 422 (1958). See also S. K. Bose, A. Gamba, and E. C. G. Sudarshan, *Phys. Rev.* **113,** 1661 (1959); P. Y. Pac. *Progr. Theoret. Phys.* **21,** 640 (1959); **22,** 857 (1959).
18. R. A. Ferrell, Thesis, Princeton University, Princeton, New Jersey, 1951 (unpublished).
19. B. Kursunoglu, *Phys. Rev.* **101,** 1419 (1956).
20. H. A. Tolhoek, *Revs. Mod. Phys.* **28,** 277 (1956).
21. F. W. Lipps and H. A. Tolhoek, *Physica* **20,** 85, 395 (1954).
22. For a general survey see, for example, M. Deutsch and O. Kofoed-Hansen, in E. Segrè (ed.), *Experimental Nuclear Physics*, John Wiley and Sons, New York, 1959, Vol. III, Part XI, especially sections 3ff. Also M. E. Rose, *Handbook of Physics*, McGraw-Hill Book Co., New York, 1958, Part 9, Chapter 5.
23. G. Wentzel, *Quantum Theory of Fields*, Interscience Publishers, New York, 1949.
24. This hypothesis was originally suggested by T. D. Lee and C. N. Yang, *Phys. Rev.* **104,** 254 (1956).
25. The first experiment which established parity non-conservation in beta decay was carried out by C. S. Wu, E. Ambler, R. W. Hayward, D. D. Hoppes, and R. P. Hudson, *Phys. Rev.* **105**, 1413 (1957). This experiment demonstrated an anisotropic angular distribution of e^- emitted by polarized Co^{60} nuclei.
26. A summary of the data as of 1957 is found in *Proceedings of the Rehovoth Conference on Nuclear Structure*, H. J. Lipkin (ed.) North Holland Publishing Co., Amsterdam, 1958. See pp. 376–403.
27. J. D. Jackson, S. B. Treiman, and H. W. Wyld, Jr., *Phys. Rev.* **106,** 517 (1957).
28. R. H. Good, Jr., and M. E. Rose, *Nuovo cimento* **14,** 872 (1959).

IV.

PARTICLE IN ELECTROMAGNETIC FIELDS

22. THE WAVE EQUATION

Classical Electromagnetic Fields

In this discussion we shall be concerned with the interaction of electrons or positrons with external electromagnetic fields. While it is possible to construct a Hamiltonian equation and a covariant wave equation for more general cases, these seem to have mainly academic interest. There is one exceptional case and that is the problem of the beta interaction which was discussed in section 21 and will again be considered in sections 25 and 42.

The electromagnetic fields are taken to be real classical Maxwell fields, and in the present theory it is assumed that they are given independently of the dynamics of the Dirac field. These fields are then described in terms of two vectors $\mathscr{E}$ and $\mathscr{H}$, the electric and magnetic fields for which the usual Maxwell equations apply. In non-rational Gaussian units these are

$$\operatorname{curl} \mathscr{H} = \frac{4\pi}{c}\,\mathbf{j}_c + \frac{1}{c}\frac{\partial \mathscr{E}}{\partial t} \tag{4.1a}$$

$$\operatorname{curl} \mathscr{E} = -\frac{1}{c}\frac{\partial \mathscr{H}}{\partial t} \tag{4.1b}$$

$$\operatorname{div} \mathscr{E} = 4\pi \rho_c \tag{4.1c}$$

$$\operatorname{div} \mathscr{H} = 0 \tag{4.1d}$$

where ρ_c and $\mathbf{j}_c$ are the *electric* charge density and current density respectively. Then from (4.1a) and (4.1c) the continuity equation follows:

$$\operatorname{div} \mathbf{j}_c + \frac{\partial \rho_c}{\partial t} = 0 \tag{4.1e}$$

Since the charge is

$$e = \int \rho_c \, d^3x$$

and this is taken to be a scalar invariant, ρ_c must have the Lorentz transformation property of the time part of a four-vector whose space part is $\mathbf{j}_c$. More exactly, the four-vector is $\mathfrak{s}_\mu = (\mathbf{j}_c, ic\rho_c)$ so that (4.1e) reads as follows:

$$\frac{\partial \mathfrak{s}_\mu}{\partial x_\mu} = 0$$

which is in covariant form.

The field equations (4.1a) and (4.1b) can be replaced by equations in the vector potential **A** and scalar potential Φ by the definitions

$$\mathscr{E} = -\frac{1}{c}\frac{\partial \mathbf{A}}{\partial t} - \nabla\Phi \tag{4.2a}$$

$$\mathscr{H} = \operatorname{curl} \mathbf{A} \tag{4.2b}$$

so that the homogeneous equations (4.1b) and (4.1d) are satisfied automatically. Furthermore, if the Lorentz condition

$$\operatorname{div} \mathbf{A} + \frac{1}{c}\frac{\partial \Phi}{\partial t} = 0 \tag{4.2c}$$

is assumed, the **A** and Φ satisfy a simple second-order wave equation. We introduce a four-vector potential $A_\mu = (\mathbf{A}, i\Phi)$ and then

$$\frac{\partial^2 A_\mu}{\partial x_\nu \, \partial x_\nu} = -\frac{4\pi}{c}\mathfrak{s}_\mu \tag{4.3}$$

For the vacuum, $\mathfrak{s}_\mu = 0$ and this is the zero mass Klein-Gordon equation.

Of course, the A_μ are still not uniquely determined because, if they are replaced by

$$A'_\mu = A_\mu + \frac{\partial G}{\partial x_\mu} \tag{4.4}$$

where G is a scalar function satisfying the zero mass Klein-Gordon equation, the field strengths

$$\mathscr{E}' = -\frac{1}{c}\frac{\partial \mathbf{A}'}{\partial t} - \nabla\Phi'$$

$$\mathscr{H}' = \operatorname{curl} \mathbf{A}'$$

are the same as $\mathscr{E}$ and $\mathscr{H}$. The transformation (4.4) is called a gauge transformation of the first kind.

To justify the description of A_μ as a four-vector it is necessary only to observe that $\partial^2/\partial x_\nu\, \partial x_\nu$ in (4.3) is an invariant operator. The Lorentz condition is

$$\frac{\partial A_\mu}{\partial x_\mu} = 0 \tag{4.2c'}$$

and is satisfied in all inertial frames if it is assumed true in any one. The Maxwell equations are then written in covariant form by introducing the antisymmetric field tensor

$$F_{\mu\nu} = \frac{\partial A_\nu}{\partial x_\mu} - \frac{\partial A_\mu}{\partial x_\nu} = -F_{\nu\mu} \tag{4.5}$$

In detailed form this is

$$F_{\mu\nu}: \quad \begin{pmatrix} 0 & \mathscr{H}_3 & -\mathscr{H}_2 & -i\mathscr{E}_1 \\ -\mathscr{H}_3 & 0 & \mathscr{H}_1 & -i\mathscr{E}_2 \\ \mathscr{H}_2 & -\mathscr{H}_1 & 0 & -i\mathscr{E}_3 \\ i\mathscr{E}_1 & i\mathscr{E}_2 & i\mathscr{E}_3 & 0 \end{pmatrix}$$

Then the Maxwell equations become

$$\frac{\partial F_{\mu\nu}}{\partial x_\nu} = \frac{4\pi}{c}\, \mathfrak{s}_\mu \tag{4.6a}$$

for the inhomogeneous equations, and for the homogeneous equations the result is

$$\epsilon_{\mu\nu\rho\lambda} \frac{\partial F_{\nu\rho}}{\partial x_\lambda} = 0 \tag{4.6b}$$

which are in manifestly covariant form. Here, again, $\epsilon_{\mu\nu\rho\lambda}$ is the completely antisymmetric unit tensor of rank four (section 14).

The Equations of Motion

In classical mechanics the equations of motion for a charged particle (charge $-e$) in a field are obtained from the free particle equations by replacing the energy p_0 by $p_0 + e\Phi$ and the momentum by $\mathbf{p} + (e/c)\mathbf{A}$. The correct Lorentz force $-e(\mathscr{E} + \mathbf{v} \times \mathscr{H}/c)$ is then obtained. It will be recalled that $-e$ is the electron charge. The same prescription is valid in non-relativistic quantum mechanics because, when the replacements

$$i\hbar \frac{\partial}{\partial t} \rightarrow i\hbar \frac{\partial}{\partial t} + e\Phi$$

$$-i\hbar \nabla \rightarrow -i\hbar \nabla + \frac{e}{c}\mathbf{A}$$

are made, the resulting wave equation is gauge invariant. This is what is meant: Let $H(A_\mu)$ be the Hamiltonian in one gauge so that

$$H(A_\mu)\psi = i\hbar \frac{\partial \psi}{\partial t}$$

Then it will be true that for another gauge (cf. 4.4),

$$H(A'_\mu)\psi' = i\hbar \frac{\partial \psi'}{\partial t}$$

where

$$\psi' = \exp\,(-ie\, G/\hbar c)\, \psi \tag{4.7}$$

Equation (4.7) is a unitary transformation. In the present connection it is called a gauge transformation of the second kind, and it is evident that the gauge transformation of the first kind is equivalent to (4.7) and consequently no physical results are altered.

Exactly the same replacements are now made in the covariant free particle Dirac equations of motion. The justification for this follows.

1. The equations are still consistent with relativity requirements.
2. They are gauge invariant exactly as described above.
3. The classical equations of motion for particles in electromagnetic fields are obtained in the appropriate limit. Also the non-relativistic quantum limit is obtained, as one should expect.

We shall defer discussion of point 3 until later.

The new form of the equation of motion is now

$$[\gamma_\mu D_\mu(-e) + k_0]\psi = 0 \tag{4.8}$$

where

$$D_\mu(-e) = \frac{\partial}{\partial x_\mu} + \frac{ie}{\hbar c} A_\mu \tag{4.9}$$

For the hermitian conjugate ψ^* we have

$$D^\times_\mu(-e)\psi^*\gamma_\mu + k_0\psi^* = 0$$

and

$$D^\times_k(-e) = \frac{\partial}{\partial x_k} - \frac{ie}{\hbar c} A_k = D_k(e)$$

$$D^\times_4(-e) = -\frac{\partial}{\partial x_4} + \frac{ie}{\hbar c} A_4 = -D_4(e)$$

Therefore, for exactly the same reason that motivated us in discussing free particles, the adjoint function

$$\bar{\psi} = \psi^*\gamma_4$$

is introduced. Then for $\bar{\psi}$ the wave equation is

$$D_\mu(e)\bar{\psi}\gamma_\mu - k_0\bar{\psi} = 0 \tag{4.10}$$

The equations for the positron will be discussed in the next section.

Since D_μ transforms under a Lorentz transformation exactly as $\partial/\partial x_\mu$, that is, like a four-vector, the argument concerning the covariance of (4.8) and (4.10) is precisely the same as for free particles. Therefore nothing further need be said about point 1.

For the gauge invariance we observe that, replacing A_μ by A'_μ and ψ by $e^{i\chi}\psi$, we have

$$\gamma_\mu\left[\frac{\partial}{\partial x_\mu} + \frac{ie}{\hbar c}\left(A_\mu + \frac{\partial G}{\partial x_\mu}\right)\right]e^{i\chi}\psi + k_0 e^{i\chi}\psi$$

$$= \gamma_\mu e^{i\chi}\left(\frac{\partial}{\partial x_\mu} + \frac{ie}{\hbar c}A_\mu\right)\psi + k_0 e^{i\chi}\psi + \frac{ie}{\hbar c}\gamma_\mu\frac{\partial G}{\partial x_\mu}e^{i\chi}\psi + i\gamma_\mu e^{i\chi}\frac{\partial \chi}{\partial x_\mu}\psi$$

The sum of the first two terms vanishes by virtue of (4.8). The sum of the second two terms will vanish if

$$\chi = -\frac{e}{\hbar c}G \tag{4.11}$$

as in (4.7). This justifies the statement made in point 2. It will be recognized that in any bilinear or quadrilinear combination of wave functions such as generally occurs in matrix elements the transformation (4.7) multiplies the wave function combination by

$$\exp\left(-i\Sigma e\, G/\hbar c\right)$$

where Σe is the sum of the charges in the initial states minus the sum of the charges in the final state. Hence, since charge is conserved, this sum is zero and the factor given above is unity.

In terms of $\boldsymbol{\alpha}$ and β the wave equation is

$$H\psi = i\hbar\frac{\partial\psi}{\partial t}$$

where

$$H = c\boldsymbol{\alpha}\cdot\vec{\boldsymbol{\pi}} + \beta mc^2 - e\Phi \tag{4.12}$$

and

$$\vec{\boldsymbol{\pi}} = \vec{\mathbf{p}} + \frac{e}{c}\mathbf{A} \tag{4.13}$$

is the standard *kinetic* momentum operator.

Since $\mathbf{A}$ is real, the continuity equation holds with the same four-current $\mathfrak{s}_\mu$ as for free particles. This is in contrast to the non-relativistic case where **A** occurs explicitly in **j**. Of course, the ψ is different so that $\psi^*\boldsymbol{\alpha}\psi$, for example, has a different value now and will certainly depend on the fields present.

It is of interest, however, to note that the fields appear explicitly when the current is decomposed into constituent parts which can be interpreted in a simple way.[1] In

$$\mathfrak{s}_\mu = (j_c)_\mu = iec\bar{\psi}\gamma_\mu\psi = \tfrac{1}{2}iec(\bar{\psi}\gamma_\mu\psi + \bar{\psi}\gamma_\mu\psi)$$

we replace $\bar{\psi}$ by $k_0^{-1}D_\nu(e)\bar{\psi}\gamma_\nu$ in one term and ψ by $-k_0^{-1}D_\nu(-e)\gamma_\nu\psi$ in the other. Then $(j_c)_\mu$ can be written as a sum of two parts, one arising from the $\partial/\partial x_\nu$ term in $D_\nu(\pm e)$ and one from the field terms. Alternatively, we separate the terms with $\mu = \nu$ from those with $\mu \neq \nu$. Then

$$(j_c)_\mu = j_\mu^{(0)} + j_\mu^{(1)}$$

where

$$j_\mu^{(0)} = \frac{ie\hbar}{2m}\frac{\partial M_{\mu\nu}}{\partial x_\nu} \tag{4.14}$$

$$j_\mu^{(1)} = \frac{ie\hbar}{2m}\left\{\left(\frac{\partial\bar{\psi}}{\partial x_\mu} - \frac{ie}{\hbar c}A_\mu\bar{\psi}\right)\psi - \bar{\psi}\left(\frac{\partial}{\partial x_\mu} + \frac{ie}{\hbar c}A_\mu\right)\psi\right\} \tag{4.15}$$

Here the $\mu \neq \nu$ terms give $j_\mu^{(0)}$ and

$$M_{\mu\nu} = -M_{\nu\mu} = \bar{\psi}\gamma_\nu\gamma_\mu\psi \tag{4.16}$$

The tensor $M_{\mu\nu}$ has space-space parts given by

$$M_{jk} = -i\epsilon_{jkl}\bar{\psi}\sigma_l\psi \tag{4.16a}$$

and time-space parts given by

$$M_{j4} = -i\bar{\psi}\alpha_j\psi \tag{4.16b}$$

so that $j_\mu^{(0)}$ can be interpreted as the current density moment associated with a magnetization (density of magnetic dipoles) and an electric polarization (density of electric dipole moment). The space part of the second term has just the *form* of the non-relativistic Schrödinger current:

$$j_k^{(1)} = \frac{ie\hbar}{2m}\left(\frac{\partial\bar{\psi}}{\partial x_k}\psi - \bar{\psi}\frac{\partial\psi}{\partial x_k}\right) + \frac{e^2}{mc}A_k\bar{\psi}\psi \tag{4.14a}$$

However, note that $\bar{\psi}$ and not ψ^* occurs here. For the non-relativistic limit where β can be replaced by 1 the distinction is irrelevant. Of course, in the frame of reference in which the electron is moving there is also a time part

$$j_4^{(1)} = \frac{e\hbar}{2mc}\left(\frac{\partial\bar{\psi}}{\partial t}\psi - \bar{\psi}\frac{\partial\psi}{\partial t}\right) + \frac{ie^2}{mc}\Phi\bar{\psi}\psi \tag{4.14b}$$

For both $j_\mu^{(0)}$ and $j_\mu^{(1)}$ the continuity equation holds.

The question of constants of the motion of (4.12) will be deferred until the study of specific fields is taken up.

Magnetic Moment of the Electron

It has already been stated that the Uhlenbeck-Goudsmit hypothesis involves the existence of a magnetic moment of the electron given in terms of an operator

$$\boldsymbol{\mu} = -\frac{e\hbar}{mc}\mathbf{s}$$

Exactly this magnetic moment, it will now be shown, emerges from the Dirac theory. The magnitude of the measured moment is then the maximum expectation value of $\boldsymbol{\mu}$, which is predicted to be

$$\mu_0 = \frac{e\hbar}{2mc}$$

To see this we construct the second-order wave equation by operating on (4.8) with $\gamma_\mu D_\mu(-e) - k_0$. Then we obtain

$$(\gamma_\mu \gamma_\nu D_\mu D_\nu - k_0^2)\psi = 0 \tag{4.17}$$

where $D = D(-e)$. The terms in $\gamma_\mu\gamma_\nu D_\mu D_\nu$ are evaluated as follows:

$$\begin{aligned}\gamma_\mu\gamma_\nu D_\mu D_\nu &= \gamma_\mu^2 D_\mu^2 + \tfrac{1}{2}\gamma_\mu\gamma_\nu(D_\mu D_\nu - D_\nu D_\mu) \\ &= \sum_\mu D_\mu^2 + \frac{ie}{2\hbar c}\gamma_\mu\gamma_\nu F_{\mu\nu}\end{aligned}$$

Then (4.17) becomes

$$\left(D_\mu D_\mu - k_0^2 + \frac{ie}{2\hbar c}\gamma_\mu\gamma_\nu F_{\mu\nu}\right)\psi = 0 \tag{4.18}$$

The first two terms give the Klein-Gordon equation with the replacement of $\partial/\partial x_\mu$ by D_μ. The space part of $D_\mu D_\mu$ is

$$D_k D_k = -\frac{1}{\hbar^2}\vec{\boldsymbol{\pi}}^2 = -\frac{1}{\hbar^2}\left(\vec{\mathbf{p}} + \frac{e}{c}\mathbf{A}\right)^2$$

so that the familiar non-relativistic kinetic energy operator results after multiplication by $-\hbar^2/2m$. The last term in (4.18) is the spin-dependent part:

$$\frac{ie}{2\hbar c}\gamma_\mu\gamma_\nu F_{\mu\nu} = -\frac{e}{\hbar c}(\boldsymbol{\sigma}\cdot\mathscr{H} - i\boldsymbol{\alpha}\cdot\mathscr{E})$$

To interpret these results in terms of a coupling energy with the field, the equation (4.18) is multiplied by $-\hbar^2/2m$, as indicated above, so that the spin-dependent interaction energy is

$$H_{sp} = \frac{e\hbar}{2mc}(\boldsymbol{\sigma}\cdot\mathscr{H} - i\boldsymbol{\alpha}\cdot\mathscr{E}) \tag{4.19}$$

By *definition* the magnetic moment operator $\boldsymbol{\mu}$ couples to the magnetic field to give a contribution

$$-\boldsymbol{\mu}\cdot\mathscr{H}$$

to H_{sp}. Therefore

$$\boldsymbol{\mu} = -\frac{e\hbar}{2mc}\boldsymbol{\sigma} = -\frac{e\hbar}{mc}\mathbf{s} \tag{4.20}$$

as predicted.

The occurrence of the antihermitian electric field interaction in (4.19) is puzzling until it is realized that (4.18), after being multiplied by $-\hbar^2/2m$, does not have the Hamiltonian form

$$H\psi = i\hbar\frac{\partial\psi}{\partial t}$$

and the operator on ψ in (4.18) need not be hermitian. If we replace $\partial^2/\partial x_4^2$ by $W^2/\hbar^2c^2$ and $W = E + mc^2$, then for

$$E \ll mc^2, \qquad e^2\Phi^2 \ll m^2c^4, \qquad e^2\mathbf{A}^2 \ll m^2c^4$$

as is appropriate in this limit, and using (4.2c′), we obtain a time-independent Hamiltonian equation valid in the non-relativistic limit:

$$\left[-\frac{\hbar^2}{2m}\nabla^2 - e\Phi + \frac{e}{mc}\mathbf{A}\cdot\vec{\mathbf{p}} + H_{sp}\right]\psi_{nr} = E\psi_{nr} \tag{4.21}$$

Again, the non-hermitian term in H_{sp} does not present a real difficulty because of the approximate nature of this equation.† The correct Hamiltonian (4.12) is hermitian. The non-relativistic limit will be studied further immediately below and the defect in the form (4.21), it will be seen, can be remedied when the limiting process is performed more systematically.

Foldy-Wouthuysen Transformation with External Fields[2]

The limiting process considered in the preceding discussion is equivalent to writing the Dirac equation as a pair of coupled equations in the large and small components and then eliminating the small component to obtain

† This does not imply that an approximate Hamiltonian cannot be hermitian. The manner in which the approximation is made is the decisive point.

a second-order equation for the large component. As was evident, this procedure suffers from the defect of giving non-hermitian operators. It is also inconvenient in that, when expectation values are to be calculated to order v^2/c^2, the small components cannot be ignored. The Foldy-Wouthuysen transformation considered in section 18 remedies both these defects and at the same time provides more physical insight into the mechanism whereby the relativistic description of the electron operates. The appearance of hermitian operators only is assured since we start with a hermitian Hamiltonian and perform only unitary transformations.

In contrast to the free particle studied before, it will be seen that it is impossible to eliminate all odd operators from the Dirac Hamiltonian in a finite sequence of transformations. This is connected with the observation that, whereas for free particles a clean-cut separation of positive and negative energy states is achieved, this is no longer the case when external fields are present. If these fields are weak† compared to mc^2, the FW transformation should converge rapidly and something of the nature of an approximate separation should be achieved. Fortunately, for electromagnetic fields this usually occurs.

The ambiguities which arise when fields are present can be illustrated by the following example. Consider a particle subject to an external static potential Φ and write $V = -e\Phi$ (for electrons). Then the wave equation for a stationary state with energy W is

$$(W - \boldsymbol{\alpha}\cdot\vec{\mathbf{p}} - \beta)\psi = V\psi \tag{4.22}$$

where ψ is time independent. Operate on (4.22) from the left with $W + \boldsymbol{\alpha}\cdot\vec{\mathbf{p}} + \beta$ to obtain

$$\begin{aligned}(W^2 - \vec{p}^2 - 1)\psi &= (W + \boldsymbol{\alpha}\cdot\vec{\mathbf{p}} + \beta)\, V\psi \\ &= \boldsymbol{\alpha}\cdot(\vec{\mathbf{p}}V)\,\psi + V(W + \boldsymbol{\alpha}\cdot\vec{\mathbf{p}} + \beta)\,\psi \\ &= \boldsymbol{\alpha}\cdot(\vec{\mathbf{p}}V)\,\psi + V(2W - V)\,\psi\end{aligned}$$

or

$$[\nabla^2 + (W - V)^2 - 1]\psi = \boldsymbol{\alpha}\cdot(\vec{\mathbf{p}}V)\,\psi \tag{4.23}$$

Consider the case of a square central well:

$$\begin{aligned} V &= -V_0 \qquad & r &< r_0 \\ V &= 0 \qquad & r &> r_0 \end{aligned}$$

Then the right side of (4.23) gives a Dirac delta function at $r = r_0$. However, if we consider $r \neq r_0$, the right side of (4.23) can be set equal to

† More precisely, the relative change of the interaction terms in a Compton wavelength and in a time interval of $\hbar/mc^2$ must be small compared to unity.

zero, this equation is readily solved in both regions, and ψ is made continuous† at r_0. Therefore we consider the equations

$$[\nabla^2 + (W - V)^2 - 1]\psi = 0 \qquad r < r_0 \tag{4.24a}$$

and

$$(\nabla^2 + W^2 - 1)\psi = 0 \qquad r > r_0 \tag{4.24b}$$

Although these equations are proper ones to use, it must be remembered that it would be incorrect to calculate all four components of ψ independently from (4.24). Instead (4.24a) and (4.24b) could be used to obtain ψ^u, the large component say, and then ψ^l obtained from

$$\psi^l = (W - V + 1)^{-1}\, \boldsymbol{\sigma}\cdot\vec{\mathbf{p}}\psi^u \tag{4.25a}$$

or, alternatively, from ψ^l we could obtain ψ^u by

$$\psi^u = (W - V - 1)^{-1}\, \boldsymbol{\sigma}\cdot\vec{\mathbf{p}}\psi^l \tag{4.25b}$$

We see that for $r > r_0$ we have free particle solutions, but it is not assumed that these are necessarily momentum eigenfunctions. It is somewhat more appropriate to consider that they are angular momentum eigenfunctions. These are studied in detail in Chapter V, but the particular form which they assume is not essential for the present discussion. In the inside region ($r < r_0$) we may select, for any W, a solution regular at $r = 0$. This means that $\psi^*\psi$ is integrable over any domain, including the origin. For $W^2 < 1$ the solutions of (4.24b) are clearly of exponential type and a square integrable solution is obtained only if the decreasing exponential solutions ($\sim \exp -[1 - W^2]^{1/2} r$) are chosen. There will consequently exist a set of discrete states in the interval $-1 \leqslant W \leqslant 1$, if it is assumed that $[(W - V)^2 - 1]r_0^2$ is sufficiently large to permit at least one level. However, when we consider $W^2 > 1$, in particular $W < -1$, we obtain results which are in complete variance with expectations based on the behavior of a non-relativistic particle. In the region $r > r_0$ we now obtain oscillatory solutions. At $r = \infty$ these are not square integrable in the sense of a bounded value of $\int d^3x \psi^*\psi$, but they are acceptable solutions in the sense that continuum solutions generally are. In general, linear combinations of the oscillatory solutions regular and irregular at $r = 0$ will be used in the outside region, and at $r = \infty$ these are standing waves. With these linear combinations a perfectly valid solution of (4.24) is obtained since the inside solution furnishes values of ψ^u and ψ^l at $r = r_0$; and (4.25a) with (4.25b) provides values of ψ^u and ψ^l at all points $r > r_0$ once the starting values are specified. Of course, here we set $V = 0$ in both equations (4.25). As a consequence we find that a particle can have deep lying negative energy states which permit a "tunneling through" to

† As required by the postulate of a probability density.

infinity in a region of classically non-allowed motion. This is, in fact, an understatement since in the region $r > r_0$ there is no exponential damping, as "tunneling" usually implies.

The situation described here is an example of the so-called Klein paradox which is a paradox only if we insist on an interpretation in which the wave functions are supposed to describe particles of definite sign of the mass. Instead, it is necessary to reject the customary intuitive notions connected with a non-relativistic description. In the presence of very strong fields the usefulness of a description in terms of positive and negative energy states is seriously impaired.

Returning to the problem of the FW transformation, the Hamiltonian is written in the form

$$H = \beta m + \Omega_e + \Omega_o \tag{4.26}$$

where Ω_e is an even operator and Ω_o is odd. These shall be assumed time independent. The rest mass term βm is considered dominant and it is desired to transform H to a new Hamiltonian in which the odd terms are of a given order in $1/m$. We shall successively transform H so that the resulting Hamiltonian contains odd operators of order $1/m$, then $1/m^2$, and finally $1/m^3$. The general prescription is to choose $\mathfrak{U}$ in

$$H' = e^{i\mathfrak{U}} H e^{-i\mathfrak{U}} \tag{4.27}$$

to be

$$\mathfrak{U} = -\frac{i}{2m}\beta\Omega_o \tag{4.28}$$

When this is done, H' contains odd terms with a factor $1/m$ or higher powers of $1/m$. If these are substituted for Ω_0 in (4.28) and a second unitary transformation is carried out, the resulting Hamiltonian H'' contains odd-order terms with a factor $1/m^2$ or higher order in $1/m$. At each stage, if the odd terms which are of order $1/m^\nu$ or higher are dropped, the resulting Hamiltonian is correct to order $1/m^\nu$.

From (4.27) we can write

$$H' = \sum_{n=0}^{\infty} \frac{1}{n!} T_n \tag{4.29a}$$

where $T_0 = H$ and

$$T_n = (i\mathfrak{U}, T_{n-1}) \tag{4.29b}$$

defines all other T_n, $n \geqslant 1$. For the leading term in T_1 we have

$$(i\mathfrak{U}, \beta m) = \tfrac{1}{2}(\beta\Omega_o, \beta)$$

Since β anticommutes with all odd operators, this is

$$(i\mathfrak{U}, \beta m) = -\Omega_o$$

which will cancel the Ω_o in $T_0 = H$. The remaining terms are: first,

$$(i\mathfrak{U}, \Omega_e) = \frac{1}{2m}(\beta\Omega_o, \Omega_e) = \frac{\beta}{2m}(\Omega_o, \Omega_e)$$

which is odd, and we have used the fact that β commutes with Ω_e; a second term is

$$(i\mathfrak{U}, \Omega_o) = \frac{1}{2m}(\beta\Omega_o, \Omega_o) = \frac{1}{m}\beta\Omega_o^2$$

and is even. There is one additional term arising from T_2 which contributes to order $1/m$. This is the term of T_2 arising from the commutator of $i\mathfrak{U}$ and the dominant term of T_1. With the numerical factor $\frac{1}{2}$ going with T_2 the relevant contribution is

$$\tfrac{1}{2}(i\mathfrak{U}, -\Omega_o) = -\frac{1}{2m}\beta\Omega_o^2$$

Hence, to order $1/m$ the Hamiltonian is

$$H' = \beta m + \Omega_e + \frac{1}{2m}\beta\Omega_o^2 + \frac{\beta}{2m}(\Omega_o, \Omega_e) \tag{4.30}$$

If it is desired to obtain the Hamiltonian correct to order $1/m$, then we carry out the same transformation but with $\mathfrak{U}$ replaced by $\mathfrak{U}'$, where

$$\begin{aligned}\mathfrak{U}' &= -\frac{i}{2m}\beta\frac{\beta}{2m}(\Omega_o, \Omega_e)\\ &= -\frac{i}{4m^2}(\Omega_o, \Omega_e)\end{aligned} \tag{4.31}$$

Then

$$H'' = e^{i\mathfrak{U}'}H'e^{-i\mathfrak{U}'}$$

is written in the form (4.29a)

$$H'' = \sum_{n=0}^{\infty}\frac{1}{n!}T'_n$$

where $T'_0 = H'$ and

$$T'_n = (i\mathfrak{U}', T'_{n-1}), \qquad n \geqslant 1$$

The mass term gives

$$(i\mathfrak{U}', \beta m) = \frac{1}{4m}((\Omega_o, \Omega_e), \beta) = -\frac{1}{2m}\beta(\Omega_o, \Omega_e)$$

which cancels the last term of (4.30). Remaining terms are of order $1/m^2$. Therefore the first three terms of (4.30) give the correct result to the desired order.

If it is desired to obtain the Hamiltonian in which odd-order terms are of order $1/m^3$, the preceding transformation which led to (4.30) must be carried further to give terms of order $1/m^2$. Then we must add the following terms from $\frac{1}{2}T_2$:

$$\frac{1}{2}(i\mathfrak{U}, (i\mathfrak{U}, \Omega_e)) = \frac{1}{8m^2}(\beta\Omega_o, \beta(\Omega_o, \Omega_e))$$

$$= -\frac{1}{8m^2}(\Omega_o, (\Omega_o, \Omega_e))$$

and

$$\frac{1}{2}(i\mathfrak{U}, (i\mathfrak{U}, \Omega_o)) = \frac{1}{4m^2}(\beta\Omega_o, \beta\Omega_o^2) = -\frac{1}{2m^2}\Omega_o^3$$

and a term from $T_3/6$:

$$\frac{1}{6}(i\mathfrak{U}, (i\mathfrak{U}, -\Omega_o)) = -\frac{1}{12m^2}(\beta\Omega_o, \beta\Omega_o^2) = \frac{1}{6m}\Omega_o^3$$

which involves the commutator of $i\mathfrak{U}$ and the dominant term of T_2. Then, to order $1/m^2$, we obtain

$$H' = \beta m + \Omega_e + \frac{1}{2m}\beta\Omega_o^2 + \frac{\beta}{2m}(\Omega_o, \Omega_e)$$
$$-\frac{1}{8m^2}(\Omega_o, (\Omega_o, \Omega_e)) - \frac{1}{3m^2}\Omega_o^3 \tag{4.32}$$

Repeating the same process gives

$$H'' = e^{i\mathfrak{U}'}H'e^{-i\mathfrak{U}'}$$

with $\mathfrak{U}'$ now given by

$$\mathfrak{U}' = -\frac{i}{2m}\beta\left[\frac{\beta}{2m}(\Omega_o, \Omega_e) - \frac{1}{3m^2}\Omega_o^3\right] \tag{4.33}$$

The commutator $(i\mathfrak{U}', \beta m)$ gives a contribution from the first term of (4.33) which cancels the fourth term of (4.32), and a contribution from the second term of (4.33) which cancels the last of (4.32). Then, in addition we obtain the following m^{-2} contribution to H'':

$$(i\mathfrak{U}', \Omega_e) = \frac{1}{4m^2}((\Omega_o, \Omega_e), \Omega_e) \tag{4.33'}$$

which is odd. All other terms are of order m^{-3}. Each succeeding term in the expansion of H'' now gives a factor m^{-2}, since this is the m-dependence of the dominant term of (4.33). Since the term (4.33′) can be removed by another unitary transformation without changing the m^{-2} terms, it follows that the Hamiltonian to second order is

$$H_{nr} = \beta m + \Omega_e + \frac{1}{2m}\beta\Omega_o^2 - \frac{1}{8m^2}(\Omega_o, (\Omega_o, \Omega_e)) \tag{4.34}$$

This result is now applied to the electron in an electromagnetic field. Then

$$\Omega_o = \boldsymbol{\alpha}\cdot(\vec{\mathbf{p}} + e\mathbf{A})$$
$$\Omega_e = -e\Phi$$

A straightforward calculation gives

$$H_{nr} = \beta m - e\Phi + \frac{\beta}{2m}(\vec{\mathbf{p}} + e\mathbf{A})^2 + \frac{e}{2m}\beta\boldsymbol{\sigma}\cdot\mathscr{H}$$
$$+ \frac{e}{4m^2}\boldsymbol{\sigma}\cdot\mathscr{E} \times (\vec{\mathbf{p}} + e\mathbf{A}) + \frac{e}{8m^2}\operatorname{div}\mathscr{E} \tag{4.35}$$

It can be checked that all terms in H_{nr} are hermitian. For positive energies β should be set equal to 1. Then, in ordinary units, and with $\beta = 1$

$$H_{nr} = mc^2 - e\Phi + \frac{1}{2m}\left(\vec{\mathbf{p}} + \frac{e}{c}\mathbf{A}\right)^2 + \frac{e\hbar}{2mc}\boldsymbol{\sigma}\cdot\mathscr{H}$$
$$+ \frac{e\hbar}{4m^2c^2}\boldsymbol{\sigma}\cdot\mathscr{E} \times \left(\vec{\mathbf{p}} + \frac{e}{c}\mathbf{A}\right) + \frac{e\hbar^2}{8m^2c^2}\operatorname{div}\mathscr{E} \tag{4.35$'$}$$

The first three terms have an obvious interpretation. Then the magnetic interaction of the field $\mathscr{H}$ with magnetic moment $\boldsymbol{\mu}$, given by (4.20), can be recognized in the fourth term. The fifth term gives the spin-orbit coupling interaction. Finally, the last term, the so-called Darwin term,[3] gives a relativistic shift to s-levels for a Coulomb field. This follows since $\operatorname{div}\mathscr{E} = 4\pi\rho_c = -4\pi e\delta(\mathbf{r})$, and in the present approximation it is proper to use non-relativistic wave functions for which only s-states have $\psi(0) \neq 0$. A simple way of interpreting this term is to recall that the electron motion is characterized by an oscillatory component which was referred to as the Zitterbewegung. If its coordinate is written $\mathbf{r} + \Delta\mathbf{r}$, where $\Delta\mathbf{r}$ is the oscillatory part, the potential Φ at the position of the electron is

$$\Phi(\mathbf{r} + \Delta\mathbf{r}) = [1 + \Delta\mathbf{r}\cdot\nabla + \tfrac{1}{2}(\Delta\mathbf{r}\cdot\nabla)^2 + \cdots]\Phi(\mathbf{r})$$

The relevant quantity is a time average of this. Thus, for the interaction energy, we obtain

$$-e\Phi(\mathbf{r}) - \frac{e}{2}\langle(\Delta\mathbf{r}\cdot\nabla)^2\rangle_{\mathrm{Av}}\Phi = -e\Phi(\mathbf{r}) - \frac{e}{6}(\Delta\mathbf{r})^2_{\mathrm{Av}}\nabla^2\Phi$$

Hence the additional energy is

$$\frac{e}{6}(\Delta\mathbf{r})^2_{\text{Av}}\,\text{div}\,\mathscr{E}$$

In this interpretation we would set (cf. 4.35′)

$$(\Delta\mathbf{r})^2_{\text{Av}} = \frac{3}{4}\left(\frac{\hbar}{mc}\right)^2$$

which is exactly the result obtained in section 18.

23. SPIN EFFECTS IN ELECTRIC AND MAGNETIC FIELDS

Polarization Effects and Covariant Spin Operator

As an application of the results of the preceding section we first consider the behavior of a spinning electron in electric and magnetic fields.[4,5] From

$$\frac{d\Omega}{dt} = \frac{i}{\hbar}(H, \Omega)$$

where $\partial\Omega/\partial t = 0$ and H is given by (4.12) we observe that, with $\Omega = \boldsymbol{\sigma}\cdot\boldsymbol{\pi}$,

$$\begin{aligned}\frac{d}{dt}\boldsymbol{\sigma}\cdot\boldsymbol{\pi} &= -\frac{ie}{\hbar}(\Phi, \boldsymbol{\sigma}\cdot\boldsymbol{\pi}) = \frac{ie}{\hbar}\boldsymbol{\sigma}\cdot(\vec{\mathbf{p}}, \Phi)\\ &= -e\boldsymbol{\sigma}\cdot\mathscr{E}\end{aligned} \tag{4.36}$$

where $\mathscr{E} = -\nabla\Phi$ is the static electric field. Therefore in a pure magnetic field $\boldsymbol{\sigma}\cdot\boldsymbol{\pi}$ is a constant of the motion. From this result it may be concluded that a longitudinally polarized electron will remain longitudinally polarized after passing through a static magnetic field. A second conclusion is that a polarized beam of electrons will not be depolarized on passing through a magnetic field if no electric field is present.

For a pure static electric field we consider $\boldsymbol{\Omega} = \boldsymbol{\pi}$. Then

$$\frac{d\boldsymbol{\pi}}{dt} = -e\mathscr{E}$$

Combining this result with (4.36) leads to the conclusion

$$\boldsymbol{\pi}\cdot\frac{d\boldsymbol{\sigma}}{dt} = 0$$

Here $\boldsymbol{\pi} = \mathbf{p}$. Therefore a beam of electrons (or μ mesons) which is originally polarized along the direction of the momentum—that is, longitudinally—will remain longitudinally polarized in passing through an electric field which does not deflect them.

The justification for the interpretation of the results given above is ultimately to be based on an appropriate definition of the spin operator in the presence of fields. This question was discussed for free particles in section 20. It was shown there that a description of the spin states could be based on the operator

$$\mathcal{O}\cdot\hat{\mathbf{n}}_0 = \hat{\mathbf{n}}_0\cdot[\boldsymbol{\sigma} + (\beta - 1)\hat{\mathbf{p}} \times (\boldsymbol{\sigma} \times \hat{\mathbf{p}})]$$

and despite the non-covariant appearance of this operator it is equivalent to the manifestly covariant

$$Q(n) = i\gamma_5\gamma_\mu n_\mu$$

where n_μ is the four-vector into which $\bar{n}_\mu = \hat{\mathbf{n}}_0, 0$ transforms. This description is based on the single-vector parameter $\hat{\mathbf{n}}_0$ which gives the spin direction in the rest system. However, when fields are present the spin direction is no longer a constant of the motion. Instead, from classical considerations, one expects a precession in a pure magnetic field, for example. Therefore $\mathcal{O}\cdot\hat{\mathbf{n}}_0$ or $Q(n)$ no longer provides a suitable description. Another way to say this is that $\mathcal{O}\cdot\hat{\mathbf{n}}_0$ does not lend itself to the gauge invariant generalization $\vec{p}_\mu \rightarrow \vec{\pi}_\mu = \vec{p}_\mu + eA_\mu$ which must be made when electromagnetic fields are present.

The required operator is obtained by noting that for free particles

$$Q(n) = T_\mu n_\mu$$

where†

$$T_\mu = \gamma_5(i\gamma_\mu - p_\mu)$$

since $n_\mu p_\mu = 0$. For free particles it follows that

$$(T_\mu, H) = 0$$

where we use $i\gamma_\mu p_\mu = -1$ as an operator relation for the relevant states. Also,

$$T_\mu p_\mu = p_\mu T_\mu = 0$$

while the commutation rules of the T_μ are‡

$$(T_\mu, T_\nu) = 2[\gamma_\mu\gamma_\nu - \delta_{\mu\nu} + i(\gamma_\mu p_\nu - p_\mu\gamma_\nu)]$$

$$(T_\mu, T_\nu)_+ = 2(\delta_{\mu\nu} + p_\mu p_\nu)$$

† These operators were first introduced by V. Bargmann and E. P. Wigner, *Proc. Natl. Acad. Sci. U.S.* **34,** 211 (1948). Their w_μ is $\frac{1}{2}T_\mu$. The T_μ are generators of a subgroup of the Lorentz transformations. They were called to my attention by D. M. Fradkin of Iowa State University.

‡ In the rest frame $T_\mu = \mathbf{T}, T_4 \rightarrow \boldsymbol{\sigma}, 0$, where odd operators are replaced by zero.

In the presence of an electromagnetic field with four-potential A_μ the T_μ is defined by

$$T_\mu = \gamma_5(i\gamma_\mu - \vec{\pi}_\mu)$$

The commutation rules with the Hamiltonian are now, for time-independent fields,

$$(\mathbf{T}, H) = -ie(\boldsymbol{\sigma} \times \mathscr{H} - \gamma_5 \mathscr{E})$$

$$(T_4, H) = e\boldsymbol{\sigma}\cdot\mathscr{E}$$

and, explicitly, $T_4 = i\boldsymbol{\sigma}\cdot\vec{\boldsymbol{\pi}}$. Consequently, when $\mathscr{E} = 0$, T_4 is a constant of the motion as is the component of $\mathbf{T}$ along $\mathscr{H}$. When $\mathscr{H} = 0$ the components of $\mathbf{T}$ perpendicular to $\mathscr{E}$ are constants of the motion.

In general,

$$\frac{dT_\mu}{d\tau} = ie\gamma_5\gamma_4 F_{\mu\nu}\gamma_\nu$$

where $F_{\mu\nu}$ is the electromagnetic field tensor introduced in section 22 and $d\tau = dt/\xi$ is the proper time interval. For slowly varying fields in which the relative change of the fields over the dimensions of a wave packet ψ are negligible,

$$\frac{d}{d\tau}\langle T_\mu \rangle = -eF_{\mu\nu}\int \psi^* i\gamma_4\gamma_5\gamma_\nu\psi \, d^3x$$

In the rest system of the particle ($\gamma_4 \approx 1$ in even operators) this is

$$\frac{d\langle T_\mu^r \rangle}{d\tau} \approx -eF_{\mu\nu}\langle T_\nu^r \rangle$$

where r refers to rest system and the gyromagnetic ratio e/mc here appears as e. Here we use $\langle \mathbf{T}^r \rangle = i\gamma_5\boldsymbol{\gamma}$, $\langle T_4^r \rangle \approx 0$. Then since $F_{jk} = \epsilon_{ijk}\mathscr{H}_i$ we see that

$$\frac{d\langle \mathbf{T}^r \rangle}{d\tau} \approx -e\langle \mathbf{T}^r \rangle \times \mathscr{H}$$

which is the classical equation of motion for the spin vector. Under a Lorentz transformation to an arbitrary coordinate system, $\langle T_\mu' \rangle = a_{\mu\nu}\langle T_\nu^r \rangle$ and

$$\frac{d\langle T_\mu' \rangle}{d\tau} = -eF_{\mu\nu}\langle T_\nu' \rangle$$

Virial Theorem[6]

As a second example we consider an entirely different question. The virial theorem in physics has a very general significance. What form does it take in the Dirac theory? In classical physics the form of this theorem is

$$-\langle \mathbf{r}\cdot\mathbf{F} \rangle_{\text{Av}} = \langle T + L_0 \rangle_{\text{Av}} \tag{4.37}$$

where $\langle\cdots\rangle_{\text{Av}}$ indicates a time average; **F** is the force, T the kinetic energy, and L_0 the Lagrangian for a free particle. Thus, in classical relativistic mechanics,[7]

$$T^2 = m^2c^4 + c^2\boldsymbol{\pi}^2, \qquad L_0 = -mc^2/\xi$$
$$\xi = (1 - v^2/c^2)^{-\frac{1}{2}}$$

The corresponding quantum form is obtained by first observing that

$$\frac{d}{dt}(\vec{\mathbf{p}}\cdot\mathbf{r} - \mathbf{r}\cdot\vec{\mathbf{p}}) = \left\langle \frac{d}{dt}\, 3\,\frac{\hbar}{i} \right\rangle = 0 \tag{4.38}$$

Angular brackets mean expectation values. Also,

$$\frac{d}{dt}\,\vec{\mathbf{p}}\cdot\mathbf{r} = \frac{i}{\hbar}\,[\vec{\mathbf{p}}\cdot(H, \mathbf{r}) - (\vec{\mathbf{p}}, H)\cdot\mathbf{r}] \tag{4.38'}$$

Since $(H, \mathbf{r}) = c\boldsymbol{\alpha}$ and $(\vec{\mathbf{p}}, H) = e\boldsymbol{\alpha}\cdot(\vec{\mathbf{p}}, \mathbf{A}) - e(\vec{\mathbf{p}}, \Phi) = e(\vec{\mathbf{p}}\boldsymbol{\alpha}\cdot\mathbf{A} - \vec{\mathbf{p}}\Phi)$, it follows that $(H, \mathbf{r})$ commutes with $\vec{\mathbf{p}}$ and $(\vec{\mathbf{p}}, H)$ commutes with $\mathbf{r}$. Therefore

$$\frac{d}{dt}\,\mathbf{r}\cdot\vec{\mathbf{p}} = \frac{i}{\hbar}\left[\mathbf{r}\cdot(H, \vec{\mathbf{p}}) - (\mathbf{r}, H)\vec{\mathbf{p}}\right] = -\frac{d}{dt}\,\vec{\mathbf{p}}\cdot\mathbf{r}$$

Thus it follows from (4.38) and (4.38′) that

$$\left\langle \frac{d}{dt}\,\mathbf{r}\cdot\vec{\mathbf{p}} \right\rangle = 0 \tag{4.39}$$

and

$$\langle \vec{\mathbf{p}}\cdot(H, \mathbf{r})\rangle = \langle(\vec{\mathbf{p}}, H)\cdot\mathbf{r}\rangle$$

Applying this to (4.12) results in

$$c\langle\boldsymbol{\alpha}\cdot\vec{\mathbf{p}}\rangle = -e\langle\mathbf{r}\cdot\nabla\Phi - \mathbf{r}\cdot\nabla\,\boldsymbol{\alpha}\cdot\mathbf{A}\rangle \tag{4.40}$$

Since **r** and **A** commute, we can replace $\vec{\mathbf{p}}$ by $\vec{\boldsymbol{\pi}}$ in (4.38). Hence

$$-\frac{1}{c}\left\langle \frac{d}{dt}\,\mathbf{r}\cdot\mathbf{A} \right\rangle = \langle\boldsymbol{\alpha}\cdot\mathbf{A}\rangle + \langle\mathbf{r}\cdot(\boldsymbol{\alpha}\cdot\nabla)\mathbf{A}\rangle = 0 \tag{4.41}$$

The quantity $\nabla\boldsymbol{\alpha}\cdot\mathbf{A}$ in (4.40) is readily evaluated since the components of $\boldsymbol{\alpha}$ are constants in the differentiation and

$$\nabla\boldsymbol{\alpha}\cdot\mathbf{A} = \alpha \times \text{curl}\,\mathbf{A} + (\boldsymbol{\alpha}\cdot\nabla)\mathbf{A}$$

Thus, for example,

$$\frac{\partial}{\partial x}(\alpha_x A_x + \alpha_y A_y + \alpha_z A_z) \equiv \alpha_y\left(\frac{\partial A_y}{\partial x} - \frac{\partial A_x}{\partial y}\right) - \alpha_z\left(\frac{\partial A_x}{\partial z} - \frac{\partial A_z}{\partial x}\right) + \alpha_x\frac{\partial A_x}{\partial x} + \alpha_y\frac{\partial A_x}{\partial y} + \alpha_z\frac{\partial A_x}{\partial z}$$

Substituting in (4.40) and using (4.41) results in

$$c\langle \boldsymbol{\alpha}\cdot\boldsymbol{\pi}\rangle = -\langle \mathbf{r}\cdot\mathbf{F}\rangle \tag{4.42}$$

where

$$\mathbf{F} = e[\nabla\Phi - \boldsymbol{\alpha} \times \text{curl } \mathbf{A}] \tag{4.42'}$$

This is just the Lorentz force when we replace the velocity by the operator $c\boldsymbol{\alpha}$.

This result can be used to calculate matrix elements in a very simple way. Since (4.42) can be written in the form

$$-\langle \mathbf{r}\cdot\mathbf{F}\rangle = \langle W - \beta mc^2 + e\Phi\rangle$$

we find, for no magnetic field,

$$c\langle \boldsymbol{\alpha}\cdot\vec{\mathbf{p}}\rangle = \langle W + e\Phi - \beta mc^2\rangle$$

For $\Phi = 0$, this becomes the free particle case and

$$c\langle \boldsymbol{\alpha}\cdot\vec{\mathbf{p}}\rangle = W - mc^2\langle\beta\rangle$$

where $W = p_0 = (p^2 + 1)^{1/2}$, and since $\langle\beta\rangle = mc^2/W$ we obtain

$$\langle \boldsymbol{\alpha}\cdot\vec{\mathbf{p}}\rangle = \frac{cp^2}{W}$$

which checks with the result $\langle\boldsymbol{\alpha}\rangle = c\mathbf{p}/W$.

An alternative method of rapid calculation of matrix elements is now illustrated. Consider that the magnetic field is absent. Then

$$\beta H + H\beta = 2(mc^2 - \beta e\Phi)$$

Therefore

$$\langle \beta(p_0 + e\Phi)\rangle = mc^2 \tag{4.43}$$

From this it can be seen that, at least in the non-relativistic limit, $\beta \to 1$, the eigenvalues W are less than mc^2 for an attractive potential, $e\Phi > 0$. This, as should be expected, will be true in general. It would follow, then, that the upper components, for which $\beta = 1$, contribute a greater amount to the average potential than do the lower components for which $\beta = -1$.

24. CHARGE CONJUGATION[8,9]

In section 17 it was seen that a plane wave for an electron ψ was transformed into a positron plane wave ψ^c by the charge conjugation operation

$$\psi^c = C^{-1}\psi^\times \tag{4.44}$$

We wish to show that there is a charge conjugation transformation in the general representation and to determine the properties which the matrix C will exhibit in this general case. For ψ we write

$$\gamma_\mu\left(\frac{\partial}{\partial x_\mu} + \frac{ie}{\hbar c} A_\mu\right)\psi + k_0\psi = 0 \tag{4.45}$$

and substitute (4.44) after taking the complex conjugate of this equation. Then we obtain

$$\gamma_k^\times\left(\frac{\partial}{\partial x_k} - \frac{ieA_k}{\hbar c}\right)C\psi^c + \gamma_4^\times\left(-\frac{\partial}{\partial x_4} + \frac{ieA_4}{\hbar c}\right)C\psi^c + k_0 C\psi^c = 0$$

Multiplying by C^{-1} from the left, we see that if

$$C^{-1}\gamma_k^\times C = \gamma_k$$

$$C^{-1}\gamma_4^\times C = -\gamma_4 \tag{4.46}$$

then we obtain for ψ^c

$$\gamma_\mu\left(\frac{\partial}{\partial x_\mu} - \frac{ie}{\hbar c} A_\mu\right)\psi^c + k_0\psi^c = 0 \tag{4.47}$$

Since this is just (4.45) with the sign of e reversed, we may interpret ψ^c as the positron wave function.

The fact that charge conjugation involves complex conjugation in any representation can be seen to be a consequence of the requirements of gauge invariance. The charge conjugation is therefore a non-linear operation:

$$\left[\sum_i a_i\psi_i\right]^c \neq \sum_i a_i\psi_i^c$$

for all constants a_i. Instead

$$\left[\sum_i a_i\psi_i\right]^c = \sum_i a_i^\times\psi_i^c$$

and the charge conjugation operator is antilinear.

Since $\gamma_k^\times$ and $-\gamma_4^\times$ obey the commutation rules of the γ_μ, it is established by the fundamental theorem of section 13 that C exists. We introduce a matrix B such that

$$C = B\gamma_4\gamma_5 \tag{4.48}$$

and B has the property that

$$\tilde{\gamma}_\mu = \gamma_\mu^\times = B\gamma_\mu B^{-1} \tag{4.49}$$

Then both equations (4.46) are fulfilled. The matrix B is now shown to be antisymmetric. The transpose of (4.49) is

$$\gamma_\mu = \tilde{B}^{-1}\tilde{\gamma}_\mu\tilde{B} = \tilde{B}^{-1}B\gamma_\mu B^{-1}\tilde{B}$$
$$= (B^{-1}\tilde{B})^{-1}\gamma_\mu B^{-1}\tilde{B}$$

Therefore $B^{-1}\tilde{B}$ commutes with all γ_μ and must be a multiple of a unit matrix.

$$B^{-1}\tilde{B} = k$$

or

$$\tilde{B} = kB$$

Transposing gives

$$B = k\tilde{B} = k^2B$$

so that $k = \pm 1$. To show that $k = -1$, consider the transpose of $iB\gamma_\mu\gamma_\nu$ where $\mu \neq \nu$. This is

$$(iB\gamma_\mu\gamma_\nu)^{\sim} = ik\tilde{\gamma}_\nu\tilde{\gamma}_\mu B = -ik\tilde{\gamma}_\mu\tilde{\gamma}_\nu B = -ik\tilde{\gamma}_\mu B\gamma_\nu = -k(iB\gamma_\mu\gamma_\nu)$$

Also, since

$$\tilde{\gamma}_5 = \gamma_5^\times = \gamma_1^\times\gamma_2^\times\gamma_3^\times\gamma_4^\times = B\gamma_5 B^{-1}$$

we obtain

$$(iB\gamma_\mu\gamma_5)^{\sim} = ik\tilde{\gamma}_5\tilde{\gamma}_\mu B = ik\tilde{\gamma}_5 B\gamma_\mu = ikB\gamma_5\gamma_\mu = -k(iB\gamma_\mu\gamma_5)$$

The choice $k = 1$ implies the existence of ten linearly independent antisymmetric matrices. Since there can only be six antisymmetric 4 by 4 matrices we conclude that $k = -1$. Thus

$$\tilde{B} = -B \tag{4.50}$$

With this result the remaining five matrices $B\gamma_\mu$ and $B\gamma_5$ are antisymmetric and with (4.50) we find $B\gamma_A$ constitutes six antisymmetric and ten symmetric matrices.

It can be further shown that B may be chosen to be unitary: Thus the hermitian conjugate of (4.49) is

$$\gamma_\mu^\times = (B^{-1})^*\gamma_\mu B^*$$

so that, with (4.49), this yields

$$B^*B\gamma_\mu = \gamma_\mu B^*B$$

Consequently B^*B, commuting with all γ_μ, is a multiple (k) of a unit matrix. Since the diagonal elements of B^*B are necessarily positive definite, $k > 0$ and k may be set equal to 1 since (4.49) does not define k.

These properties of B may now be used to establish some properties of C. From (4.48) we see that

$$\tilde{C} = \tilde{\gamma}_5\tilde{\gamma}_4\tilde{B} = -\tilde{\gamma}_5\tilde{\gamma}_4 B = -B\gamma_5\gamma_4 = B\gamma_4\gamma_5 = C$$

Thus C is symmetric. It is also easy to show that C is unitary if B is. Then

$$C^*C = (B\gamma_4\gamma_5)^*(B\gamma_4\gamma_5) = \gamma_5\gamma_4 B^* B\gamma_4\gamma_5 = 1$$

It is now seen that charge conjugation does not change the norm of ψ:

$$(\psi^c, \psi^c) = (C^{-1}\psi^\times, C^{-1}\psi^\times) = (\psi^\times, CC^{-1}\psi^\times) = (\psi, \psi)^\times$$

and (ψ, ψ) is real. The same is therefore true for any linear combination $\sum_i a_i\psi_i$ with complex coefficients a_i. This result is to be expected in view of the interpretation of ψ^c as the positron state.

Finally, the charge conjugation property is reciprocal. This means that the charge conjugate of ψ^c is ψ:

$$(\psi^c)^c = C^{-1}(\psi^c)^\times = C^{-1}C^{-1\times}\psi$$

But C^{-1} is C^* and $(C^{-1})^\times$ is $C^{*\times} = \tilde{C} = C$. Thus $C^{-1}C^{-1\times} = C^*C = 1$. This proves the theorem.

As before, any operator equation

$$\Omega\psi = \omega\psi$$

where ω is a number, on charge conjugation becomes

$$\Omega^c\psi^c = \omega^\times\psi^c$$

where

$$\Omega^c = C^{-1}\Omega^\times C \tag{4.51}$$

and, for hermitian Ω, $\omega = \omega^\times$.

The correspondence between positive energy positron states and negative energy electron states should not be a property of a particular Lorentz frame but should be independent of which inertial system is used. This means that charge conjugation should be covariant. With $\psi^\times = C\psi^c$ under a Lorentz transformation, $\psi(x) \to \psi'(x')$; then if

$$\psi'(x') = \Lambda\psi(x)$$

we should also have

$$\psi^{c\prime}(x') = \Lambda\psi^c(x)$$

This implies that

$$\psi'^c(x') = C^{-1}\psi'^\times(x') = C^{-1}\Lambda^\times\,\psi^\times(x)$$

should be equal to

$$\psi^{c\prime}(x') = \Lambda\psi^c(x) = \Lambda C^{-1}\,\psi^\times(x)$$

Therefore we require that

$$C^{-1}\Lambda^{\times} = \Lambda C^{-1}$$

or, equivalently,

$$\Lambda^{\times} C = C\Lambda \tag{4.52}$$

This constitutes an additional condition on Λ. For instance, for

$$\Lambda = e^{\frac{1}{2}\gamma_j\gamma_k\theta} \qquad (j \neq k)$$

and

$$C = \gamma_2$$

in the standard representation, the condition (4.52) reduces to

$$\gamma_j^{\times}\gamma_k^{\times}\gamma_2 = \gamma_2\gamma_j\gamma_k$$

Since in this representation γ_2 is real while γ_1 and γ_3 are pure imaginary, it is seen that the condition is indeed satisfied. For a Lorentz transformation with uniform velocity the Λ used in section 14 will satisfy (4.52) if

$$\alpha_k^{\times}\gamma_2 = \gamma_2\alpha_k$$

Again α_2 is pure imaginary and anticommutes with γ_2 while α_1 and α_3 are real and commute with γ_2. Hence the condition is again satisfied.

It will be realized that the relations

$$\sigma_k^c = -\sigma_k, \qquad \alpha_k^c = \alpha_k$$

and the like are unchanged under a change of representation. Also

$$\left\{c\boldsymbol{\alpha}\cdot\left(\vec{\mathbf{p}} + \frac{e}{c}\mathbf{A}\right) + \beta mc^2 - e\Phi\right\}^c = -\left\{c\boldsymbol{\alpha}\cdot\left(\vec{\mathbf{p}} - \frac{e}{c}\mathbf{A}\right) + \beta mc^2 + e\Phi\right\}$$

The minus sign in front of the curly bracket on the right is cancelled in the equation of motion by another minus sign arising from charge conjugation of the operator $i\hbar\, \partial/\partial t$.

It is important to recognize that any particular Lorentz transformation can always be replaced by two (or any number of) other Lorentz transformations and conversely. Therefore if (4.52) is valid for two transformations L_1 and L_2 with corresponding Λ_1 and Λ_2 it must also be true for the Lorentz transformation obtained by applying them in succession. That this is so is seen at once. If

$$\Lambda_1^{\times} C = C\Lambda_1$$

$$\Lambda_2^{\times} C = C\Lambda_2$$

then

$$(\Lambda_2\Lambda_1)^{\times} C = \Lambda_2^{\times}\Lambda_1^{\times} C = \Lambda_2^{\times} C\Lambda_1$$

$$= C\Lambda_2\Lambda_1$$

It follows that the property (4.52) is preserved through any number of Lorentz transformations. Improper transformations are discussed in the next section, and it will be seen that (4.52) still applies.

25. SPACE AND TIME REFLECTION

In this section it is our purpose to investigate the transformation properties of the Dirac equations of motion under the improper Lorentz transformations

$$x_k' = -x_k, \qquad x_4' = x_4 \tag{4.53}$$

which is the space inversion of coordinates, and

$$x_k' = x_k, \qquad x_4' = -x_4 \tag{4.54}$$

or time reversal. In each case $\det a = -1$. The case of reflection in a plane, say $x_1' = -x_1$, $x_\mu' = x_\mu$ for $\mu \neq 1$, is included in (4.53) since the complete space reflection followed or preceded by a rotation around the x_1- or x_1'-axis through an angle π reproduces the reflection in the x_2–x_3 plane. Clearly, Lorentz transformations of the type (4.53) and (4.54) commute with all the three-space rotations although not with the general continuous Lorentz transformation.

In the following discussion we shall trace the arguments concerning the space and time inversion in classical and in non-relativistic quantum mechanics, and this will shed considerable light on the discussion of the corresponding problem with the Dirac equation.

Space Reflection

If we consider a charged particle in an electromagnetic field, then the equations of motion

$$m\frac{d}{dt}\frac{\mathbf{v}}{(1 - v^2/c^2)^{1/2}} = \mathbf{F} = -e(\mathscr{E} + \mathbf{v} \times \mathscr{H}/c)$$

with $\mathbf{v} = d\mathbf{x}/dt$ are unchanged under the space reflection (4.54) provided that

$$\begin{aligned} \mathbf{v}' &= -\mathbf{v} \\ \mathscr{H}'(x') &= \mathscr{H}(x) \\ \mathscr{E}'(x') &= -\mathscr{E}(x) \end{aligned} \tag{4.55}$$

where the charge $-e$ is an invariant. Here $\mathbf{x}'(= -\mathbf{x})$ on the left refers to the same point in space as $\mathbf{x}$ does on the right. Therefore at a given point, described by different coordinates in the two reference frames, $\mathscr{H}$ does not change (axial vector) and $\mathscr{E}$ does (polar vector).

The transformations (4.55) are in accord with the deductions from the form invariance of the Maxwell equations. Thus

$$-e = \iiint_{-\infty}^{\infty} \rho_c(x)\, d^3x$$

is transformed to

$$-e' = \iiint_{-\infty}^{\infty} \rho_c(x)\, d^3x'$$

since the three sign changes in going from d^3x to d^3x' compensate the three sign changes required to interchange the limits in the integrals. Since

$$-e' = -e = \iiint_{-\infty}^{\infty} \rho_c'(x')\, d^3x'$$

we conclude that ρ_c is a scalar. From (4.1c) $\mathscr{E}$ is a polar vector and from (4.1b) $\mathscr{H}$ is an axial vector. Then from (4.1a) we conclude

$$\mathbf{j}'(x') = -\mathbf{j}(x)$$

so that, as expected, the continuity equation is

$$\frac{\partial \mathfrak{s}'_\mu(x')}{\partial x'_\mu} = 0$$

unchanged in form. From (4.2b) we conclude $A'_k(x') = -A_k(x)$, and from (4.2a) $\Phi'(x') = \Phi(x)$. Hence it is still true that

$$A'_\mu(x') = a_{\mu\nu}A_\nu(x) \tag{4.56}$$

In a quantum theory the space reflection requires

$$\vec{\mathbf{p}}' = -\vec{\mathbf{p}}, \qquad \mathbf{l}' = \mathbf{l}$$

and since reflections commute with rotations it follows that

$$\mathbf{J}' = \mathbf{J}$$

for all angular momentum operators. Then the commutation rules

$$(x_j, x_k) = (\vec{p}_j, \vec{p}_k) = 0$$

$$(\vec{p}_j, x_k) = -i\hbar\delta_{jk}$$

$$\mathbf{J} \times \mathbf{J} = i\mathbf{J}$$

are all unchanged by the space reflection. It follows then, from the known properties of transformation theory, that there exists a unitary transformation Λ such that

$$\psi'(x') = \Lambda\psi(x)$$

The non-relativistic equation

$$\left\{\frac{1}{2m}\left(\vec{\mathbf{p}} + \frac{e}{c}\mathbf{A}\right)^2 - e\Phi\right\}\psi(x) = i\hbar\frac{\partial\psi(x)}{\partial t} \tag{4.57}$$

goes over into the corresponding primed equations with Λ equal to any operator which commutes with the Hamiltonian in curly brackets. Since a second application of Λ gives the same coordinate system with which one started, $\Lambda^2 = 1$ and the eigenvalues are ± 1. These are the well-known even, odd parity states. Thus

$$\psi'(x') = \pm\psi(x)$$

implies that for every $\psi(\mathbf{x})$ there is a function $\psi(-\mathbf{x})$ which is also an eigenfunction of the energy operator with the same eigenvalue.

We may now consider the space reflection in the Dirac theory. Writing (4.8) in the primed coordinate system, for example,

$$\gamma_\mu\left(\frac{\partial}{\partial x'_\mu} + \frac{ie}{\hbar c}A'_\mu(x')\right)\psi'(x') + k_0\psi'(x') = 0 \tag{4.8$'$}$$

becomes

$$\Lambda^{-1}\gamma_\mu\epsilon_\mu\left(\frac{\partial}{\partial x_\mu} + \frac{ie}{\hbar c}A_\mu(x)\right)\Lambda\psi(x) + k_0\psi(x) = 0$$

where $\epsilon_k = -1$, $\epsilon_4 = +1$. Consequently,

$$\Lambda^{-1}\gamma_\mu\Lambda = a_{\mu\nu}\gamma_\nu \tag{4.58}$$

as before and, in detailed form, this is

$$\begin{aligned}\Lambda^{-1}\gamma_k\Lambda &= -\gamma_k\\ \Lambda^{-1}\gamma_4\Lambda &= \gamma_4\end{aligned} \tag{4.58$'$}$$

From the second of these equations Λ must be a linear combination of γ_4, $\gamma_1\gamma_2$, $\gamma_2\gamma_3$, $\gamma_3\gamma_1$, $\gamma_1\gamma_5$, $\gamma_2\gamma_5$, and $\gamma_3\gamma_5$. However, of these only γ_4 has the property that it anticommutes with all γ_k. Hence

$$\Lambda = i\gamma_4 \tag{4.59}$$

The choice of phase in (4.59) is arbitrary so far as (4.58) is concerned, but the factor i is inserted so that the relation

$$\Lambda^\times C = C\Lambda$$

is fulfilled. In this way the space-reversed positron is the charge conjugate of the space-reversed electron. The fact that $\Lambda \sim \gamma_4$ is hardly surprising in view of the remark made above that γ_4 times space inversion commutes with the Dirac Hamiltonian and the additional circumstance that

$$\gamma_\mu\left(\frac{\partial}{\partial x_\mu} + \frac{ie}{\hbar c} A_\mu\right) + k_0 = \frac{c}{\hbar}\gamma_4\left(H - i\hbar\frac{\partial}{\partial t}\right)$$

with H given by (4.12).

It should be emphasized that the covariance of the Dirac equation under space inversion is in no way at variance with the breakdown of parity conservation in beta decay. This phenomenon is a manifestation of the properties of the beta interaction. Whether or not parity conservation is required for an electron or positron in an electromagnetic field is a matter for experiment alone to decide, and present data are entirely in agreement with the position that the electromagnetic interaction is parity-conserving. When one deals with a neutral particle like the neutrino (see Chapter VII) there will be no *a priori* reason for insisting on a parity-conserving Hamiltonian.

Time Reflection

Considering first the classical problem of the motion of a charged particle in an electromagnetic field, we find from the Maxwell equations that under time reflection

$$A'_\mu(x') = -a_{\mu\nu}A_\nu(x) \tag{4.60}$$

This is seen by noting that, with e a scalar,

$$\rho'_c = \rho_c$$

but

$$\mathbf{j}'_c = -\mathbf{j}_c$$

as is required to preserve the form of the continuity equation. Then from (4.1c)

$$\mathscr{E}' = \mathscr{E}$$

and from (4.1b)

$$\mathscr{H}' = -\mathscr{H}$$

Thus Eq. (4.1a) is fulfilled in the primed fields and current density, with primed coordinates (x'_μ). Consequently, from (4.2b), $\mathbf{A}' = -\mathbf{A}$ and from (4.2a), $\Phi' = \Phi$. This gives (4.60); the sign change as compared to (4.56) will be seen to have profound consequences.

For the classical orbits we see that, with

$$\mathbf{v}' = -\mathbf{v}$$

the Lorentz force and therefore the equations of motion do not change under time inversion. This means that, if an orbit exists in which a particle goes from A to B, with momentum $\mathbf{p}_A$ at $t = 0$ and $\mathbf{p}_B$ at time t, then another orbit exists in which the particle retraces its path and goes from B to A with momenta $-\mathbf{p}_B$ at B and $-\mathbf{p}_A$ at A. This is, of course, the original orbit run backwards in time as in a reversed motion picture.

Turning to the spin-independent non-relativistic theory, we see that if $\psi'(\mathbf{x}', t')$ satisfies (4.57) with primed variables, then

$$\left\{\frac{1}{2m}\left(\vec{\mathbf{p}} - \frac{e}{c}\mathbf{A}\right)^2 - e\Phi\right\}\psi'(\mathbf{x}', t') = -i\hbar\frac{\partial\psi'(\mathbf{x}', t')}{\partial t}$$

with $t' = -t$. Taking the complex conjugate of this equation converts it to (4.57). Therefore

$$\psi'(\mathbf{x}', t') = \psi^{\times}(\mathbf{x}, t) \tag{4.61}$$

expresses the time reversal properties in this case. The occurrence of the antilinear complex conjugation operation could have been foreseen by noting that none of the commutation rules is changed by time inversion but the operator equation

$$\frac{d\Omega}{dt} = \frac{i}{\hbar}(H, \Omega)$$

is changed to the extent of replacing i with $-i$, which is just the effect of complex conjugation. This, of course, does not occur with space reflection.

The next step is the consideration of the Pauli equation. This is written in the form

$$\left[H_{nr} + \mu_0\boldsymbol{\sigma}\cdot\mathscr{H}\right]\psi(t) = i\hbar\frac{\partial\psi(t)}{\partial t}$$

where H_{nr} is the Hamiltonian in (4.57). Writing this in the primed system gives

$$H'_{nr}\psi'(-t) - \mu_0\boldsymbol{\sigma}\cdot\mathscr{H}\,\psi'(-t) = -i\hbar\frac{\partial\psi'(-t)}{\partial t}$$

In H'_{nr} the vector potential $\mathbf{A}' = -\mathbf{A}$ occurs. We again take the complex conjugate and set

$$\psi'^{\times}(-t) = \Lambda^{\times}\psi(t)$$

where Λ is a linear operator. We remember that $H'^{\times}_{nr} = H_{nr}$, and this gives

$$\Lambda^{-1\times}H_{nr}\Lambda^{\times}\,\psi(t) - \mu_0\Lambda^{-1\times}\,\boldsymbol{\sigma}^{\times}\cdot\mathscr{H}\Lambda^{\times}\psi(t) = i\hbar\,\frac{\partial\psi(t)}{\partial t}$$

Therefore it is required that

$$\Lambda^{-1\times}\boldsymbol{\sigma}^{\times}\Lambda^{\times} = -\boldsymbol{\sigma} \tag{4.62a}$$

and

$$\Lambda^{-1\times}H_{nr}\Lambda^{\times} = H_{nr} \tag{4.62b}$$

It is clear from (4.62a) that Λ must be a 2 by 2 matrix in spin space. This would commute with H_{nr}, which is a unit matrix in this space and so (4.62b) is satisfied. Writing (4.62a) in the form

$$\boldsymbol{\sigma}\Lambda = -\Lambda\boldsymbol{\sigma}^{\times}$$

we see that, in the standard representation of the Pauli matrices where σ_2 is pure imaginary and σ_1, σ_3 are real, Λ is proportional to σ_2. We choose a phase consistent with $\Lambda^{\times}C = C\Lambda$ and write

$$\Lambda = i\sigma_2 \tag{4.63}$$

which is real. Of course, (4.63) will hold under a unitary transformation also. The final result for a Pauli electron is then

$$\psi'(\mathbf{x}, t') = i\sigma_2\psi^{\times}(\mathbf{x}, t) \tag{4.64}$$

The persistent appearance of the antilinear complex conjugation is to be expected and will, of course, appear in the Dirac formalism as well.

Proceeding as before, we write (4.8′) for the Dirac particle and insert

$$A'_{\mu} = -a_{\mu\nu}A_{\nu}$$

to obtain

$$\left\{\gamma_{\mu}\epsilon_{\mu}\left(\frac{\partial}{\partial x_{\mu}} - \frac{ie}{\hbar c}A_{\mu}\right) + k_0\right\}\psi'(\mathbf{x}, t') = 0$$

where $\epsilon_k = 1$, $\epsilon_4 = -1$. If there were no field present it would be possible to write a linear relation

$$\psi'(\mathbf{x}, t') = \Lambda\,\psi(\mathbf{x}, t) \tag{4.65}$$

with

$$\begin{aligned} \gamma_k\Lambda &= \Lambda\gamma_k \\ \gamma_4\Lambda &= -\Lambda\gamma_4 \end{aligned} \tag{4.66}$$

with the solution

$$\Lambda = \gamma_1\gamma_2\gamma_3 = \gamma_5\gamma_4 \tag{4.67}$$

However, this choice would not restore (4.8) when $A_{\mu} \neq 0$ since the sign of the charge would be reversed. The time-reversed solution (4.65) would then correspond to opposite charge! To remedy this situation we need the complex conjugation operation. Therefore we write

$$\psi'^{\times}(\mathbf{x}, t') = C\Lambda\psi(\mathbf{x}, t) \tag{4.68}$$

The charge conjugation matrix C is inserted for convenience. Noting that $A_\mu^\times = \epsilon_\mu A_\mu$ (no sum on μ) and that $(\partial/\partial x_\mu)^\times = \epsilon_\mu(\partial/\partial x_\mu)$ (again no sum on μ), we obtain (4.8) provided that

$$(C\Lambda)^{-1}\gamma_\mu^\times C\Lambda = \gamma_\mu$$

or

$$\Lambda^{-1}C^{-1}\gamma_\mu^\times C\Lambda = \gamma_\mu$$

From (4.46) it is seen that this reduces to

$$\Lambda^{-1}\gamma_k\Lambda = \gamma_k$$

$$\Lambda^{-1}\gamma_4\Lambda = -\gamma_4 \tag{4.66'}$$

so that Λ is the same as in (4.65) and the special solution (4.67) applies. It is therefore still true that

$$\Lambda^{-1}\gamma_\mu\Lambda = a_{\mu\nu}\gamma_\nu$$

and (4.53) gives $a_{\mu\nu} = \epsilon_\mu\,\delta_{\mu\nu}$ (no sum on μ). Of course, Λ now plays an entirely different role in the Lorentz transformation, as compared to transformations with $a_{44} \geqslant 1$.

In order that time reversal and charge conjugation commute we require that

$$(\psi^c)' = (\psi')^c$$

The left-hand side is

$$C^\times\Lambda^\times\psi^{c\times} = C^\times\Lambda^\times(C^{-1}\psi^\times)^\times = C^\times\Lambda^\times C^{-1\times}\psi$$

The right-hand side is

$$C^{-1}(C^\times\Lambda^\times\psi^\times)^\times = C^{-1}C\Lambda\psi = \Lambda\psi$$

Equating the operators and taking the complex conjugate gives

$$C\Lambda C^{-1} = \Lambda^\times$$

or

$$C\Lambda = \Lambda^\times C$$

which is just (4.52). Thus, with (4.52) fulfilled, charge conjugation is covariant under all Lorentz transformations. The solution $\Lambda = \gamma_5\gamma_4 = \gamma_1\gamma_2\gamma_3$ does indeed fulfill this relation with $C = \gamma_2$. In the standard representation $\Lambda = \gamma_1\gamma_2\gamma_3$ is real, and this is just the condition for (4.52) to be correct. From the definition of B given in (4.48) it is seen that (4.68) is alternatively written

$$\psi'^\times(\mathbf{x}, t') = B\psi(\mathbf{x}, t) \tag{4.68'}$$

With $C = \gamma_2$ the matrix B is

$$B = C\gamma_5\gamma_4 = \gamma_2\gamma_5\gamma_4 = -\gamma_1\gamma_3 = i\sigma_2 \tag{4.68''}$$

so that (4.68′) reduces to (4.64), the transformation equation of the Pauli electron. In the present context, however, σ_2 is a 4 by 4 matrix. Thus both the large and the small components transform like the Pauli functions.

It is a consequence of (4.52) that if a sequence of Lorentz transformations is carried out the transformation matrix Λ is the product of the Λ-matrices for the individual transformations. This is valid for all types of transformations. For example, consider a time reflection carried out first. Then

$$x'_\mu = b_{\mu\nu} x_\nu$$
$$\psi'^\times(x') = C\Lambda_b \psi(x)$$
$$b_{\mu\nu}\gamma_\nu = \Lambda_b^{-1}\gamma_\mu\Lambda_b$$

Then, if this is followed by a Lorentz transformation which does not involve time reflection, we have

$$x''_\lambda = a_{\lambda\mu} x'_\mu$$
$$\psi''(x'') = \Lambda_a \psi'(x')$$
$$a_{\lambda\mu}\gamma_\mu = \Lambda_a^{-1}\gamma_\lambda\Lambda_a$$

The net transformation gives

$$x''_\lambda = a_{\lambda\mu} b_{\mu\nu} x_\nu = c_{\lambda\nu} x_\nu$$

and

$$\begin{aligned} c_{\lambda\nu}\gamma_\nu = a_{\lambda\mu} b_{\mu\nu}\gamma_\nu &= a_{\lambda\mu}\Lambda_b^{-1}\gamma_\mu\Lambda_b \\ &= \Lambda_b^{-1}\Lambda_a^{-1}\gamma_\lambda\Lambda_a\Lambda_b \\ &= (\Lambda_a\Lambda_b)^{-1}\gamma_\lambda\Lambda_a\Lambda_b \\ &= \Lambda_c^{-1}\gamma_\lambda\Lambda_c \end{aligned}$$

where

$$\Lambda_c = \Lambda_a\Lambda_b$$

Also

$$\psi''(x'') = \Lambda_a C^\times \Lambda_b^\times \psi^\times(x)$$

or

$$\begin{aligned} \psi''^\times(x'') &= \Lambda_a^\times C\Lambda_b\psi(x) \\ &= C\Lambda_c\psi(x) \end{aligned}$$

Any matrix compounded from continuous space and time reflection matrices will also satisfy (4.52).[10] If

$$\Lambda_a^\times C = C\Lambda_a$$

and

$$\Lambda_b^\times C = C\Lambda_b$$

then for $\Lambda_c = \Lambda_a\Lambda_b$ we see that

$$\begin{aligned}\Lambda_c^\times C &= \Lambda_a^\times\Lambda_b^\times C = \Lambda_a^\times C\Lambda_b \\ &= C\Lambda_a\Lambda_b = C\Lambda_c\end{aligned}$$

as stated above. Thus (4.52) characterizes all Lorentz transformations.

Transformation of the Adjoint Function

In order to study the time reflection properties of the covariants $\bar{\psi}\gamma_A\psi$ (see section 14) it is necessary to determine the connection between $\bar{\psi}'(x')$ and $\bar{\psi}(x)$. For a transformation without time reflection it was seen in Chapter II that

$$\bar{\psi}'(x') = \bar{\psi}(x)\gamma_4\Lambda^*\gamma_4 \tag{4.69}$$

On the other hand, for a time reflection

$$\begin{aligned}(\bar{\psi}'(x'))^\times &= (\psi'^*(x')\gamma_4)^\times \\ &= (\psi'^\times)^*\gamma_4^\times = (C\Lambda\psi)^*\gamma_4^\times \\ &= \psi^*\Lambda^*C^*\gamma_4^\times \\ &= \bar{\psi}\gamma_4\Lambda^*C^{-1}\gamma_4^\times \\ &= -\bar{\psi}\gamma_4\Lambda^*\gamma_4C^{-1}\end{aligned} \tag{4.70}$$

since $C^* = C^{-1}$ and $C^{-1}\gamma_4^\times = -\gamma_4C^{-1}$. This result certainly differs from (4.69). However, this is expected since ψ itself transforms in a different way for time reversal than in other cases. In fact, in section 14 it was shown that

$$\gamma_4\Lambda^*\gamma_4 = \Lambda^{-1}$$

when $a_{44} > 1$. Now when $a_{44} \leqslant -1$ it will be shown that

$$\gamma_4\Lambda^*\gamma_4 = -\Lambda^{-1}$$

In section 14 it was shown that

$$\Lambda\gamma_4\Lambda^*\gamma_4 = k \tag{4.71}$$

where $k^2 = 1$ and therefore $k = \pm 1$.

To see that k is identical with the sign of a_{44}, which is what is needed to complete the proof, we multiply

$$a_{4\rho}\gamma_\rho = \Lambda^{-1}\gamma_4\Lambda$$

from the left and then a second time from the right by γ_4 and add the resulting equations to get

$$a_{4\rho}(\gamma_4\gamma_\rho + \gamma_\rho\gamma_4) = \gamma_4\Lambda^{-1}\gamma_4\Lambda + \Lambda^{-1}\gamma_4\Lambda\gamma_4 \tag{4.72}$$

We use $\gamma_4\gamma_\rho + \gamma_\rho\gamma_4 = 2\delta_{4\rho}$ and

$$\gamma_4\Lambda^{-1} = k\Lambda^*\gamma_4 \tag{4.71'}$$

which is obtained from (4.71) by taking the inverse of that equation. This is used in the first term on the right of (4.72). In the second term use

$$\Lambda\gamma_4 = k\gamma_4\Lambda^{*-1}$$

which is the inverse of (4.71′). Then (4.72) becomes

$$2a_{44} = k[\Lambda^*\Lambda + \Lambda^{-1}\Lambda^{*-1}]$$

The matrix in square brackets is now seen to be diagonal, and from its structure its elements must be positive definite. Therefore the sign of k is the sign of a_{44} and the proof is thereby completed. Substituting the result in (4.70) gives

$$(\bar{\psi}')^\times = \bar{\psi}\Lambda^{-1}C^{-1} \tag{4.73}$$

Transformation of the Bilinear Covariants under Time Reflection

In section 14 the transformation properties of the bilinear covariants $\bar{\psi}\gamma_B\phi$ were investigated for continuous Lorentz transformations. The results obtained there also apply to space reflections which involve only "linear" transformation. However, for time reflections, with the antilinear transformation appearing, a separate investigation is necessary and a different result may be expected.

The transformation rule for ψ and ϕ is given by (4.68) and for $\bar{\psi}$, $\bar{\phi}$ by (4.73). Then

$$\begin{aligned}\bar{\psi}'\gamma_B\phi' &= (\bar{\psi}'^\times\gamma_B^\times\phi'^\times)^\times \\ &= (\bar{\psi}\Lambda^{-1}C^{-1}\gamma_B^\times C\Lambda\phi)^\times \\ &= (\psi^*\gamma_4\Lambda^{-1}C^{-1}\gamma_B^\times C\Lambda\phi)^\times \\ &= (\psi^*\gamma_4\Lambda^{-1}C^{-1}\gamma_B^\times C\Lambda\phi)^*\end{aligned}$$

since the covariant is a 1 by 1 and complex conjugation is equivalent to hermitian conjugation. We use $\gamma_4\Lambda^{-1} = -\Lambda^*\gamma_4$ and obtain

$$\begin{aligned}\bar{\psi}'\gamma_B\phi' &= -(\psi^*\Lambda^*\gamma_4C^{-1}\gamma_B^\times C\Lambda\phi)^* \\ &= (\psi^*\Lambda^*C^{-1}\gamma_4^\times\gamma_B^\times C\Lambda\phi)^*\end{aligned}$$

since $\gamma_4C^{-1} = -C^{-1}\gamma_4^\times$.

The matrix $C^{-1}\gamma_4^\times\gamma_B^\times C$ is related in a simple way to $C\gamma_4\gamma_BC^{-1}$. Moreover,

$$C\gamma_4\gamma_BC^{-1} = -\zeta\tilde{\gamma}_B\tilde{\gamma}_4 \tag{4.74}$$

where

$$\zeta = 1 \qquad \text{for } \gamma_B = 1,\ i\gamma_5\gamma_\mu,\ \gamma_5$$

$$\zeta = -1 \qquad \text{for } \gamma_B = \gamma_\mu,\ i\gamma_\mu\gamma_\nu \qquad (\mu \neq \nu)$$

Taking the complex conjugate of (4.74) gives

$$C^{\times}\gamma_4^{\times}\gamma_B^{\times}C^{-1\times} = -\zeta(\gamma_4\gamma_B)^*$$

or

$$C^{-1}\gamma_4^{\times}\gamma_B^{\times}C = -\zeta(\gamma_4\gamma_B)^*$$

by the properties of C: $C^{-1} = C^*$, $C = \tilde{C}$. Then

$$\begin{aligned}\bar{\psi}'\gamma_B\phi' &= -\zeta(\psi^*\Lambda^*\gamma_B^*\gamma_4\Lambda\phi)^* \\ &= -\zeta(\phi^*\Lambda^*\gamma_4\gamma_B\Lambda\psi) \\ &= -\zeta\bar{\phi}\gamma_4\Lambda^*\gamma_4\gamma_B\Lambda\psi \\ &= \zeta\bar{\phi}\Lambda^{-1}\gamma_B\Lambda\psi \end{aligned} \tag{4.75}$$

where the last step follows from $\gamma_4\Lambda\gamma_4\Lambda^* = -1$ or $\gamma_4\Lambda^*\gamma_4 = -\Lambda^{-1}$; cf. equations immediately preceding (4.71).

We see from (4.75) that if ψ and ϕ are the same the only change in the transformation law is the factor ζ. Thus, for the V and T covariants, a minus sign is introduced as compared to (2.74′) and (2.75′). In general, then, the transformation laws could be written as in section 14 but with a factor $S(a_{44}) = a_{44}/|a_{44}|$ inserted for the V and T covariants. It is important to realize, however, that when $\psi \neq \phi$ that time reflection reverses the roles of these two. This is intuitively obvious when $\psi(\phi)$ represent, as in beta interactions, a particle which appears in the final (initial) state.

The result (4.75) will now be applied to the study of time reversal properties of interaction constructed from contractions of covariants. We consider, as a special case, a term of the type

$$H_B = C_B K_B(ab)\, K_B(cd) + C_B^{\times} K_B^*(ab)\, K_B^*(cd)$$

where

$$K_B(ab) \equiv \bar{\psi}^a\gamma_B\psi^b$$

and similarly for $K_B(cd)$. The C_B are ordinary numbers playing the role of coupling constants. We wish to investigate the consequences of the assumption: H_B is invariant under time reversal. It will be evident that the conclusion will also apply to an interaction of the form $\Sigma_B H_B$.

We observe that

$$\begin{aligned}K_B^*(ab) &= (\bar{\psi}^a\gamma_B\psi^b)^* \\ &= (\psi^{a*}\gamma_4\gamma_B\psi^b)^* \\ &= \psi^{b*}\gamma_B^*\gamma_4\psi^a \\ &= \bar{\psi}^b\gamma_4\gamma_B^*\gamma_4\psi^a\end{aligned}$$

We shall use the hermitian γ_B so that we can write†

$$K_B^*(ab) = \epsilon_B K_B(ba)$$

where $\epsilon_B = 1(-1)$ if γ_4 and γ_B commute (anticommute). Moreover,

$$K_B'(ab) = \zeta_B \bar{\psi}^b \Lambda^{-1} \gamma_B \Lambda \psi^a$$

where we have recognized that ζ depends on γ_B by writing ζ_B. With $\Lambda = \gamma_5\gamma_4$ we have

$$\Lambda^{-1}\gamma_B\Lambda = \gamma_4\gamma_5\gamma_B\gamma_5\gamma_4 = \eta_B\gamma_4\gamma_B\gamma_4$$

where $\eta_B = 1(-1)$ according to whether γ_B and γ_5 commute or anticommute. Hence

$$K_B'(ab) = \zeta_B\eta_B K_B^*(ab)$$

Similarly,

$$K_B^{*\prime}(ab) = \zeta_B\eta_B K_B(ab)$$

The same results apply for $K_B'(cd)$ and $K_B^{*\prime}(cd)$ with the same phase factors. Hence, since $\zeta_B^2 = \eta_B^2 = 1$,

$$H_B' = C_B K_B^*(ab)\, K_B^*(cd) + C_B^\times K_B(ab)\, K_B(cd)$$

When this is compared with H_B it is seen that the consequence of the assumption of time reversal invariance is

$$C_B = C_B^\times \tag{4.76}$$

or the coupling coefficients must be real.[11]

Unitary Transformations

In the discussion of charge conjugation, given in section 24, it was stated that the relation between a given matrix Ω and the corresponding charge conjugate matrix Ω^c was independent of the representation. However, it does not follow that, if the charge conjugation matrix has a particular realization, say γ_2 as in the standard representation, in another representation it will be the transform of γ_2, that is, $S\gamma_2S^{-1}$. Our purpose here is three-fold. First we determine the relation between C in different representations. Second, we show that when ψ undergoes a unitary transformation

$$\Psi(x) = S\psi(x) \tag{4.77}$$

† Although this result is not actually needed in the present connection it is cited to show the connection of the hermitian conjugate covariants to the reverse decay processes. If γ_B is antihermitian there is an additional minus sign in the connection between $K_B^*(ab)$ and $K_B(ba)$ which disappears in the product entering H_B. The same remark applies in the time-reversed H_B.

then the charge conjugate function undergoes the same transformation:

$$\Psi^c(x) = S\psi^c(x)$$

Finally, it will be demonstrated that the unitary transformation is covariant under all Lorentz transformations; that is, if (4.77) applies in one reference frame it also applies in any other with the same S.

To avoid confusion we use capital letters Ψ, Γ_μ rather than primes to designate the wave function and Dirac matrices obtained after the S transformation. As usual, primes are reserved to designate the wave functions obtained after a Lorentz transformation. Then if

$$(\gamma_\mu D_\mu + k_0)\psi(x) = 0$$

the transformation (4.77) gives

$$(\Gamma_\mu D_\mu + k_0)\Psi(x) = 0$$

where

$$\Gamma_\mu = S\gamma_\mu S^{-1} \tag{4.78}$$

Of course, the commutation relations

$$\Gamma_\mu \Gamma_\nu + \Gamma_\nu \Gamma_\mu = 2\delta_{\mu\nu}$$

are valid and Γ_μ can be chosen hermitian. Therefore, by a previous argument, S can be chosen unitary and we shall so choose it. Thus

$$S^* = S^{-1} \tag{4.79}$$

For definiteness, we refer to the Γ_μ representation as the "new" representation in contrast to the "old" representation where the Dirac matrices are written γ_μ. In the old representation we use C_0 for charge conjugation and the associated B_0 as defined by (4.48). In the new representation these are replaced by C_n and B_n. Thus

$$C_n^{-1}\Gamma_\mu^{\times} C_n = \epsilon_\mu \Gamma_\mu \tag{4.80}$$

$\epsilon_k = 1$, $\epsilon_4 = -1$, and

$$B_n \Gamma_\mu B_n^{-1} = \Gamma_\mu^{\times} \tag{4.81}$$

Substituting (4.78) into (4.81) yields

$$\begin{aligned} B_n S\gamma_\mu S^{-1} B_n^{-1} &= S^{\times}\gamma_\mu^{\times} S^{-1\times} \\ &= \tilde{S}^{-1} B_0 \gamma_\mu B_0^{-1} \tilde{S} \end{aligned}$$

by (4.49) and (4.79). Multiplying on the left by $\gamma_\mu S^{-1} B_n^{-1}$ and on the right by $\tilde{S}^{-1} B_0 \gamma_\mu$, we obtain

$$S^{-1} B_n^{-1} \tilde{S}^{-1} B_0 \gamma_\mu = \gamma_\mu S^{-1} B_n^{-1} \tilde{S}^{-1} B_0$$

This result states that $S^{-1}B_n^{-1}\tilde{S}^{-1}B_0$ commutes with all γ_μ and must therefore be a multiple of a unit matrix:

$$B_0 = k\tilde{S}B_nS \tag{4.82}$$

By taking the hermitian conjugate of (4.49) the result

$$\gamma_\mu^\times = B_0^{-1*}\gamma_\mu B_0^*$$

is obtained. Then with (4.49) we deduce that

$$B_0^*B_0\gamma_\mu = \gamma_\mu B_0^*B_0$$

and hence $B_0^*B_0$ is a multiple of a unit matrix which is, moreover, positive. Since a scale factor is left open in the definition of B_0 it can be chosen so that B_0 is unitary. Precisely the same argument with Γ_μ and B_n shows that B_n can be chosen unitary. Consequently (4.82) becomes

$$\begin{aligned} 1 = B_0^*B_0 &= |k|^2S^*B_n^*\tilde{S}^*\tilde{S}B_nS \\ &= |k|^2S^*B_n^*B_nS = |k|^2S^*S = |k|^2 \end{aligned}$$

Therefore it is permissible to choose $k = 1$, and when this is done

$$B_0 = \tilde{S}B_nS$$

or

$$B_n = S^\times B_0 S^{-1}$$

For the charge conjugation matrix

$$\begin{aligned} C_n = B_n\Gamma_4\Gamma_5 &= S^\times B_0 S^{-1}S\gamma_4\gamma_5 S^{-1} \\ &= S^\times C_0 S^{-1} \end{aligned} \tag{4.83}$$

This is the desired connection between C_n and C_0, the charge conjugation matrices in the two representations.

The properties $C_0 = \tilde{C}_0$ and $C_0^* = C_0^{-1}$ are preserved under the unitary transformation:

$$\tilde{C}_n = S^{-1}\tilde{C}_0\tilde{S}^\times = S^\times C_0 S^* = C_n$$

and

$$\begin{aligned} C_n^*C_n &= S^{-1*}C_0^*S^{\times*}S^\times C_0S^{-1} \\ &= SC_0^{-1}S^{\times-1}S^\times C_0S^{-1} \\ &= SC_0^{-1}C_0S^{-1} = 1 \end{aligned}$$

From (4.83) the validity of the initial statement of this paragraph can be checked. For example, if ω and Ω represent an operator in the old and new representations and if

$$\omega^c = \eta\omega$$

where $\eta = \pm 1$, then with $\Omega = S\omega S^{-1}$ we find

$$\begin{aligned}\Omega^c &= C_n^{-1}\Omega^\times C_n \\ &= SC_0^{-1}S^{-1\times}S^\times\omega^\times S^{-1\times}S^\times C_0 S^{-1} \\ &= SC_0^{-1}\omega^\times C_0 S^{-1} = S\omega^c S^{-1} \\ &= \eta S\omega S^{-1} = \eta\Omega\end{aligned}$$

as required.

The second problem is the determination of the charge conjugate of ψ in the new representation: Ψ^c. This is now obtained immediately.

$$\begin{aligned}\Psi^c &= C_n^\times \Psi^\times \\ &= SC_0^\times S^{-1\times}S^\times\psi^\times \\ &= SC_0^\times\psi^\times \\ &= S\psi^c\end{aligned}$$

Thus ψ^c and ψ transform in exactly the same way.

With regard to Lorentz transformations we consider first those which do not involve time reflection. We wish to show that if $\psi'(x') = \Lambda_0\psi(x)$ then, under (4.77), $\Psi'(x') = S\psi'(x')$ and $\Psi'(x') = \Lambda_n\Psi(x)$. Here Λ_0 and Λ_n are the Λ transformation matrices in the old and new representations respectively. We find with (4.78) that

$$\begin{aligned}a_{\mu\nu}\Gamma_\nu &= S\Lambda_0^{-1}S^{-1}S\gamma_\mu S^{-1}S\Lambda_0 S^{-1} \\ &= S\Lambda_0^{-1}S^{-1}\Gamma_\mu S\Lambda_0 S^{-1} \\ &\equiv \Lambda_n^{-1}\Gamma_\mu\Lambda_n\end{aligned}$$

so that

$$\Lambda_n = S\Lambda_0 S^{-1} \tag{4.84}$$

as could be expected. It is also true that

$$\Lambda_n^\times C_n = C_n\Lambda_n$$

which should be compared with (4.52), and

$$\Lambda_n\Gamma_4\Lambda_n^*\Gamma_4 = S(a_{44})$$

as was the case in the old representation.

For the transformation of $\Psi'(x')$ we see that

$$\begin{aligned}\Psi'(x') &= \Lambda_n\Psi(x) = S\Lambda_0 S^{-1}S\psi(x) \\ &= S\Lambda_0\psi(x) \\ &= S\psi'(x')\end{aligned}$$

We turn now to the Lorentz transformation with time reflection, and we shall show that the same result holds. We write

$$\Psi'(x') = (C_n\Lambda_n\Psi(x))^\times = (C_n\Lambda_n S\psi(x))^\times$$
$$= C_n^\times\Lambda_n S^\times\psi^\times(x)$$

But $\psi'(x') = C_0^\times\Lambda_0^\times\psi^\times(x)$ and so

$$\Psi'(x') = C_n^\times\Lambda_n^\times S^\times\Lambda_0^{\times-1}C_0^{\times-1}\psi'(x')$$

We use (4.83) and (4.84) to obtain

$$\Psi'(x') = (SC_0^\times S^{-1\times})(S^\times\Lambda_0^\times S^{-1\times})(S^\times\Lambda_0^{\times-1}C_0^{\times-1})\psi'(x')$$
$$= SC_0^\times\Lambda_0^\times\Lambda_0^{\times-1}C_0^{\times-1}\psi'(x')$$
$$= SC_0^\times C_0^{\times-1}\psi'(x')$$
$$= S\psi'(x')$$

as was stated.

PROBLEMS

1. Show that the space part of the current density $j_\mu^{(0)}$ defined in (4.14) is

$$\mathbf{j}^{(0)} = \frac{e\hbar}{2m}\,\text{curl}\;\bar{\psi}\boldsymbol{\sigma}\psi$$

2. Show that the expectation value of β for any state must satisfy the inequality

$$-1 \leqslant \langle\beta\rangle \leqslant 1$$

3. Find a matrix B satisfying (4.49) when the standard representation is used. Choose the arbitrary factor in B so that B is unitary. What arbitrariness remains? With this B find the charge conjugation matrix C.

4. Pauli has used a charge conjugation matrix C_p for which

$$C_p\gamma_\mu C_p^{-1} = -\gamma_\mu^\times$$

Show that the charge conjugate wave function is

$$\psi^c = C_p^{-1}\tilde{\bar{\psi}}$$

5. Find a representation in which C is the unit matrix so that charge conjugation is identical with complex conjugation. Find a representation in which $C = -\gamma_5$ where γ_5 is in the standard representation.[12] Write the wave equation for zero rest mass.

6. Give an argument, based on the gauge transformation, which would show that the charge conjugation operation must involve complex conjugation.

7. Show that the time-reversed wave function $\psi'(\mathbf{x}, t')$ is equal to $\Lambda\psi^c(\mathbf{x}, t)$ where Λ is defined in (4.66) and (4.52) is assumed to be fulfilled.

8. Consider an interaction of the form

$$H_B = C_B(\bar{\psi}^a\gamma_B\psi^b)(\bar{\psi}^c\gamma_B\psi^d) + C'_B(\bar{\psi}^a\gamma_B\gamma_5\psi^b)(\bar{\psi}^c\gamma_B\psi^d) + \text{hermitian conjugate}$$

Show that the consequence of invariance of H_B under space reflection is $C'_B = 0$. Alternatively, if $H'_B = -H_B$, then $C_B = 0$.

9. Show that covariants formed with $\Psi = S\psi$ are exactly the same as those formed with ψ, where the S transformation is unitary.

10. The Majorana representation of the Dirac matrices is one in which the three Dirac α_k are real while β is pure imaginary. More specifically, it is stipulated that the transformation to the Majorana representation leaves α_1 and α_3 unchanged and replaces α_2 and β with $-\beta$ and α_2 respectively. Find the S matrix connecting the Majorana and standard representations. Take the former to be the "new" representation. Find the charge conjugation matrix in the Majorana representation. In the Majorana representation find the Λ matrix which effects the Lorentz transformations for (a) a space rotation around the z-axis; (b) a uniform translation along the x-axis; (c) a space reflection: $x'_k = -x_k$, $x'_4 = x_4$; and (d) a time reflection: $x'_k = x_k$, $x'_4 = -x_4$.

11. Show that the adjoint $\bar{\Psi}$ in the new representation is connected to the adjoint $\bar{\psi}$ in the old representation by

$$\bar{\Psi}(x) = \bar{\psi}(x)S$$

12. If $BB^* = 1$ show that C and C_n are both unitary.

13. Feynman and Gell-Mann[13] have pointed out that, instead of using four-component wave functions satisfying linear equations, one could use two coupled second-order equations with two-component functions. Find a pair of equations of this type equivalent to the standard Dirac equations.

14. In a nuclear beta transition the final and initial states, ψ_f and ψ_i, are stationary states of a Hamiltonian which is assumed to have the form $H_N = \boldsymbol{\alpha}\cdot\vec{\mathbf{p}} + \beta M + V$, where V is an even operator. Using the FW transformation to first order in M^{-1}, evaluate the parts of the beta interaction (see Chapter III, Eq. 3.77) which contain odd operators in the nuclear space.

15. For a Lorentz transformation in which $\psi'(x') = \Lambda\psi(x)$ show that

$$\bar{\psi}'T'_\mu\psi' = S(a_{44})(\det a)a_{\mu\nu}\bar{\psi}T_\nu\psi$$

and for $\psi'(x') = \Lambda C^\times\psi^\times(x)$ show that the above is changed to the extent of a minus sign.

REFERENCES

1. W. Gordon, *Z. Physik* **50,** 630 (1927).
2. L. Foldy and S. A. Wouthuysen, *Phys. Rev.* **78,** 29 (1950).
3. C. G. Darwin, *Proc. Roy. Soc.* (*London*) **A 118,** 654 (1928).
4. H. A. Tolhoek and S. R. de Groot, *Physica* **17,** 17 (1951).
5. K. M. Case, *Phys. Rev.* **106,** 173 (1957).
6. M. E. Rose and T. A. Welton, *Phys. Rev.* **86,** 432 (1952); R. M. Schectman and R. H. Good, Jr., *Am. J. Phys.* **25,** 219 (1956).

7. H. Goldstein, *Classical Mechanics*, Addison-Wesley Publishing Co., Cambridge, Mass., 1953, Chapter 6.
8. W. Pauli, *Ann. inst. Henri Poincaré* **6,** 109 (1936).
9. R. H. Good, Jr., *Revs. Mod. Phys.* **27,** 187 (1955).
10. G. Racah, *Nuovo cimento* **14,** 322 (1937).
11. L. C. Biedenharn and M. E. Rose, *Phys. Rev.* **83,** 459 (1951).
12. Cf. W. L. Bade and H. Jehle, *Revs. Mod. Phys.* **25,** 714 (1953).
13. R. P. Feynman and M. Gell-Mann, *Phys. Rev.* **109,** 193 (1958).

V.

Dirac particle in a central field

This chapter is devoted to some of the most important applications of the theory which arise in connection with central field problems. The wave functions obtained for hydrogen-like atoms in the Kepler problem will also be applied to perturbation calculations wherein the perturbed Hamiltonian does not possess spherical symmetry.

26. WAVE EQUATION IN POLAR COORDINATES

We recognize at the outset that the central field problems which arise in actual applications are not strictly one-body problems but present for consideration at least a two-body problem in which the second "particle" is the atomic nucleus.† Since the electron in an atom perturbs the nuclear structure in an entirely negligible way and whatever perturbation exists reacts back on the electron to a very small extent, the nucleus can be treated classically as a source of the static central field. The motion of the center of mass of the system can be eliminated in a trivial way by taking the mass of the nucleus to be infinite. Alternatively, one can replace the electron mass m which appears in the following equations, when ordinary units are introduced, by the reduced mass. The latter does not have a unique definition in relativistic problems,[1] but this ambiguity is mitigated by the circumstance that the description of the nuclear motion can be taken to be non-relativistic with a high degree of accuracy. Whatever course is followed, the error introduced is less than one part in 10^3, and this is of order or less than the radiative corrections.[C] In the following treatment $\mathbf{r}$ is the vector defining the position of the Dirac particle relative to the source of the field.

† Many electron atoms are briefly discussed in section 29.

To obtain the polar form of the wave equation we consider a stationary state of energy W in a field with a central potential energy $V(r)$ and transform the kinetic energy term $\boldsymbol{\alpha}\cdot\vec{\mathbf{p}}$. To do this use is made of the identity

$$\nabla = \hat{\mathbf{r}}(\hat{\mathbf{r}}\cdot\nabla) - \hat{\mathbf{r}} \times (\hat{\mathbf{r}} \times \nabla)$$
$$= \hat{\mathbf{r}}\frac{\partial}{\partial r} - i\frac{\hat{\mathbf{r}}}{r} \times \mathbf{l} \tag{5.1}$$

where, as usual, $\mathbf{l} = -i\mathbf{r} \times \nabla$ is the orbital angular momentum in the rational relativistic units used here. From (5.1) the kinetic energy operator becomes

$$\boldsymbol{\alpha}\cdot\vec{\mathbf{p}} = -i\alpha_r\frac{\partial}{\partial r} - \frac{1}{r}\boldsymbol{\alpha}\cdot\hat{\mathbf{r}} \times \mathbf{l}$$

If in

$$\boldsymbol{\alpha}\cdot\mathbf{A}\,\boldsymbol{\alpha}\cdot\mathbf{B} = \mathbf{A}\cdot\mathbf{B} + i\boldsymbol{\sigma}\cdot\mathbf{A} \times \mathbf{B}$$

we set $\mathbf{A} = \hat{\mathbf{r}}$, $\mathbf{B} = \mathbf{l}$ we find

$$\sigma_r\boldsymbol{\sigma}\cdot\mathbf{l} = i\boldsymbol{\sigma}\cdot\hat{\mathbf{r}} \times \mathbf{l}$$

Hence

$$\boldsymbol{\alpha}\cdot\vec{\mathbf{p}} = -i\alpha_r\frac{\partial}{\partial r} + i\frac{\alpha_r}{r}\boldsymbol{\sigma}\cdot\mathbf{l}$$

This result may be substituted in the wave equation and, using the K operator defined in section 12, we obtain

$$W\psi = H\psi = \left[i\gamma_5\sigma_r\left(\frac{\partial}{\partial r} + \frac{1}{r} - \frac{\beta}{r}K\right) + V + \beta\right]\psi \tag{5.2}$$

This is the wave equation in polar form.

As is evident from section 12 and from the fact that $\mathbf{j}^2$, j_z, and K commute with $V(r)$, these three operators commute with H. We shall be interested in a representation which diagonalizes these three operators in addition to H. The eigenvalues of $\mathbf{j}^2$, j_z, and K are $j(j+1)$, μ, and $-\kappa$ respectively. As has already been mentioned, the operator of space inversion times β is also diagonalized in this representation. Writing

$$\psi = \begin{pmatrix}\psi^u\\ \psi^l\end{pmatrix}$$

we have

$$(\boldsymbol{\sigma}\cdot\mathbf{l} + 1)\psi^u = -\kappa\psi^u$$
$$(\boldsymbol{\sigma}\cdot\mathbf{l} + 1)\psi^l = \kappa\psi^l$$
$$\mathbf{j}^2\psi^n = j(j+1)\psi^n$$
$$j_z\psi^n = \mu\psi^n$$

where, in the last two equations, $n = u$ or l. Since ψ^u and ψ^l are two-component spinors, it follows that they are proportional to χ_κ^μ and $\chi_{-\kappa}^\mu$ respectively; cf. Eq. (1.60′). Therefore we may write for ψ

$$\psi = \psi_\kappa^\mu = \begin{pmatrix} g(r)\chi_\kappa^\mu \\ if(r)\chi_{-\kappa}^\mu \end{pmatrix} \tag{5.3}$$

where $g(r)$ and $f(r)$ are radial functions which will, in general, depend on κ. The phase i is introduced to make the radial equations for f and g explicitly real. For bound states and continuum standing waves f/g will be real.

Inserting (5.3) in (5.2) we obtain the two relations resulting from equating upper and lower components on each side of the wave equation:

$$(W - V - 1)g\chi_\kappa^\mu = \left[-\left(\frac{df}{dr} + \frac{f}{r}\right) + \frac{\kappa f}{r}\right]\chi_\kappa^\mu$$

$$(W - V + 1)f\chi_{-\kappa}^\mu = \left[\frac{dg}{dr} + \frac{g}{r} + \frac{\kappa g}{r}\right]\chi_{-\kappa}^\mu$$

Here $\sigma_r\chi_\kappa^\mu = -\chi_{-\kappa}^\mu$ has been used; cf. (1.65′). From these we arrive finally at the radial equations

$$\begin{aligned} \frac{df}{dr} &= \frac{\kappa - 1}{r}f - (W - 1 - V)g \\ \frac{dg}{dr} &= (W - V + 1)f - \frac{\kappa + 1}{r}g \end{aligned} \tag{5.4}$$

It is often convenient to use

$$\begin{aligned} u_1 &= rg \\ u_2 &= rf \end{aligned} \tag{5.4′}$$

for which the alternative radial equations

$$\frac{d}{dr}\begin{pmatrix} u_1 \\ u_2 \end{pmatrix} = \begin{pmatrix} -\kappa/r & W + 1 - V \\ -(W - 1 - V) & \kappa/r \end{pmatrix}\begin{pmatrix} u_1 \\ u_2 \end{pmatrix} \tag{5.5}$$

apply.

To obtain the corresponding results for the positron we recall that the charge conjugate solution is

$$\psi^c = \gamma_2\psi^\times$$

in this representation. However, in applying the charge conjugate operation it must be remembered that it applies to the time-dependent functions and therefore if $i\,\partial\psi/\partial t = W\psi$ then $i\,\partial\psi^c/\partial t = -W\psi^c$. Hence the radial functions must be altered to the extent of changing the sign of W. If we call these altered radial functions f^c and g^c we obtain

$$(\psi_\kappa^\mu)^c = \begin{pmatrix} -f^c\sigma_2\chi_{-\kappa}^{\mu\times} \\ ig^c\sigma_2\chi_\kappa^{\mu\times} \end{pmatrix}$$

From (1.60′),

$$\sigma_2\chi_\kappa^{\mu\times} = \sum_m C(l\tfrac{1}{2}j; \mu - m, m)\sigma_2\,\chi^m(-)^{\mu-m}Y_l^{m-\mu}$$

But

$$\sigma_2\chi^m = i(-)^{m-\frac{1}{2}}\chi^{-m}$$

So

$$\sigma_2\chi_\kappa^{\mu\times} = i(-)^{\mu-\frac{1}{2}}\sum_m C(l\tfrac{1}{2}j; \mu - m, m)\chi^{-m}Y_l^{m-\mu}$$

The summation letter m can be replaced by $-m$ and the relation

$$C(l\tfrac{1}{2}j; -\mu - m, m) = (-)^{l+\frac{1}{2}-j}C(l\tfrac{1}{2}j; \mu + m, -m)$$

is used. The validity of the latter may be verified from (1.59). Then

$$\sigma_2\chi_\kappa^{\mu\times} = i(-)^{l-j+\mu}\chi_\kappa^{-\mu}$$

The reversal of the sign of μ is just what is expected from $j_z^c = -j_z$. Using this last result, we obtain

$$(\psi_\kappa^\mu)^c = (-)^{l-j+\mu+1}\begin{pmatrix} -if^c\chi_{-\kappa}^{-\mu} \\ g^c\chi_\kappa^{-\mu} \end{pmatrix} \tag{5.6}$$

Comparing this result with (5.3), we see that (apart from a phase) (5.6) is obtained from the former by making the replacements: $-\kappa$ for κ, $-ig^c$ for f, $-if^c$ for g, μ for $-\mu$. If these replacements are made in (5.4) and the sign of W is changed, the result is

$$\begin{aligned} \frac{df^c}{dr} &= \frac{\kappa - 1}{r}f^c - (W - 1 + V)g^c \\ \frac{dg^c}{dr} &= (W + V + 1)f^c - \frac{\kappa + 1}{r}g^c \end{aligned} \tag{5.7}$$

In other words, since f^c and g^c are regular solutions as are f and g, the charge conjugate radial functions are obtained from the f and g of (5.4) by changing the sign of V. For a positron in an electrostatic field (5.6) applies with f and g obtained from (5.4) but with the sign of Z reversed. Therefore a positron wave function is

$$(\psi_\kappa^\mu)_{\text{pos}} = \begin{pmatrix} -if(-Z)\chi_{-\kappa}^{-\mu} \\ g(-Z)\chi_\kappa^{-\mu} \end{pmatrix} \tag{5.6′}$$

and the eigenvalues of $(\mathbf{j}^2)^c$ and j_z^c are $j(j+1)$ and μ respectively. If we apply the space inversion operator βI_s to ψ_{pos}, the eigenvalue is $(-)^{l_\kappa+1}$ where for the electron the same operator gives $(-)^{l_\kappa}$. But $\beta^c I_s$ applied to ψ_{pos} again gives $(-)^{l_\kappa}\psi_{\text{pos}}$.

27. FREE PARTICLE SOLUTIONS

The angular momentum representation for free particles is obtained through use of solutions of (5.4) or (5.5) with $V = 0$. In general, a second-order equation for u_1 (or u_2) can be obtained by elimination of one of these radial functions. For u_1 this second-order equation is, for any central V,

$$\frac{d^2u_1}{dr^2} + \frac{dV/dr}{W - V + 1}\frac{du_1}{dr} + \left[(W - V)^2 - 1 - \frac{\kappa(\kappa + 1)}{r^2} + \frac{\kappa}{r}\frac{dV/dr}{W - V + 1}\right]u_1 = 0 \quad (5.8)$$

For $V = 0$ this becomes

$$\frac{d^2u_1}{dr^2} + \left[p^2 - \frac{\kappa(\kappa + 1)}{r^2}\right]u_1 = 0 \quad (5.9)$$

where $p^2 = W^2 - 1$. The solution regular at $r = 0$ is

$$u_1 = Arj_l(pr) \quad (5.10)$$

Here A is a normalization constant. For u_2 the first of Eqs. (5.5) is used to give

$$u_2 = \frac{1}{W + 1}\left(\frac{d}{dr} + \frac{\kappa}{r}\right)u_1$$

For the spherical Bessel functions we use the relations

$$j_l'(x) = \frac{l}{x}j_l - j_{l+1} = -\frac{l + 1}{x}j_l + j_{l-1}$$

where prime means differentiation with respect to the argument $x = pr$. With these relations and the relation $l - \bar{l} = S_\kappa = \kappa/|\kappa|$, we find

$$u_2 = AS_\kappa\frac{pr}{W + 1}j_{\bar{l}}(pr) \quad (5.11)$$

which applies for both signs of κ. For a constant potential, W is simply replaced by $W - V$ throughout.

If the free particle wave function

$$\psi_\kappa^\mu = \begin{pmatrix} j_l \chi_\kappa^\mu \\ \dfrac{ipS_\kappa}{W+1} j_{\bar{l}} \chi_{-\kappa}^\mu \end{pmatrix} \tag{5.12}$$

is compared with the plane wave solutions ($W = p_0$) it is clear that the spin orientation quantum number, i.e., the eigenvalue of $\mathcal{O}_z$, has been replaced by μ, the eigenvalue of j_z. This does not mean that a direct replacement is made but rather that the operators play similar roles in a given physical situation. For example, a polarized particle would be represented by an ensemble in which states of different μ would have unequal weights. The precise relation between the two representations is obtained by an expansion of the plane wave into angular momentum waves similar to that carried out in section 8. We write

$$U_\pm e^{i\mathbf{p}\cdot\mathbf{r}} = \sum_{\kappa\mu} a_{\kappa\mu} \psi_\kappa^\mu \tag{5.13}$$

where $U_\pm$ is given in (3.7) and ψ_κ^μ in (5.12). Then we require that the equations

$$\left(\frac{p_0+1}{2p_0}\right)^{1/2} \chi^m = \sum_{\kappa\mu} a_{\kappa\mu} j_l(pr) \chi_\kappa^\mu \tag{5.13a}$$

$$\left(\frac{p_0+1}{2p_0}\right)^{1/2} \boldsymbol{\sigma}\cdot\mathbf{p}\chi^m = \frac{ip}{p_0+1} \sum_{\kappa\mu} S_\kappa a_{\kappa\mu} j_{\bar{l}}(pr) \chi_{-\kappa}^\mu \tag{5.13b}$$

be fulfilled. Here $m = \pm\frac{1}{2}$. The first equation is satisfied for

$$a_{\kappa\mu} = 4\pi i^l \left(\frac{p_0+1}{2p_0}\right)^{1/2} C(l\tfrac{1}{2}j;\mu-m,m)\, Y_l^{\mu-m\times}(\hat{\mathbf{p}}) \tag{5.14}$$

as comparison with (1.69) shows. That this value of the $a_{\kappa\mu}$ also satisfies the second equation (5.13b) will be immediately apparent. In fact, we know that the small component of the plane wave is obtained from the large component by applying the operator $\boldsymbol{\sigma}\cdot\vec{\mathbf{p}}/(W+1)$ to the latter. Since the large component of the plane wave is equal to the large component in the expansion (5.13) with $a_{\kappa\mu}$ given by (5.14), it follows that the proof of the statement consists in showing that $\boldsymbol{\sigma}\cdot\vec{\mathbf{p}}/(W+1)$ applied to $\psi^u = j_l\chi_\kappa^\mu$ gives the small component of the spherical waves. But this is true, since it is just the condition used to find the small component in ψ_κ^μ. The expansion of the plane wave is, therefore, obtained from that of the large component, which is

$$\psi_{\text{large}} = 4\pi\left(\frac{p_0+1}{2p_0}\right)^{1/2} \sum_{\kappa\mu} i^l C(l\tfrac{1}{2}j;\mu-m,m)\, j_l(pr)\, Y_l^{\mu-m*}(\hat{\mathbf{p}})\, \chi_\kappa^\mu \tag{5.15}$$

An expansion of this type is useful in scattering theory; see section 33. A corresponding expansion for particles in a central field will be discussed later (section 34).

It is useful to observe that, for **p** along the z-axis, $\mu = m = \pm\frac{1}{2}$.

28. GENERAL PROPERTIES OF THE RADIAL FUNCTIONS

Normalization of Bound State Wave Functions

For many problems, and for the Coulomb field in particular, the bound state solutions are rather complicated functions and the problem of normalizing them by direct methods of calculation is rather formidable. Fortunately, there exists a comparatively simple method for carrying out the normalization.[2]

First it is desirable to introduce the concept of "left" and "right" solutions. Since the normalization requires that

$$\int \psi^*\psi\, d^3x = \int_0^\infty r^2(f^2+g^2)\, dr = 1$$

it is clearly necessary that $\psi^*\psi$ be integrable over any domain in configuration space. It is possible to find solutions which are integrable at the left end of the interval $0 \leqslant r \leqslant \infty$; that is, they are regular at $r = 0$. These will, in general, not be integrable as $r \to \infty$ unless the energy parameter W is given one of the values corresponding to the appropriate discrete spectrum. Such solutions, which depend on W, will be called left or L solutions. Similarly, it is always possible and usually easy to construct solutions which vanish at infinity in such a way that $\psi^*\psi$ is integrable there. Such solutions will not be integrable at $r = 0$ unless W has one of the appropriate values (eigenvalues). Such solutions we shall call "right" or R solutions. If an L solution is made to coincide with an R solution at any point r_1 say, that is,

$$f_{\rm L}(r_1) = f_{\rm R}(r_1)$$
$$g_{\rm L}(r_1) = g_{\rm R}(r_1)$$

then they will coincide at all r and the solution obtained will be an eigensolution. The solution is then both an L solution and an R solution. The continuity conditions at any point r_1 constitute a condition on W yielding the correct spectrum of energy values. Actually, since an overall scale factor is not fixed until the normalization is applied, it is only necessary that

$$\rho_L(r_1) \equiv \frac{f_L(r_1)}{g_L(r_1)} = \rho_R(r_1) \equiv \frac{f_R(r_1)}{g_R(r_1)}$$

In fact, $\rho(r)$ is uniquely determined by the radial equations (5.4) or (5.5) and the stipulation of a regularity condition either at $r = 0$ or at $r = \infty$. Again, ρ_R and ρ_L are functions of W as well as of r.

We now consider two time-dependent solutions corresponding to different energies W and W'. They are

$$\Psi = \psi e^{-iWt}$$

$$\Psi' = \psi' e^{-iW't}$$

where the prime refers to the energy W'. The four-current formed from Ψ and Ψ' fulfills a continuity equation. Thus

$$\operatorname{div} \Psi'^* \boldsymbol{\alpha} \Psi + \frac{\partial \Psi'^* \Psi}{\partial t} = 0$$

or

$$\operatorname{div} \Psi'^* \boldsymbol{\alpha} \Psi = i(W - W')\Psi'^* \Psi$$

Integrating over a closed volume we obtain

$$\int \Psi'^* \alpha_n \Psi \, dS = i(W - W') \int \Psi'^* \Psi \, d^3x$$

where α_n is the component of $\boldsymbol{\alpha}$ along the outward normal on the surface S bounding the volume of integration. Now we let $W' = W + dW$ and obtain

$$\int \frac{\partial \psi^*}{\partial W} \alpha_n \psi \, dS = -i \int \psi^* \psi \, d^3x$$

since there is no outward current for a stationary state; that is,

$$\int \psi^* \alpha_n \psi \, dS = 0$$

We now specialize the volume of integration to be a spherical shell with radii r_1 and r_2. Then, introducing $u_1 = rg$ and $u_2 = rf$, we find

$$\left[u_2 \frac{\partial u_1}{\partial W} - u_1 \frac{\partial u_2}{\partial W} \right]_{r_1}^{r_2} = \int_{r_1}^{r_2} (u_1^2 + u_2^2) \, dr \qquad (5.16)$$

Taking $r_1 = 0$ and $r_2 = r$, the contribution to the left side of (5.16) from $r = r_1 = 0$ vanishes if u_1 and u_2 are the radial functions of an L solution. Hence

$$u_1^2 \frac{\partial \rho_L}{\partial W} = -\int_0^r (u_1^2 + u_2^2)\, dr \tag{5.17}$$

where

$$\rho_L = \left(\frac{u_2}{u_1}\right)_L$$

For $r_1 = r$ and $r_2 = \infty$ the contribution from r_2 on the left side of (5.16) will vanish if u_1 and u_2 are radial functions of the R type. Hence

$$u_1^2 \frac{\partial \rho_R}{\partial W} = \int_r^\infty (u_1^2 + u_2^2)\, dr \tag{5.18}$$

and

$$\rho_R = \left(\frac{u_2}{u_1}\right)_R$$

We combine (5.17) and (5.18) and the normalized solution at any point r is given by

$$u_1^2 = \left[\frac{\partial \rho_R}{\partial W} - \frac{\partial \rho_L}{\partial W}\right]^{-1}_{W_n} \tag{5.19}$$

where W_n is one of the eigenvalues of W and n represents the set of quantum numbers required to specify these eigenvalues.

The normalization procedure is then as follows. From (5.4) or (5.5) one constructs solutions for any W which are regular at $r = 0$. One also constructs solutions regular at $r = \infty$. From these ρ_R and ρ_L are obtained as functions of W. The L and R solutions will each contain a normalization constant. From either the L or R solutions the correct W_n are obtained. The ratios ρ_R and ρ_L do not depend on the normalization constants. Hence, by differentiation with respect to W and substitution of W_n, the right side of (5.19) is calculated. Equating this to u_1^2 obtained from R *or* L solutions† with $W = W_n$ gives the value of the normalization constant to within the usual phase ± 1. This procedure will be carried out in detail for the Coulomb field in the next section.

In connection with these questions it is useful to examine the asymptotic form of (5.5) in the case of practical interest: $V(r) \to 0$ as $r \to \infty$. Then, for large r,

$$\frac{du_1}{dr} = -\frac{\kappa}{r} u_1 + (W + 1) u_2$$

$$\frac{du_2}{dr} = -(W - 1) u_1 + \frac{\kappa}{r} u_2$$

† After setting $W = W_n$ these solutions are identical to within the unfixed normalization constant.

The asymptotic solutions are

$$u_1 = A(r, W)e^{-\lambda r} + B(r, W)e^{\lambda r}$$
$$(W + 1)u_2 = -\lambda A'(r, W)e^{-\lambda r} + \lambda B'(r, W)e^{\lambda r}$$

where

$$\lambda = (1 - W^2)^{1/2}, \qquad A' = A - \frac{1}{\lambda}\frac{dA}{dr}, \qquad B' = B + \frac{1}{\lambda}\frac{dB}{dr}$$

The terms in κ/r in the differential equations and also the contribution from the potential energy V serve to determine the functions $A(r, W)$ and $B(r, W)$. These will generally have the form of finite powers of r. From the result just given it is seen that a bound state requires

$$-1 < W < 1 \tag{5.20}$$

This demonstrates a general result that all bound states must be in the interval from -1 to $+1$ or, in ordinary units, from $-mc^2$ to mc^2. In particular cases, of course, it is possible that the spectrum of discrete eigenvalues is restricted to an even smaller range. The Coulomb field is a case in point. In the asymptotic form of u_1 the term in $e^{\lambda r}$ must vanish. Thus the eigenvalues W_n may be obtained as roots of the equation

$$\lim_{r\to\infty} B(r, W_n) = 0 \tag{5.21}$$

We must also have $\lim B'(r, W_n) = 0$ and this will be the case where $B(r, W)$ has a factor which depends on W alone and which vanishes for $W = W_n$—see (5.42) below—or where $dB/dr \ll B$ for large r.

The term $A(r, W) \exp(-\lambda r)$ is, of course, the asymptotic form of the R solution.

Nodes of the Radial Functions[3]

In the non-relativistic central field problem we know that for given orbital angular momentum the solution for the bound state with lowest energy is nodeless if we exclude the possible zero at the origin and the point at infinity. In this open interval from 0 to ∞ the number of nodes increases by one in going from one state to the next of higher energy. There is a corresponding result in the relativistic central field problem, but the situation is more complicated because there are now two radial functions.†

† Of course, we can also write the non-relativistic radial equations as two coupled first-order differential equations. This can be done in many ways. For example, if $r\mathscr{R}$, where $\mathscr{R}$ is the radial wave function, is set equal to u_1 and $dr\mathscr{R}/dr$ is set equal to u_2, we obtain a pair of equations of the general character of (5.5). However, the connection between u_1 and u_2 is somewhat more involved in the relativistic case. This is reflected in the radically different second-order equation (5.8).

We first recognize that the quantity $W - 1 - V$ in (5.5) is similar to $E - V$, the kinetic energy in the non-relativistic case. In the non-relativistic case nodes of the radial wave function can occur only in the region of classically allowed motion, that is, where $E - V > 0$. Of course, we consider only proper wave functions with W or E equal to one of the eigenvalues. It is now easy to see that exactly the same result applies in the relativistic case: nodes can occur only where $W - 1 - V > 0$. We shall prove this in the practical case that V is everywhere negative and a monotonic increasing function of r. Thus $W - 1 - V = 0$ at only one point.† In (5.5) we set

$$G = r^{\kappa}u_1, \qquad F = r^{-\kappa}u_2$$

Then in the open interval 0 to ∞ in which the end points are excluded, nodes of f and g coincide with nodes of F and G. We see that

$$\frac{dF}{dr} = -r^{-2\kappa}(W - 1 - V)G; \qquad \frac{dG}{dr} = r^{2\kappa}(W + 1 - V)F$$

Now we consider a node of F at $r = r_1$ and arbitrarily assume that $F < 0$ for $r < r_1$ and $F > 0$ for $r > r_1$. If $W - 1 - V < 0$, and since $W + 1 - V$ is everywhere >0, it follows that, at r_1, G is positive and goes through a minimum; that is, the curvature of G is positive. This behavior is impossible because F and G must both vanish at ∞. Thus, for some $r = r_2 > r_1$, the function F must reach a maximum beyond which F decreases. The point r_2 is defined so that between r_1 and r_2 there are no roots or extrema of F. At r_2 then, G must vanish. But, since at r_1 we saw that $G > 0$ and $d^2G/dr^2 > 0$, it follows that between r_1 and r_2 the function G must reach a maximum. This is not possible because at such a point F would vanish, contrary to assumption.

On the other hand, if $W - 1 - V > 0$ then at r_1 where $F = 0$ and $dF/dr > 0$ the function $G < 0$ and $dG/dr = 0$. Moreover, $d^2G/dr^2 > 0$ so that G reaches a minimum at r_1. This is a valid type of solution. For $r > r_1$, F and G may have other zeros or G may approach zero without crossing the axis. In that case F reaches a maximum for some $r > r_1$ and then approaches zero without crossing the axis for any larger value of r.

This discussion also illustrates a point which is fairly obvious. It is impossible for f and g, or F and G, to vanish simultaneously at any point where V is finite. If both f and g or F and G were to vanish at the same point, the equations, (5.4) for example, show that f and g would vanish everywhere. A second remark which is at the base of our discussion

† The proof can be generalized to show that nodes occur only where $(W - V)^2 - 1 > 0$. When $V \leqslant 0$ this is identical with the condition $W - V - 1 > 0$.

concerns the fact that where V is continuous f and g must be not only continuous (which is always necessary) but they must also have continuous first derivatives.

To discuss the nodes of f and g it is useful to introduce $\rho = f/g$ once more. For ρ we have the Ricatti equation

$$\frac{d\rho}{dr} = \frac{2\kappa\rho}{r} - (W - 1 - V) - (W + 1 - V)\rho^2 \tag{5.22}$$

If we also introduce φ according to

$$f = \rho \sin \varphi$$

$$g = \rho \cos \varphi$$

it is seen that

$$\frac{\partial \rho}{\partial r} = (1 + \rho^2)\frac{\partial \varphi}{\partial r}$$

Therefore, where $g = 0$ and hence $\rho = \infty$, $\partial\rho/\partial r$ and $\partial\varphi/\partial r$ are both negative ($V < 0$). Where $f = 0$, $\rho = 0$, both $\partial\rho/\partial r$ and $\partial\varphi/\partial r$ have the opposite sign to $W - 1 - V$. But, since this must be positive where nodes occur, $\partial\rho/\partial r$ and $\partial\varphi/\partial r$ are negative again. Hence, in the f-g plane, the vector representing f and g rotates clockwise whenever it crosses the axes $f = 0$ or $g = 0$ with r increasing. From the discussion of the functions of F and G it is seen that the nodes of f and g alternate; that is, between every pair of adjacent nodes of f (or g) there is one node of g (or f).

For an eigensolution

$$\rho(\infty) = -\frac{\lambda}{W + 1} = -\left(\frac{1 - W}{1 + W}\right)^{1/2} < 0 \tag{5.23}$$

Hence at ∞ the functions f and g have opposite signs. Thus, to determine the relative number of nodes of f and g, we must examine the behavior at the origin. Two cases suffice for the discussion: $V(0) =$ constant and $V(r) = -\zeta/r$ for small r with $\zeta > 0$.[2-4] In the first case the behavior at the origin is the same as in the free particle case; see Eq. (5.12). Thus, for small r,

$$f/g > 0 \quad \text{for} \quad \kappa > 0$$

$$f/g < 0 \quad \text{for} \quad \kappa < 0$$

For a Coulomb-like behavior of V near $r = 0$ we find from (5.5) that

$$u_1 = Ar^\gamma, \qquad u_2 = Br^\gamma$$

for small r and

$$A(\kappa + \gamma) = \zeta B$$

$$B(\kappa - \gamma) = \zeta A$$

so that

$$\gamma^2 = \kappa^2 - \zeta^2$$

The regular solutions (for all κ) must correspond to $\zeta^2 < 1$ and $\gamma > 0$. Hence

$$\lim_{r\to 0} \frac{f}{g} = \frac{B}{A} = \frac{\kappa + \gamma}{\zeta} \tag{5.24}$$

Thus, for $\kappa > 0$, $f/g > 0$ and, for $\kappa < 0$, $f/g < 0$ just as in the first case discussed. For $\kappa > 0$, the angle φ at $r = 0$ is in the first or third quadrant and, for $\kappa < 0$, $\varphi(0)$ is in the second or fourth quadrant. At $r = \infty$ we have φ in the second or fourth quadrant.

It follows that for $\kappa > 0$ the number of f nodes exceeds the number of g nodes by 1, while for $\kappa < 0$ the numbers of nodes of f and g are equal. It is seen that the number of nodes of the large component g in every case follows the same rule that applies to the non-relativistic radial function. The bound state eigenfunctions for a Coulomb field are studied below, and the results are shown in Figs. 5.2 through 5.5. These may be compared with the statements made here.

29. COULOMB FIELD. BOUND STATES

We shall consider hydrogen-like atoms for which

$$V = -Ze^2/r$$

although for many electron atoms screening corrections due to the presence of other electrons constitute an appreciable modification of the energy. The radial equations (5.5) are now

$$\begin{aligned} \frac{du_1}{dr} &= -\frac{\kappa u_1}{r} + \left(W + 1 + \frac{\zeta}{r}\right) u_2 \\ \frac{du_2}{dr} &= -\left(W - 1 + \frac{\zeta}{r}\right) u_1 + \frac{\kappa u_2}{r} \end{aligned} \tag{5.25}$$

where $\zeta = e^2 Z = \alpha Z < 1$. In these equations the substitutions

$$\begin{aligned} u_1 &= (1 + W)^{1/2} e^{-\lambda r}(\varphi_1 + \varphi_2) \\ u_2 &= (1 - W)^{1/2} e^{-\lambda r}(\varphi_1 - \varphi_2) \end{aligned} \tag{5.26}$$

are made. Here $\lambda = (1 - W^2)^{1/2}$ as before. If we also use

$$x = 2\lambda r$$

the resulting equations are

$$\begin{aligned}\frac{d\varphi_1}{dx} &= \left(1 - \frac{\zeta W}{\lambda x}\right)\varphi_1 - \left(\frac{\kappa}{x} + \frac{\zeta}{\lambda x}\right)\varphi_2 \\ \frac{d\varphi_2}{dx} &= \left(-\frac{\kappa}{x} + \frac{\zeta}{\lambda x}\right)\varphi_1 + \frac{\zeta W}{\lambda x}\varphi_2\end{aligned} \tag{5.27}$$

These equations are solved by substituting the power series:

$$\varphi_1 = x^\gamma \sum_{m=0}^{\infty} \alpha_m x^m$$

$$\varphi_2 = x^\gamma \sum_{m=0}^{\infty} \beta_m x^m$$

which, after like powers of x are equated, gives the recurrence relations

$$\begin{aligned}\alpha_m(m+\gamma) &= \alpha_{m-1} - \frac{W\zeta}{\lambda}\alpha_m - \left(\kappa + \frac{\zeta}{\lambda}\right)\beta_m \\ \beta_m(m+\gamma) &= \left(-\kappa + \frac{\zeta}{\lambda}\right)\alpha_m + \frac{W\zeta}{\lambda}\beta_m\end{aligned} \tag{5.28}$$

For $m > 0$ this determines all α_m and β_m in terms of α_0 and β_0. For $m = 0$ we find a pair of homogeneous linear equations in α_0 and β_0 which are consistent if and only if the determinant of the coefficients vanishes:

$$\begin{vmatrix} \gamma + \zeta W/\lambda & \kappa + \zeta/\lambda \\ \kappa - \zeta/\lambda & \gamma - \zeta W/\lambda \end{vmatrix} = 0$$

or

$$\gamma^2 - \zeta^2 W^2/\lambda^2 = \kappa^2 - \frac{\zeta^2}{\lambda^2}$$

Using the value of λ given above, we obtain

$$\gamma^2 = \kappa^2 - \zeta^2$$

as above. The regular solutions are obtained by taking the *positive* square root:†

$$\gamma = (\kappa^2 - \zeta^2)^{1/2} \tag{5.29}$$

Using this value of γ we have

$$\frac{\beta_m}{\alpha_m} = -\frac{\zeta/\lambda - \kappa}{\zeta W/\lambda - \gamma - m} = \frac{\kappa - \zeta/\lambda}{n' - m}$$

† For the negative root, $r^2(f^2 + g^2) \approx r^{-2\gamma}$ near $r = 0$, and this gives a divergent result for $\gamma \geqslant \frac{1}{2}$. The minimum γ occurs for $\kappa^2 = 1$ so that in this case the negative root would require $\zeta \geqslant \frac{1}{2}\sqrt{3}$ or $Z \geqslant 109$. For $\kappa^2 > 1$ there is no value of Z which permits a regular solution to be constructed.

where

$$n' = \zeta W/\lambda - \gamma \tag{5.30}$$

Inserting this into the first of Eqs. (5.28) yields the result

$$\begin{aligned}\alpha_m &= -\frac{n' - m}{m(2\gamma + m)}\alpha_{m-1} = (-)^m \frac{(n' - 1)\cdots(n' - m)}{m!(2\gamma + 1)\cdots(2\gamma + m)}\alpha_0 \\ &= \frac{(1 - n')(2 - n')\cdots(m - n')}{m!(2\gamma + 1)\cdots(2\gamma + m)}\alpha_0\end{aligned} \tag{5.31}$$

and

$$\beta_m = (-)^m \frac{n'\cdots(n' - m + 1)}{m!(2\gamma + 1)\cdots(2\gamma + m)}\beta_0 \tag{5.32}$$

From the second of (5.28),

$$\frac{\alpha_0}{\beta_0} = -\frac{\gamma - W\zeta/\lambda}{\kappa - \zeta/\lambda} = \frac{n'}{\kappa - \zeta/\lambda} \tag{5.32'}$$

These results may now be used in the power series for φ_1 and φ_2. When this is done we recognize that the series φ_1 and φ_2 are confluent hypergeometric functions. These functions can be defined by

$$\begin{aligned}F(a, c, x) &= 1 + \frac{a}{c}x + \frac{a(a + 1)}{c(c + 1)}\frac{x^2}{2!} + \cdots \\ &= \sum_{m=0}^{\infty} \frac{a_m}{c_m}\frac{x^m}{m!}\end{aligned} \tag{5.33}$$

where

$$a_m = \frac{(a + m - 1)!}{(a - 1)!} = \frac{\Gamma(a + m)}{\Gamma(a)}$$

The series (5.33) converges uniformly over the entire complex plane. In terms of the confluent hypergeometric function

$$\varphi_1 = \alpha_0 x^\gamma F(1 - n', 2\gamma + 1, x) \tag{5.34}$$

$$\begin{aligned}\varphi_2 &= \beta_0 x^\gamma F(-n', 2\gamma + 1, x) \\ &= \frac{\kappa - \zeta/\lambda}{n'}\alpha_0 x^\gamma F(-n', 2\gamma + 1, x)\end{aligned} \tag{5.35}$$

The asymptotic behavior of (5.33) is given by[5]

$$F(a, c, x) = \frac{\Gamma(c)}{\Gamma(c - a)}(-x)^{-a}\left[1 + O\left(\frac{1}{x}\right)\right] + \frac{\Gamma(c)}{\Gamma(a)}e^x x^{a-c}\left[1 + O\left(\frac{1}{x}\right)\right]$$

As a consequence, as $r \to \infty$, f and g behave like $e^{\lambda r}$ and are not regular at infinity. Therefore the series (5.34) and (5.35) must be so terminated that both of the confluent hypergeometric functions are simply polynomials. This means that n' is a non-negative integer: $n' = 0, 1, 2, \ldots$. The case $n' = 0$ gives an acceptable solution since then $\alpha_0 = 0$ (see below). The integer n' gives the number of nodes of φ_2, and it will be seen that this is the same as the number of nodes of g. In addition to n', it is useful to introduce the principal quantum number n where

$$n = n' + k = n' + |\kappa|$$

Then Eq. (5.30) gives the eigenvalues

$$W_{nk} = \left[1 + \left(\frac{\zeta}{n' + \gamma}\right)^2\right]^{-1/2} = \left[1 + \left(\frac{\zeta}{n - k + \gamma}\right)^2\right]^{-1/2} \tag{5.36}$$

The eigenvalues are seen to lie in the interval

$$\gamma_1 \leqslant W_n < 1 \tag{5.37}$$

where the lower limit corresponds to the $1s_{1/2}$ state: $\kappa = -1$, $n' = 0$, $n = 1$. In (5.37) we have attached a subscript to γ which gives the value of k: $\gamma_1 = (1 - \zeta^2)^{1/2}$ is the $1s_{1/2}$ energy.

From the result (5.36) it is seen that W depends only on n and k; the non-relativistic degeneracy for the Coulomb field is partially lifted. Whereas for principal quantum number n the $2n^2$ states described by $0 \leqslant l \leqslant n - 1$, $-l \leqslant m_l \leqslant l$, and $m_s = \pm\frac{1}{2}$ had the non-relativistic binding $1 - W = \frac{1}{2}\zeta^2/n^2$, now the levels with the same n and l but with $j = l \pm \frac{1}{2}$ are split. These levels correspond to $\kappa = k = j_1 + \frac{1}{2}$ and $\kappa = -k - 1 = -j_1 - 3/2 = -j_2 - \frac{1}{2}$. Here $j_1 = l - \frac{1}{2}$ and $j_2 = l + \frac{1}{2}$. The level with the higher j lies higher as the x-ray data require.[6] This splitting represents a spin-orbit energy, but only in the non-relativistic limit will it be the same as the values given in section 7.

In Fig. 5.1 the predicted position of the levels for $n = 1$ and 2 is shown for $Z = 82$ and for both the relativistic (r) and non-relativistic (nr) cases. Note that the scales for $n = 1$ and 2 are not the same. The numbers on the ordinate scale are $W_{nk} - 1$. We see that the relativistic binding is greater, and this is generally the case.

Since W_{nk} for given n depends on $k = |\kappa|$ but not on the sign of κ, it follows that the levels of the same j and n are predicted to be degenerate. This degeneracy which, of course, also exists in the non-relativistic energy, is an accidental degeneracy peculiar to the Coulomb field. In many-electron atoms, where V deviates from a Coulomb field due to screening, the level with lower l lies below that with higher l. However, in hydrogen where no screening is involved there is nevertheless a very small $2s_{1/2}$–$2p_{1/2}$ splitting which is the well-known Lamb shift.[6] In frequency units this splitting is 1057 megacycles per second, and so $\Delta E/E_{2s} = 1.4 \times 10^{-3}$. This is of the same order as other radiative corrections (for instance, the correction to the magnetic moment).

Expanding (5.36) in powers of $\zeta = \alpha Z$, we see that

$$W_n - 1 = E_n = -\frac{1}{2}\frac{\zeta^2}{n^2} + \zeta^4\left(\frac{3}{8n^4} - \frac{1}{2kn^3}\right) + O(\zeta^6) \qquad (5.38)$$

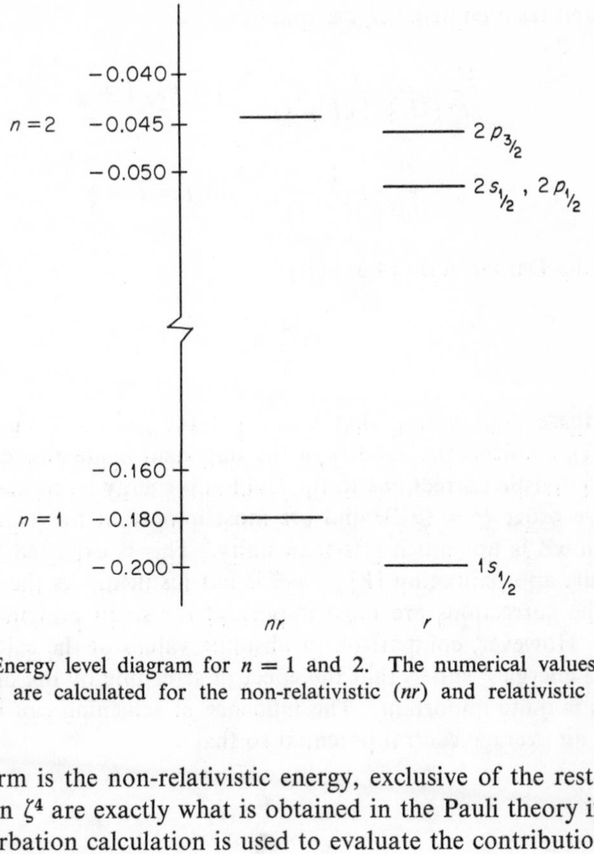

Figure 5.1 Energy level diagram for $n = 1$ and 2. The numerical values refer to $W_{nk} - 1$ and are calculated for the non-relativistic (*nr*) and relativistic (*r*) cases for $Z = 82$.

The first term is the non-relativistic energy, exclusive of the rest energy. The terms in ζ^4 are exactly what is obtained in the Pauli theory if a first-order perturbation calculation is used to evaluate the contribution of the sum of the following three terms:

(i) the additional energy due to variation of mass with velocity† $-\frac{1}{2}(E - V)^2$;

(ii) the spin-orbit coupling as given in Chapter I;

(iii) the Darwin "fluctuation" term given in Chapter IV.

† The kinetic energy is $(1 + p^2)^{1/2}$, where p is the *local* momentum. Expanding in powers of p^2, the p^4 term gives $-\frac{1}{2}(E - V)^2$, where $p^2 = 2(E - V)$ to this order.

The first term (i) contributes to $W - 1$ the amount

$$-\frac{1}{2}[E^2 + 2E\zeta\langle r^{-1}\rangle + \zeta^2\langle r^{-2}\rangle] = -\frac{1}{2}\left[\frac{1}{4}\frac{\zeta^4}{n^4} - \frac{\zeta^4}{n^4} + \frac{\zeta^4}{n^3(l+\frac{1}{2})}\right]$$

$$= -\frac{\zeta^4}{2n^4}\left(\frac{n}{l+\frac{1}{2}} - \frac{3}{4}\right)$$

The second term contributes (section 7)

$$\frac{\zeta^4}{2n^3}\frac{1}{(2l+1)(l+1)} \qquad \text{for } j = l + \tfrac{1}{2}$$

and

$$-\frac{\zeta^4}{2n^3}\frac{1}{l(2l+1)} \qquad \text{for } j = l - \tfrac{1}{2}$$

Finally, the Darwin term (4.35) gives

$$\frac{\zeta^4}{2n^3}\delta_{l0}$$

Adding these (and noting that $k = l + 1$ for $j = l + \frac{1}{2}$ and $k = l$ for $j = l - \frac{1}{2}$), confirms the validity of the statement made above.

The relativistic corrections to the Coulomb energy levels are seen to be of relative order $\zeta^2 = (\alpha Z)^2$ and are most important for heavy elements for which αZ is not much less than unity. This is expected because for large Z the approximation $|V| \ll mc^2$ is not justified. As the form (5.38) shows, the corrections are most important for small principal quantum number. However, comparison of absolute values of the calculated and measured energies[7] shows that the effect of screening by the other atomic electrons is quite important. The influence of screening can be included by using an average central potential so that

$$V = -\frac{\zeta}{r}S(r)$$

where the screening factor S depends on the choice of model. Numerical integration of the radial equations with S given by the Thomas-Fermi-Dirac model with exchange effects included yields energy values in reasonably good agreement with observations.[8] The influence of screening is essential for the splitting of levels with the same j. It is also not negligible for the fine-structure splitting, and calculated values[9] are in good agreement with the measured ones.

Returning to the wave functions, we discuss first the case $n' = 0$ which requires separate comment. From (5.32′) it is seen that if $\kappa > 0$ it is necessary that

$$\kappa = k = \zeta/\lambda$$

This gives

$$W = (1 - \zeta^2/k^2)^{1/2}$$

which agrees with (5.36). For $\kappa < 0$ we would obtain $\alpha_0 = 0$ when $n' = 0$. That is, α_0/n' is finite. In this case $\varphi_1 = 0$ and φ_2 takes the simple form

$$\varphi_2 = \alpha_0'(\kappa - \zeta/\lambda)x^\gamma$$

where $\alpha_0' = \alpha_0/n'$ is a normalization constant.

To determine α_0 in the general case we proceed as outlined in the preceding section. Starting with (5.5), we introduce

$$u_1 = (1 + W)^{1/2}(\Phi_1 + \Phi_2)$$
$$u_2 = (1 - W)^{1/2}(\Phi_1 - \Phi_2)$$

and the variable $x = 2\lambda r = 2(1 - W^2)^{1/2}r$. From the resulting differential equations for Φ_1 and Φ_2,

$$\frac{d\Phi_1}{dx} = \left(\frac{1}{2} - \frac{\zeta W}{\lambda x}\right)\Phi_1 - \left(\frac{\kappa}{x} + \frac{\zeta}{\lambda x}\right)\Phi_2$$

$$\frac{d\Phi_2}{dx} = \left(-\frac{\kappa}{x} + \frac{\zeta}{\lambda x}\right)\Phi_1 - \left(\frac{1}{2} - \frac{\zeta W}{\lambda x}\right)\Phi_2 \tag{5.39}$$

we eliminate Φ_1 to obtain a second-order equation for Φ_2:

$$\frac{d^2\Phi_2}{dx^2} + \frac{1}{x}\frac{d\Phi_2}{dx} + \left[-\frac{1}{4} + \left(\frac{\zeta W}{\lambda} + \frac{1}{2}\right)\frac{1}{x} - \frac{\gamma^2}{x^2}\right]\Phi_2 = 0$$

This equation can be put in normal form by using

$$\mathfrak{M} = x^{1/2}\Phi_2$$

as dependent variable. Then

$$\frac{d^2\mathfrak{M}}{dx^2} + \left[-\frac{1}{4} + \left(\frac{\zeta W}{\lambda} + \frac{1}{2}\right)\frac{1}{x} - \frac{\gamma^2 - \frac{1}{4}}{x^2}\right]\mathfrak{M} = 0 \tag{5.40}$$

The solution of (5.40) regular at the origin is[10]

$$\mathfrak{M}_{k',\gamma}(x) = x^{\gamma+1/2}e^{-1/2x}F(\tfrac{1}{2} + \gamma - k', 2\gamma + 1, x) \tag{5.41}$$

with

$$k' = (\zeta W/\lambda) + \tfrac{1}{2} \tag{5.41'}$$

This agrees with the results already obtained. A solution regular at $x = \infty$ is the Whittaker function,[10] $\mathfrak{W}_{k',\gamma}(x)$, which, for our purposes, can be defined by†

$$\mathfrak{W}_{k',\gamma}(x) = \frac{\Gamma(-2\gamma)}{\Gamma(\frac{1}{2} - \gamma - k')}\,\mathfrak{M}_{k',\gamma}(x) + \frac{\Gamma(2\gamma)}{\Gamma(\frac{1}{2} + \gamma - k')}\,\mathfrak{M}_{k',-\gamma}(x) \tag{5.42}$$

The asymptotic expansion of $\mathfrak{W}_{k'\gamma}(x)$ for large x is[10]

$$\mathfrak{W}_{k'\gamma}(x) \sim e^{-\frac{1}{2}x} x^{k'} \times \left\{1 + \sum_{\nu=1}^{\infty} \frac{[\gamma^2 - (k' - \frac{1}{2})^2][\gamma^2 - (k' - \frac{3}{2})^2] \cdots [\gamma^2 - (k' - \nu + \frac{1}{2})^2]}{\nu! x^\nu}\right\} \tag{5.43}$$

Equating $\mathfrak{W}_{k'\gamma}$ and $\mathfrak{M}_{k'\gamma}$ so that they are identical functions to within a constant factor yields the result (5.36) for the energy. This is most readily seen from (5.42), which requires that $\Gamma(\frac{1}{2} + \gamma - k') = \infty$ or

$$\tfrac{1}{2} + \gamma - k' = -n' \tag{5.43$'$}$$

where n' is a non-negative integer. For Φ_2 we write

$$\Phi_2 = x^{-\frac{1}{2}} \mathfrak{W}_{k',\gamma}(x) \tag{5.44a}$$

For Φ_1 we use the second equation in (5.39) and the relation[5]

$$\begin{aligned} \frac{d}{dx} F(a, c, x) &= \frac{a}{c} F(a + 1, c + 1, x) \\ &= \frac{a - c}{c} F(a, c + 1, x) + F(a, c, x) \end{aligned} \tag{5.43$''$}$$

to obtain

$$\Phi_1 = x^{-\frac{1}{2}} (\kappa + \zeta/\lambda) \mathfrak{W}_{k'-1,\gamma}(x) \tag{5.44b}$$

Consequently,

$$\rho_{\mathrm{R}} = \left(\frac{1 - W}{1 + W}\right)^{\frac{1}{2}} \frac{(\kappa + \zeta/\lambda)\mathfrak{W}_{k'-1,\gamma} - \mathfrak{W}_{k',\gamma}}{(\kappa + \zeta/\lambda)\mathfrak{W}_{k'-1,\gamma} + \mathfrak{W}_{k',\gamma}} \tag{5.45}$$

This result is to be differentiated with respect to W, and after differentiation (5.43′) is used. If we evaluate (5.19) at $r = 0$, in the sense of a limit for small r, it is unnecessary to consider $\partial\rho_{\mathrm{L}}/\partial W$ as (5.17) and (5.18) show that

$$\lim_{r\to 0} \left(\frac{\partial\rho_{\mathrm{L}}/\partial W}{\partial\rho_{\mathrm{R}}/\partial W}\right) = -\lim_{r\to 0} r[u_1^2 + u_2^2] = 0$$

† The notation used here corresponds to Whittaker and Watson's notation in the following way: $\gamma = m$, $k' = k$, $\mathfrak{M}_{k',\gamma} = M_{km}$, $\mathfrak{W}_{k',\gamma} = W_{km}$. Equation (5.42) appears on p. 346 of reference 10.

In calculating $\partial\rho_R/\partial W$ it is unnecessary to differentiate $\mathfrak{M}_{k,-\gamma}(x)$ because it is multiplied by $[\Gamma(\frac{1}{2}+\gamma-k')]^{-1}$ which eventually is set equal to zero. No indeterminate forms arise thereby. Finally, we notice that only the leading terms in $\mathfrak{M}_{k',\pm\gamma}$ need be considered since we are to take the limit of $\partial\rho_R/\partial W$ at $r = 0$. In evaluating $(\partial\rho_R/\partial W)_{W_n}$ we need to use

$$\left[\frac{\partial}{\partial W}\frac{1}{\Gamma(\frac{1}{2}+\gamma-k')}\right]_{W_n} = \frac{(-)^{n'+1}}{\pi}n'!\left(\frac{\partial k'}{\partial W}\right)_{W_n}$$
$$= \frac{(-)^{n'+1}n'!}{\pi}\zeta\left[1+\left(\frac{n'+\gamma^2}{\zeta}\right)\right]^{3/2}$$

in which elementary properties of the gamma function are used.† The remaining details of the rather lengthy manipulations may be left to the reader. The result is expressible in terms of a value of α_0^2. Taking the negative square root as a matter of convention we get

$$\alpha_0 = -\frac{\lambda n'}{\Gamma(2\gamma+1)}\left[\frac{\Gamma(2\gamma+n'+1)}{2\zeta(-\kappa+\zeta/\lambda)n'!}\right]^{1/2} \tag{5.46}$$

in which the value of λ must be inserted according to

$$\lambda = \left[1+\left(\frac{n'+\gamma}{\zeta}\right)^2\right]^{-1/2}$$
$$= \zeta[n^2 - 2n'(k-\gamma)]^{-1/2} \tag{5.46'}$$

The final results for the bound state wave functions are obtained from (5.26), (5.34), and (5.46). They are

$$f = -\frac{2^{1/2}\lambda^{5/2}}{\Gamma(2\gamma+1)}\left[\frac{\Gamma(2\gamma+n'+1)(1-W)}{n'!\,\zeta(\zeta-\lambda\kappa)}\right]^{1/2}(2\lambda r)^{\gamma-1}e^{-\lambda r}$$
$$\times\,[n'F(-n'+1, 2\gamma+1, 2\lambda r) - (\kappa-\zeta/\lambda)F(-n', 2\gamma+1, 2\lambda r)] \tag{5.47}$$

$$g = \frac{2^{1/2}\lambda^{5/2}}{\Gamma(2\gamma+1)}\left[\frac{\Gamma(2\gamma+n'+1)(1+W)}{n'!\,\zeta(\zeta-\lambda\kappa)}\right]^{1/2}(2\lambda r)^{\gamma-1}e^{-\lambda r}$$
$$\times\,[-n'F(-n'+1, 2\gamma+1, 2\lambda r) - (\kappa-\zeta/\lambda)F(-n', 2\gamma+1, 2\lambda r)] \tag{5.48}$$

In the non-relativistic limit ζ^2 is neglected compared to unity, so that $\gamma = k$, W is set equal to 1 and $\lambda = \zeta/n$. Then f vanishes and g becomes

† $[d\log\Gamma(z)/dz]_{z=-n'+\epsilon} = -1/\epsilon$ for $\epsilon \ll 1$. Also,

$$\Gamma(-n'+\epsilon) = \pi/(n')!\sin(n'+1-\epsilon)\pi$$

Table 5.1. Parameters Defining the K and L Shell Radial Wave Functions for the Coulomb Field

Subshell	γ	W	λ	a_0	a_1	c_0	c_1	N
$K\,(1s_{1/2})$ $\kappa = -1$	$(1-\zeta^2)^{1/2}$	γ	ζ	1	0	1	0	$\dfrac{(2\zeta)^{\gamma+1/2}}{[2\Gamma(2\gamma+1)]^{1/2}}$
$L_{\mathrm{I}}\,(2s_{1/2})$ $\kappa = -1$	$(1-\zeta^2)^{1/2}$	$\left(\dfrac{1+\gamma}{2}\right)^{1/2}$	$\dfrac{\zeta}{2W}$	$2(W+1)$	$-\dfrac{\zeta}{W}\dfrac{2W+1}{2\gamma+1}$	$2W$	$-\dfrac{\zeta}{W}\dfrac{2W+1}{2\gamma+1}$	$\dfrac{(2\zeta)^{\gamma+1/2}}{2(2W)^{\gamma+1}}\left[\dfrac{2\gamma+1}{\Gamma(2\gamma+1)(2W+1)}\right]^{1/2}$
$L_{\mathrm{II}}\,(2p_{1/2})$ $\kappa = 1$	$(1-\zeta^2)^{1/2}$	$\left(\dfrac{1+\gamma}{2}\right)^{1/2}$	$\dfrac{\zeta}{2W}$	$2W$	$-\dfrac{\zeta}{W}\dfrac{2W-1}{2\gamma+1}$	$2(W-1)$	$-\dfrac{\zeta}{W}\dfrac{2W-1}{2\gamma+1}$	$\dfrac{(2\zeta)^{\gamma+1/2}}{2(2W)^{\gamma+1}}\left[\dfrac{2\gamma+1}{\Gamma(2\gamma+1)(2W-1)}\right]^{1/2}$
$L_{\mathrm{III}}\,(2p_{3/2})$ $\kappa = -2$	$(4-\zeta^2)^{1/2}$	$\frac{1}{2}\gamma$	$\frac{1}{2}\zeta$	1	0	1	0	$\dfrac{\zeta^{\gamma+1/2}}{[2\Gamma(2\gamma+1)]^{1/2}}$

the non-relativistic radial function, as can be seen by use of the contiguous relation

$$xF(a + 1, c + 1, x) = cF(a + 1, c, x) - cF(a, c, x)$$

All the states with $k = 1$ exhibit a weak (but square integrable) divergence of f and g at $r = 0$. This is typical of the relativistic wave functions. It

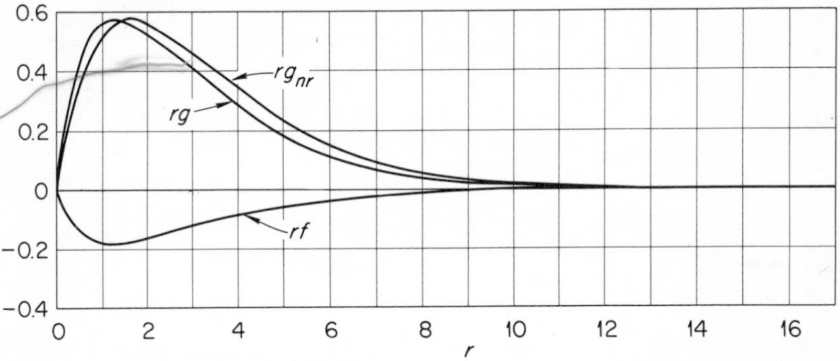

Figure 5.2 Normalized radial wave functions multiplied by r for the $1s_{1/2}$ state and $Z = 82$. The abscissa gives r in units of $\hbar/mc$. The subscript nr refers to the non-relativistic radial function.

does not appear in the non-relativistic radial function because it is there assumed that $V \ll mc^2$, which is clearly invalid near $r = 0$. Then only the centrifugal term $l(l + 1)/r^2$ determines the small r behavior. In the relativistic case the second-order equation contains $V^2 = \zeta^2/r^2$, which counteracts the centrifugal repulsion to some extent and reduces the exponent in the indicial behavior of the wave functions from $k - 1$ to $\gamma - 1$.

For the K and L shells the wave functions f and g may be written as follows:

$$f = -N(1 - W)^{1/2} r^{\gamma - 1} e^{-\lambda r}(a_0 + a_1 r) \tag{5.49a}$$

$$g = N(1 + W)^{1/2} r^{\gamma - 1} e^{-\lambda r}(c_0 + c_1 r) \tag{5.49b}$$

Table 5.1 gives the values of N, γ, λ and a_i, c_i. For the K shell we have $n = 1$, $n' = 0$, $\kappa = -1$. For L_{I}: $n = 2$, $n' = 1$, $\kappa = -1$; L_{II}: $n = 2$, $n' = 1$, $\kappa = 1$; L_{III}: $n = 2$, $n' = 0$, $\kappa = -2$. In Figs. 5.2 to 5.5 these radial functions multiplied by r are given in graphical form for $Z = 82$ together with the non-relativistic rg. It is apparent that for $1s_{1/2}$ and $2p_{3/2}$ (K and L_{III} respectively), the ratio f/g is constant and, in fact, equal to $\rho(\infty) = -(1 - W)^{1/2}/(1 + W)^{1/2}$ as would be required. From (5.22) it is seen that this occurs only for the Coulomb field and then only for $n' = 0$, $\kappa < 0$. In these cases $W = \gamma/k$ in general.

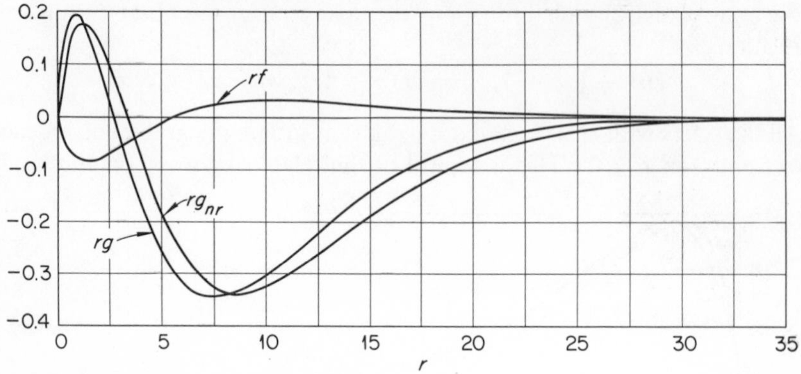

Figure 5.3 Same as Fig. 5.2 but for the $2s_{1/2}$ state.

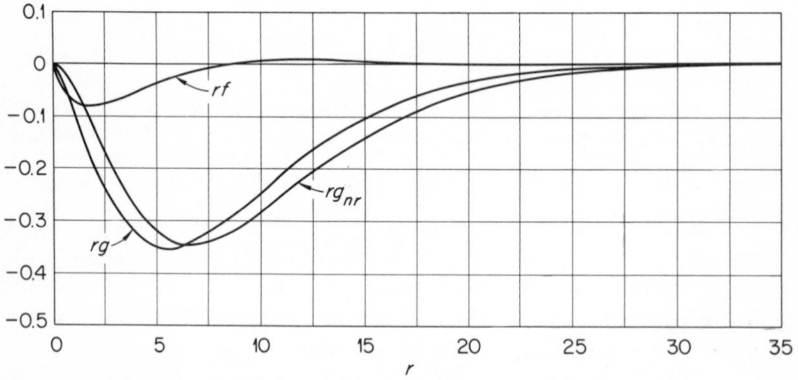

Figure 5.4 Same as Fig. 5.2 but for the $2p_{1/2}$ state. The infinite slope of rg at $r = 0$ is not discernible on this scale.

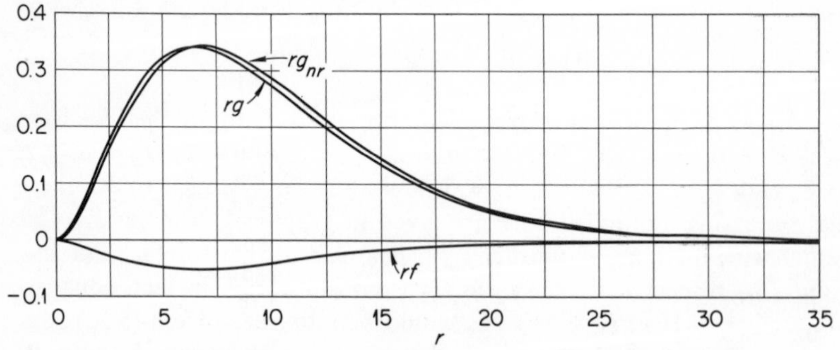

Figure 5.5 Same as Fig. 5.2 but for the $2p_{3/2}$ state.

The ratio of the magnitudes of small to large component is of the order $\rho(\infty) \sim \zeta = \alpha Z$. However, large departures from this ratio occur, especially near nodes of f or g or both. The order of magnitude of $|(g - g_{nr})/g_{nr}|$ is $(\alpha Z)^2$ except, of course, where one of these radial functions has a node.

30. ANOMALOUS ZEEMAN EFFECT

In a homogeneous magnetic field $\mathscr{H}$ in addition to the Coulomb field the Hamiltonian for an electron is

$$H = H_0 + H'$$

where H_0 is the Hamiltonian with the Coulomb field and

$$H' = e\boldsymbol{\alpha}\cdot\mathbf{A} = -\frac{e}{2}\boldsymbol{\alpha}\cdot\mathbf{r}\times\mathscr{H} \tag{5.50}$$

In this relativistic formulation of the anomalous Zeeman effect it is apparent that there are no explicit $\mathbf{A}^2$ terms. These appear only in a second-order equation, and therefore the present treatment includes, among other effects, the influence of the $\mathbf{A}^2$ term previously neglected.

If the z-axis is chosen as the direction of the magnetic field, the perturbation (5.50) becomes

$$H' = -\frac{e}{2}\mathscr{H}(\alpha_x y - \alpha_y x) \tag{5.51}$$

The total Hamiltonian still commutes with j_z since

$$(\tfrac{1}{2}\sigma_z, \alpha_x y - \alpha_y x) = i(\boldsymbol{\alpha}\cdot\mathbf{r} - \alpha_z z) = -(l_z, \alpha_x y - \alpha_y x)$$

Therefore matrix elements of H' exist only between states of the same μ. However, $\boldsymbol{j}^2$ does not commute with H', as may be verified directly.† The matrix elements of H' with the wave functions in the angular momentum representation are

$$(\psi_\kappa^\mu|H'|\psi_{\kappa'}^\mu) = -\frac{ie}{2}\mathscr{H}[(g_\kappa\chi_\kappa^\mu|(\boldsymbol{\sigma}\times\mathbf{r})_z|f_{\kappa'}\chi_{-\kappa'}^\mu)$$
$$- (f_\kappa\chi_{-\kappa}^\mu|(\boldsymbol{\sigma}\times\mathbf{r})_z|g_{\kappa'}\chi_{\kappa'}^\mu)] \tag{5.52}$$

The second term in (5.52) can be put into a form similar to the first by noting that $\sigma_r\chi_\kappa^\mu = -\chi_{-\kappa}^\mu$ and

$$\sigma_r\boldsymbol{\sigma}\times\mathbf{r}\,\sigma_r = -\boldsymbol{\sigma}\times\mathbf{r}$$

† A simple way to see this is to note that H' transforms under rotations like a first-rank tensor (or a first-order spherical harmonic). Therefore it can connect states with angular momentum j' and j if $\Delta(jj'\,1)$ is fulfilled: $j' = j, j \pm 1$.

Hence[11]

$$(\psi_\kappa^\mu|H'|\psi_{\kappa'}^\mu) = -\frac{ie\mathscr{H}}{2} R_{\kappa\kappa'} A_{\kappa\kappa'}$$

where

$$R_{\kappa\kappa'} = \int_0^\infty r^3(g_\kappa f_{\kappa'} + g_{\kappa'} f_\kappa)\, dr$$

is a radial matrix element symmetric in κ, κ' and

$$A_{\kappa\kappa'} = \int d\Omega(\chi_\kappa^\mu|(\boldsymbol{\sigma} \times \mathbf{r})_z|\chi_{-\kappa'}^\mu) \tag{5.53}$$

is an angular integral. Using

$$\sigma_x\chi^m = \chi^{-m}$$
$$\sigma_y\chi^m = i(-)^{½-m}\chi^{-m}$$

and the definition (1.60′) of the spin-angular functions, we obtain the result

$$A_{\kappa\kappa'} = i\left(\frac{8\pi}{3}\right)^{½}\Big\{C(l\tfrac{1}{2}j;\mu-\tfrac{1}{2},\tfrac{1}{2})\,C(\bar{l}'\tfrac{1}{2}j';\mu+\tfrac{1}{2},-\tfrac{1}{2})\int d\Omega\, Y_l^{\mu-½\times}Y_1^{-1}Y_{\bar{l}'}^{\mu+½}$$
$$+ C(l\tfrac{1}{2}j;\mu+\tfrac{1}{2},-\tfrac{1}{2})\,C(\bar{l}'\tfrac{1}{2}j';\mu-\tfrac{1}{2},\tfrac{1}{2})\int d\Omega Y_l^{\mu+½\times}Y_1^{1}Y_{\bar{l}'}^{\mu-½}\Big\}$$

The angular integrals are†

$$\int d\Omega Y_l^{\mu\pm½\times}Y_1^{\pm1}Y_{\bar{l}'}^{\mu\mp½} = \left[\frac{3}{4\pi}\frac{2\bar{l}'+1}{2l+1}\right]^{½} C(\bar{l}'1l;00)\,C(\bar{l}'1l;\mu\mp\tfrac{1}{2},\pm1) \tag{5.53′}$$

and

$$A_{\kappa\kappa'} = i\left[\frac{2(2\bar{l}'+1)}{2l+1}\right]^{½} C(\bar{l}'1l;00)$$
$$\times \sum_\tau C(l\tfrac{1}{2}j;\mu-\tau,\tau)\,C(\bar{l}'\tfrac{1}{2}j';\mu+\tau,-\tau)\,C(\bar{l}'1l;\mu+\tau,-2\tau) \tag{5.54}$$

From this result it is apparent that

$$\bar{l}' + 1 + l = \text{even integer}$$
$$j' - j = 0, \pm1$$

as is evident from the odd parity property of $(\boldsymbol{\sigma} \times \mathbf{r})_z/r$ and its rotational properties. In addition, $l - \bar{l}' = \pm1$ from the triangular condition $\Delta(l\bar{l}'1)$. Since $\bar{l}' = l' - S_{\kappa'}$ it follows that $l' + l$ must be even and $l - l' = 0, \pm2$. The diagonal matrix elements of H' exist for all states: $\kappa = \kappa' = k$, $j = j' = k - \frac{1}{2}$, $l = l' = k - 1$, $\bar{l}' = k - 2$. The non-diagonal matrix

† Reference A, p. 62.

elements which do not vanish occur between the following pairs of states: (a): $\kappa = -k$, $\kappa' = k + 1$, $j = k - \frac{1}{2} = j' - 1$, $l = k - 1 = l' - 2$, $\bar{l}' = k$; (b): $\kappa = k$, $\kappa' = -k - 1$, $j = k - \frac{1}{2} = j' - 1$, $l = l' = k$, $\bar{l}' = k + 1$. Some examples of (a) are $s_{1/2} - d_{3/2}$, $p_{3/2} - f_{5/2}$ and of (b) are $p_{1/2} - p_{3/2}$, $d_{3/2} - d_{5/2}$. Obviously, the value of μ for the two coupled states must be the same.

In constructing the secular determinant for the operator H' we shall restrict our consideration to states within a given shell, neglecting matrix elements between states in different shells since their energy separation is large. In particular we consider the K and L shells. The only non-diagonal matrix elements are between $2p_{1/2}$ and $2p_{3/2}$ for $\mu = \pm\frac{1}{2}$. In order to calculate $A_{\kappa\kappa'}$ in general we need vector addition coefficients of the type $C(j_1 1 j; m - m_2, m)$. These are listed in Table 5.2.[B] Using these results and the $C(l\frac{1}{2}j; m - m_2, m_2)$ given in (1.59), it is a straightforward procedure to calculate $A_{\kappa\kappa'}$ for all relevant cases. For the diagonal elements we find

$$A_{kk} = \frac{4il\mu}{4l^2 - 1}, \qquad k = l$$

$$A_{-k,-k} = -\frac{4i(l + 1)\mu}{(2l + 1)(2l + 3)}, \qquad k = l + 1$$

or, in general,

$$A_{\kappa\kappa} = \frac{4i\kappa\mu}{4k^2 - 1} \tag{5.54'}$$

For the non-diagonal elements the results are

$$A_{k,-k-1} = i\,\frac{[(l + \frac{1}{2})^2 - \mu^2]^{1/2}}{2l + 1}, \qquad l = k$$

$$A_{-k,k+1} = -i\,\frac{[(l + \frac{3}{2})^2 - \mu^2]^{1/2}}{2l + 3}, \qquad l = k - 1$$

For s states in the K and L shells the total energy is simply

$$W = W_{n1} - \frac{2e\mathscr{H}}{3} R^{(n)}_{-1,-1}\mu \tag{5.55}$$

where we have emphasized that the radial matrix element depends on the principal quantum number n. For the M shell and higher shells this result will not apply because of non-diagonal elements between $ns_{1/2}$ and $nd_{3/2}$.

For the p-states in the L shell we obtain a simple result for $2p_{3/2}$, $\mu = \pm\frac{3}{2}$:

$$W = W_{22} \mp \tfrac{2}{5}e\mathscr{H}R_{-2,-2} \tag{5.55a}$$

Table 5.2. Vector Addition Coefficients $C(j_1 1 j; m - m_2, m_2)$

j	$m_2 = 1$	$m_2 = 0$	$m_2 = -1$
$j_1 + 1$	$\left[\frac{(j_1 + m)(j_1 + m + 1)}{(2j_1 + 1)(2j_1 + 2)}\right]^{1/2}$	$\left[\frac{(j_1 - m + 1)(j_1 + m + 1)}{(2j_1 + 1)(j_1 + 1)}\right]^{1/2}$	$\left[\frac{(j_1 - m)(j_1 - m + 1)}{(2j_1 + 1)(2j_1 + 2)}\right]^{1/2}$
j_1	$-\left[\frac{(j_1 + m)(j_1 - m + 1)}{2j_1(j_1 + 1)}\right]^{1/2}$	$\frac{m}{[j_1(j_1 + 1)]^{1/2}}$	$\left[\frac{(j_1 - m)(j_1 + m + 1)}{2j_1(j_1 + 1)}\right]^{1/2}$
$j_1 - 1$	$\left[\frac{(j_1 - m)(j_1 - m + 1)}{2j_1(2j_1 + 1)}\right]^{1/2}$	$-\left[\frac{(j_1 - m)(j_1 + m)}{j_1(2j_1 + 1)}\right]^{1/2}$	$\left[\frac{(j_1 + m + 1)(j_1 + m)}{2j_1(2j_1 + 1)}\right]^{1/2}$

For $\mu = \pm\frac{1}{2}$ we use the secular determinant

$$\begin{vmatrix} W_{21} + (2p_{1/2}|H'|2p_{1/2}) - W & (2p_{1/2}|H'|2p_{3/2}) \\ (2p_{3/2}|H'|2p_{1/2}) & W_{22} + (2p_{3/2}|H'|2p_{3/2}) - W \end{vmatrix} = 0 \quad (5.56)$$

We find from the above that

$$(2p_{1/2}|H'|2p_{1/2}) = \tfrac{2}{3}e\mathscr{H}R_{11}\mu \quad (5.56a)$$

$$(2p_{3/2}|H'|2p_{3/2}) = -\tfrac{4}{15}e\mathscr{H}R_{-2,-2}\mu \quad (5.56b)$$

$$(2p_{1/2}|H'|2p_{3/2}) = (2p_{3/2}|H'|2p_{1/2}) \quad (5.56c)$$

$$= \frac{e\mathscr{H}}{6}\left(\frac{9}{4} - \mu^2\right)^{1/2} R_{1,-2}$$

The roots of (5.56) are

$$W = \tfrac{1}{2}\{W_{21} + W_{22} + H'_{1/2 1/2} + H'_{3/2 3/2} \pm [(\Delta W + H'_{3/2 3/2} - H'_{1/2 1/2})^2 + 4(H'_{3/2 1/2})^2]^{1/2}\} \quad (5.57)$$

where $\Delta W = W_{22} - W_{21}$ is the $2p_{3/2} - 2p_{1/2}$ splitting without magnetic field. In (5.57) we have used an obvious abbreviation for the matrix elements of H'.

The radial integrals are obtained from the results of the preceding section. A straightforward calculation gives

$$R^{(1)}_{-1,-1} = -\tfrac{1}{2}(2\gamma_1 + 1) \quad (5.58a)$$

$$R^{(2)}_{-1,-1} = -\frac{W(2W+1)}{\zeta}(1 - W^2)^{1/2} \quad (5.58b)$$

$$R_{11} = \frac{W(2W-1)}{\zeta}(1 - W^2)^{1/2} \quad (5.58c)$$

where $W = W_{21}$.

$$R_{-2,-2} = -\tfrac{1}{2}(2\gamma_2 + 1) \quad (5.58d)$$

$$R_{1,-2} = -\frac{2^{\gamma_1+\gamma_2+1}W_1^{\gamma_2+1}(2W_1+1)^{1/2}\Gamma(\gamma_1+\gamma_2+2)}{\zeta(1+W_1)^{\gamma_1+\gamma_2+2}[\Gamma(2\gamma_1+1)\Gamma(2\gamma_2+1)]^{1/2}}$$
$$\times \left\{[(1-W_1)(1+W_2)]^{1/2}\left[W_1 - \frac{\gamma_1+\gamma_2+2}{(2W_1+1)(W_1+1)}\right]\right.$$
$$\left. + [(1-W_2)(1+W_1)]^{1/2}\left[W_1 - 1 - \frac{\gamma_1+\gamma_2+2}{(2W_1+1)(W_1+1)}\right]\right\} \quad (5.58e)$$

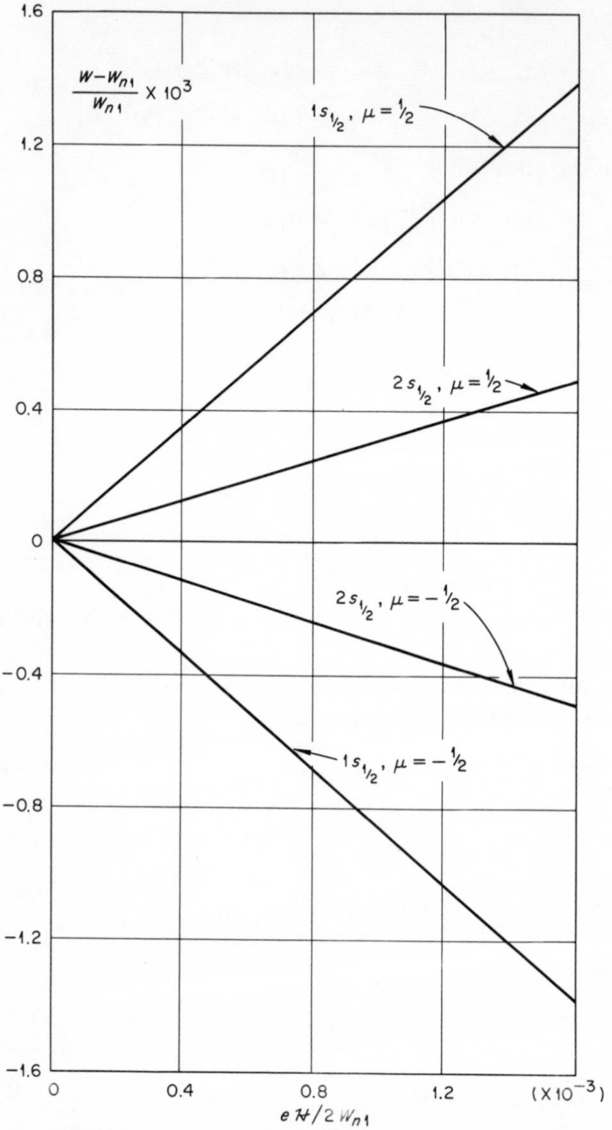

Figure 5.6 Magnetic energy for s-levels, (K and L_{I} shells) $Z = 82$. The ordinate gives the additional energy due to the homogeneous magnetic field in units of the Coulomb energy. The abscissa is $\mu_0 \mathscr{H}/W_{nk}$, where $\mu_0 = e/2$ is the Bohr magneton. Both ordinate and abscissa scales are different for $1s_{\frac{1}{2}}$ and $2s_{\frac{1}{2}}$, but the slope of the lines is independent of the scale factor W_{n1}. The Coulomb values are $1 - W_{11} = 0.1989$ and $1 - W_{21} = 0.0510$.

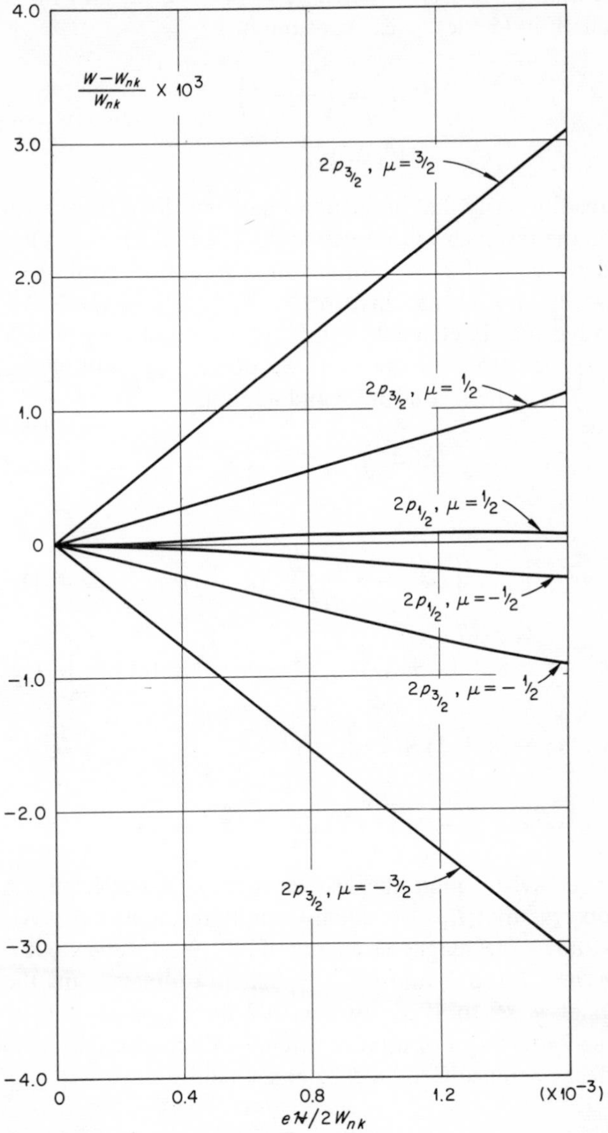

Figure 5.7 The magnetic energy for the $2p$ levels and for $Z = 82$. The coordinates are the same as in Fig. 5.6 and the unit of energy is slightly different for $2p_{1/2}$ and $2p_{3/2}$. The Coulomb value of $1 - W_{22}$ is 0.0458.

For greater clarity we have written $\gamma_k = (k^2 - \zeta^2)^{1/2}$, and in (5.58e) the subscript on W in (5.58e) gives the value of k:

$$W_1 = \left(\frac{1 + \gamma_1}{2}\right)^{1/2}$$

$$W_2 = \tfrac{1}{2}\gamma_2$$

We can readily verify that in the non-relativistic limit these results indeed go over into the results given in section 7. The radial matrix elements are, in fact, independent of Z in the limit $Z \to 0$ because, while $f \sim \alpha Zg$, the matrix element of r always involves a factor $1/\lambda \sim 1/\alpha Z$. Indeed, the diagonal radial matrix elements can be written in a form which displays this in an explicit way. From (5.4) we obtain, by multiplying the first equation by f and the second by g and adding,

$$f\frac{df}{dr} + g\frac{dg}{dr} = 2fg + \frac{\kappa - 1}{r}f^2 - \frac{\kappa + 1}{r}g^2$$

Therefore

$$\begin{aligned} 2\int_0^\infty r^3 fg\,dr &= \int_0^\infty \left[r^3\left(f\frac{df}{dr} + g\frac{dg}{dr}\right) - (\kappa - 1)r^2 f^2 + (\kappa + 1)r^2 g^2\right] dr \\ &= -\tfrac{3}{2} + (\kappa + 1)\int_0^\infty r^2 g^2\,dr - (\kappa - 1)\left[1 - \int_0^\infty r^2 g^2\,dr\right] \\ &= -(\kappa + \tfrac{1}{2}) + 2\kappa\int_0^\infty r^2 g^2\,dr \\ &= \kappa - \tfrac{1}{2} - 2\kappa\int_0^\infty r^2 f^2\,dr \end{aligned} \tag{5.59}$$

In the non-relativistic limit the last term may be neglected. As a final check we observe that $R_{1,-2}$ is equal to unity in the non-relativistic limit. Figure 5.6 shows the magnetic energy $W/W_{n1} - 1$ versus $e\mathscr{H}/2W_{n1}$ for the s-states ($n = 1$ and 2) and for $Z = 82$. In ordinary units the abscissa is the ratio of $\mu_0\mathscr{H}$ to W_{n1}. In Fig. 5.7 the corresponding results are given for the $2p$ states. For a more extended discussion of the anomalous Zeeman effect reference C should be consulted.

31. HYPERFINE STRUCTURE[12,13]

The relativistic corrections to the hyperfine structure can be determined in a manner very similar to that used in the treatment of the anomalous Zeeman effect. We must now consider the entire system of nucleus plus electron. If the nuclear spin is I, the angular momentum of the nuclear plus electron system is F where $F(F+1)$ is the eigenvalue of $\mathbf{F}^2 = (\mathbf{I} + \mathbf{j})^2$. The total system of nucleus plus electron is described by a wave function

$$\Psi_F^m = \sum_\mu C(IjF; m-\mu,\mu)\Phi_I^{m-\mu}\psi_j^\mu$$

Here Φ is the nuclear wave function and ψ_j^μ is the same as ψ_κ^μ introduced in (5.3).

The perturbation is

$$H' = e\boldsymbol{\alpha}\cdot\mathbf{A} = e\boldsymbol{\alpha}\cdot\frac{\mathfrak{m}\times\mathbf{r}}{r^2} = e\mathfrak{m}\cdot\frac{\mathbf{r}\times\boldsymbol{\alpha}}{r^3} \tag{5.60}$$

In (5.60) $\mathfrak{m}$ is the nuclear magnetic moment operator, which is

$$\mathfrak{m} = g_N\mu_N\mathbf{I}, \qquad \mu_N = \frac{e\hbar}{2Mc}$$

with M the proton mass and g_N the nuclear gyromagnetic ratio. The first-order perturbation energy is then

$$W' = eg_N\mu_N \sum_{\mu\mu'} C(IjF; m-\mu,\mu)\, C(IjF; m-\mu',\mu') \times (Im-\mu|\mathbf{I}|Im-\mu')\cdot\left(j\mu\left|\frac{\mathbf{r}\times\boldsymbol{\alpha}}{r^3}\right|j\mu'\right) \tag{5.61}$$

The matrix element (5.61) can be worked out by methods described in reference A† with the result

$$W' = eg_N\mu_N\frac{F(F+1) - I(I+1) - j(j+1)}{2[I(I+1)j(j+1)]^{1/2}}(I\|\mathbf{I}\|I)\left(j\left\|\frac{\mathbf{r}\times\boldsymbol{\alpha}}{r^2}\right\|j\right) \tag{5.62}$$

where the double-barred quantities are "reduced matrix elements" which can be defined by

$$(Im|I_z|Im) = C(I1I; m0)(I\|\mathbf{I}\|I)$$

and

$$\left(j\mu\left|\frac{(\mathbf{r}\times\boldsymbol{\alpha})_z}{r^3}\right|j\mu\right) = C(j1j;\mu0)\left(j\left\|\frac{\mathbf{r}\times\boldsymbol{\alpha}}{r^3}\right\|j\right)$$

It follows‡ that

$$(I\|\mathbf{I}\|I) = [I(I+1)]^{1/2}$$

and

$$\left(j\left\|\frac{\mathbf{r}\times\boldsymbol{\alpha}}{r^3}\right\|j\right) = \frac{[j(j+1)]^{1/2}}{\mu}\left(j\mu\left|\frac{(\mathbf{r}\times\boldsymbol{\alpha})_z}{r^3}\right|j\mu\right)$$

† Chapter VI, particularly Eq. (6.21).
‡ Reference A, pp. 85–88 and Eq. (5.13).

Hence

$$W' = \frac{1}{2} eg_N\mu_N[F(F+1) - I(I+1) - j(j+1)]\left(j\mu \left| \frac{(\mathbf{r} \times \boldsymbol{\alpha})_z}{r^3} \right| j\mu\right)\mu^{-1} \tag{5.63}$$

The matrix element in (5.63) is exactly like the one worked out in the preceding section except for a change in the radial integrals. Taking over those results, we have

$$\left(j\mu \left| \frac{(\mathbf{r} \times \boldsymbol{\alpha})_z}{r^3} \right| j\mu\right) = -iA_{\kappa\kappa}\mathscr{R}_\kappa \tag{5.64}$$

where $A_{\kappa\kappa}$ is defined in (5.53) and

$$\mathscr{R}_\kappa = 2\int_0^\infty g_\kappa f_\kappa \, dr \tag{5.64'}$$

From (5.54′) we obtain the result[14–16]

$$W' = \frac{2\kappa}{4k^2 - 1} eg_N\mu_N[F(F+1) - I(I+1) - j(j+1)]\mathscr{R}_\kappa \tag{5.65}$$

The radial integrals for the K and L shell states are

$$\mathscr{R}_{-1}(1s_{1/2}) = -\frac{2\zeta^3}{\gamma_1(2\gamma_1 - 1)} \tag{5.66a}$$

$$\mathscr{R}_{-1}(2s_{1/2}) = -\frac{\zeta^2}{2W^2} \frac{(1 - W^2)^{1/2}}{(2W - 1)(2W^2 - 1)(4W^2 - 3)} \tag{5.66b}$$

$$\mathscr{R}_2(2p_{1/2}) = \frac{\zeta^2}{2W^2} \frac{(1 - W^2)^{1/2}}{(2W + 1)(2W^2 - 1)(4W^2 - 3)} \tag{5.66c}$$

$$\mathscr{R}_{-2}(2p_{3/2}) = -\frac{\zeta^3}{4\gamma_2(2\gamma_2 - 1)} \tag{5.66d}$$

In the non-relativistic limit all these radial integrals are proportional to $(\alpha Z)^3$, as they should be.[17] To obtain an idea of the magnitude of the corrections to the non-relativistic limit we give the expansion of $\mathscr{R}_\kappa$ to two terms:

$$\mathscr{R}_{-1}(1s_{1/2}) \cong -2\zeta^3(1 + \tfrac{3}{4}\zeta^2)$$

$$\mathscr{R}_{-1}(2s_{1/2}) \cong -\frac{\zeta^3}{4}\left(1 + \frac{17}{8}\zeta^2\right)$$

$$\mathscr{R}_1(2p_{1/2}) \cong \frac{\zeta^3}{12}\left(1 + \frac{47}{24}\zeta^2\right)$$

$$\mathscr{R}_{-2}(2p_{3/2}) \cong -\frac{\zeta^3}{24}\left(1 + \frac{7}{24}\zeta^2\right)$$

In all cases the hyperfine multiplet splitting has been increased. For $Z = 82$, $\zeta = 0.60$ and the relativistic correction is quite appreciable.

32. COULOMB FIELD CONTINUUM STATES

When $W \geqslant 1$ the energy spectrum for the Coulomb field is continuous and the wave functions which are regular at $r = 0$ become standing waves. To obtain these wave functions we consider the counterpart of (5.39). That is, we set

$$\begin{aligned} u_1 &= (W+1)^{1/2}(\Phi_1 + \Phi_2) \\ u_2 &= i(W-1)^{1/2}(\Phi_1 - \Phi_2) \end{aligned} \tag{5.67}$$

and use

$$p = (W^2 - 1)^{1/2}$$

in place of λ. Hence p is the magnitude of the local momentum at $r = \infty$. If we set

$$x = 2ipr$$

we obtain

$$\frac{d\Phi_1}{dx} = \left(\frac{1}{2} + \frac{i\zeta W}{px}\right)\Phi_1 - \left(\frac{\kappa}{x} - \frac{i\zeta}{px}\right)\Phi_2 \tag{5.68a}$$

$$\frac{d\Phi_2}{dx} = -\left(\frac{\kappa}{x} + \frac{i\zeta}{px}\right)\Phi_1 - \left(\frac{1}{2} + \frac{i\zeta W}{px}\right)\Phi_2 \tag{5.68b}$$

If we take the complex conjugate of these equations, remembering that x is pure imaginary, we find

$$\frac{d\Phi_1^\times}{dx} = -\left(\frac{1}{2} + \frac{i\zeta W}{px}\right)\Phi_1^\times - \left(\frac{\kappa}{x} + \frac{i\zeta}{px}\right)\Phi_2^\times$$

$$\frac{d\Phi_2^\times}{dx} = -\left(\frac{\kappa}{x} - \frac{i\zeta}{px}\right)\Phi_1^\times + \left(\frac{1}{2} + \frac{i\zeta W}{px}\right)\Phi_2^\times$$

These equations are identical with (5.68a) and (5.68b) if we set

$$\Phi_1^\times = \Phi_2 \tag{5.69}$$

Hence u_1 and u_2 can be chosen real, as is obvious from the original radial equations. These real functions will therefore give standing waves.† Eliminating Φ_2, we find for Φ_1 the second-order equation

$$\frac{d^2\Phi_1}{dx^2} + \frac{1}{x}\frac{d\Phi_1}{dx} - \left[\frac{1}{4} + \left(\frac{1}{2} + \frac{i\zeta W}{p}\right)\frac{1}{x} + \frac{\gamma^2}{x^2}\right]\Phi_1 = 0$$

† The extension to outgoing or ingoing waves will be obvious from the sequel.

where γ has the same meaning as before. To put this in normal form we again write

$$\mathfrak{M} = x^{1/2}\Phi_1$$

and find

$$\frac{d^2\mathfrak{M}}{dx^2} - \left[\frac{1}{4} + \left(\frac{1}{2} + \frac{i\zeta W}{p}\right)\frac{1}{x} + \frac{\gamma^2 - \frac{1}{4}}{x^2}\right]\mathfrak{M} = 0 \tag{5.70}$$

This should be compared with the corresponding equation (5.40) in the bound state problem. The regular (at $r = 0$) solution of (5.70) is

$$\mathfrak{M}(x) = x^{\gamma + 1/2}e^{-x/2}F(\gamma + 1 + iy, 2\gamma + 1, x)$$

where we have introduced

$$y = \zeta W/p$$

We set

$$\begin{aligned}\Phi_1 &= N(\gamma + iy)e^{i\eta}(2pr)^\gamma e^{-ipr}F(\gamma + 1 + iy, 2\gamma + 1, 2ipr)\\ &\equiv N(\gamma + iy)e^{i\eta}(2p)^\gamma\Phi(r)\end{aligned}$$

where N is a real normalization factor which, for the moment, is irrelevant. The phase η must now be determined so that Φ_2 evaluated from (5.68a) is indeed $\Phi_1^\times$. This requires that

$$e^{-2i\eta} = -\frac{\gamma + iy}{\gamma - iy}\frac{r}{\kappa - iy/W}\left[\frac{1}{\Phi^\times}\frac{d\Phi}{dr} - ip\left(1 + \frac{y}{pr}\right)\frac{\Phi}{\Phi^\times}\right]$$

The evaluation of $\exp(-2i\eta)$ is facilitated by the use of Kummer's formula[10]

$$e^{-x/2}F(\gamma + 1 + iy, 2\gamma + 1, x) = e^{x/2}F(\gamma - iy, 2\gamma + 1, -x)$$

With this and the additional help of the contiguous relation

$$xF(a + 1, c + 1, x) = c[F(a + 1, c, x) - F(a, c, x)]$$

of the hypergeometric function, we find

$$e^{2i\eta} = -\frac{\kappa - iy/W}{\gamma + iy} \tag{5.71'}$$

For the radial functions we can now write

$$\begin{aligned}rf &= i(W - 1)^{1/2}N(2pr)^\gamma\{(\gamma + iy)e^{-ipr+i\eta}\\ &\qquad\times F(\gamma + 1 + iy, 2\gamma + 1, 2ipr) - \text{c.c.}\}\\ rg &= (W + 1)^{1/2}N(2pr)^\gamma\{(\gamma + iy)e^{-ipr+i\eta}\\ &\qquad\times F(\gamma + 1 + iy, 2\gamma + 1, 2ipr) + \text{c.c}\}\end{aligned} \tag{5.71}$$

where N is again the normalization factor and η is the phase determined by (5.71′) to within an additive multiple of π. In (5.71) c.c. means complex conjugate.

The solutions are now normalized in the energy scale. This means that, if ψ_W and $\psi_{W'}$ are solutions corresponding to energies W and W',

$$\int d^3x\ \psi^*_{W'}\psi_W = \delta(W - W') \tag{5.72}$$

An alternative normalization is to one particle in a sphere of very large radius R. If at $r = \infty$

$$\begin{aligned} rf &= -A(W-1)^{1/2}\sin(pr+\delta) \\ rg &= A(W+1)^{1/2}\cos(pr+\delta) \end{aligned} \tag{5.73}$$

then the normalization in the sphere requires that

$$\int d^3x\ \psi^*\psi = \int_0^R r^2(f^2+g^2)\,dr = A^2WR = 1$$

Then

$$A = (WR)^{-1/2}$$

For normalization according to (5.72)†

$$A = (\pi p)^{-1/2} \tag{5.74}$$

We use the asymptotic behavior of the confluent hypergeometric functions.[5] The relevant part of this in our case is

$$F(a, c, x) \to \frac{\Gamma(c)}{\Gamma(a)}\, x^{a-c}e^x + \cdots$$

so that at $r \to \infty$

$$rf \to i(W-1)^{1/2}N\Gamma(2\gamma+1)(2pr)^\gamma\left[\frac{(\gamma+iy)e^{ipr+i\eta}}{\Gamma(\gamma+1+iy)}(2ipr)^{iy-\gamma} - \text{c.c.}\right]$$

$$rg \to (W+1)^{1/2}N\Gamma(2\gamma+1)(2pr)^\gamma\left[\frac{(\gamma+iy)e^{ipr+i\eta}}{\Gamma(\gamma+1+iy)}(2ipr)^{iy-\gamma} + \text{c.c.}\right]$$

We write

$$\frac{\gamma+iy}{\Gamma(\gamma+1+iy)} = \frac{\exp[-i\arg\Gamma(\gamma+iy)]}{|\Gamma(\gamma+iy)|}$$

$$(2ipr)^{iy} = e^{-\pi y/2}e^{iy\log 2pr}$$

$$i^{-\gamma} = e^{-\pi i\gamma/2}$$

† Cf., for example, reference C, p. 23.

Then rf and rg have the asymptotic behavior given by (5.73), where

$$A = \frac{2Ne^{-\pi y/2}\Gamma(2\gamma + 1)}{|\Gamma(\gamma + iy)|} \tag{5.74$'$}$$

and

$$\delta \equiv \delta_\kappa = y \log 2pr - \arg \Gamma(\gamma + iy) + \eta - \tfrac{1}{2}\pi\gamma \tag{5.75}$$

The occurrence of the r-dependent logarithm term is characteristic of the Coulomb field and arises from the slow decrease of $V(r)$. For $\lim rV \to 0$ as $r \to \infty$ it would not appear. This r-dependent phase will not affect any physical results of the Coulomb field alone. For example, it will not appear in interference terms in scattering amplitudes since the log term is independent of κ.

The energy scale normalization fixes N when (5.74) and (5.74′) are compared. The final results are then

$$rf = \frac{i(W-1)^{1/2}(2pr)^\gamma e^{\pi y/2}|\Gamma(\gamma+iy)|}{2(\pi p)^{1/2}\Gamma(2\gamma+1)} \{e^{-ipr+i\eta}(\gamma+iy) \times F(\gamma+1+iy, 2\gamma+1, 2ipr) - \text{c.c.}\} \tag{5.76}$$

$$rg = \frac{(W+1)^{1/2}(2pr)^\gamma e^{\pi y/2}|\Gamma(\gamma+iy)|}{2(\pi p)^{1/2}\Gamma(2\gamma+1)} \{e^{-ipr+i\eta}(\gamma+iy) \times F(\gamma+1+iy, 2\gamma+1, 2ipr) + \text{c.c.}\} \tag{5.77}$$

Since η is defined only to within an additive multiple of π, there is the usual sign ambiguity in f and g, but f/g is unambiguous. The only factor in f_κ and g_κ which depends on the sign of κ is $e^{\pm i\eta}$.

For many purposes, in particular the calculation of radial matrix elements involving f or g, the integral representation of these functions is useful. With the same normalization as in (5.76) and (5.77) we have[5,18]

$$r\begin{Bmatrix} f \\ g \end{Bmatrix} = \begin{Bmatrix} i(W-1)^{1/2} \\ (W+1)^{1/2} \end{Bmatrix} \frac{e^{\pi y/2}(\frac{1}{2}pr)^\gamma}{2(\pi p)^{1/2}|\Gamma(\gamma+iy)|} \times \left[e^{i\eta}\int_{-1}^{+1} e^{iprx}(1-x)^{\gamma-1-iy}(1+x)^{\gamma+iy}\,dx \mp \text{c.c.}\right] \tag{5.77$'$}$$

Expansion of $\exp(iprx)$ and integration term by term give the series solutions again.

The asymptotic behavior of the solution (5.76) and (5.77) is

$$rf = -\left(\frac{W-1}{\pi p}\right)^{1/2} \sin(pr + \delta) \tag{5.78a}$$

$$rg = \left(\frac{W+1}{\pi p}\right)^{1/2} \cos(pr + \delta) \tag{5.78b}$$

where the phase δ is given in (5.75).

Clearly, wherever a physical problem involves emission of electrons into the continuum these wave functions will be important. Examples of their application occur in electron scattering, internal conversion, photoelectric effect, nuclear beta decay, and electron-positron pair formation. They would also be relevant for many other problems which have hitherto been solved only with approximate wave functions. Among these we may mention bremsstrahlung and Auger emission. Approximate wave functions are therefore of some utility and will be discussed in the next chapter. A formal application to scattering will be made later on in this chapter.

It will be recognized that the same weak singularity as appeared in the bound state wave functions occurs in the continuum solutions at $r = 0$ for $j = \frac{1}{2}$. This behavior in both continuum and bound solutions implies a marked modification of the description of processes in which the small r region is important. Internal conversion is a case in point. However, in all such cases it may be necessary to remember that at very small distances the potential energy function is again modified by the effect of the finite size of the nucleus. This problem will also be discussed in the next chapter. Finally, it is of interest to note that screening effects on the continuum solutions are usually less important than for the bound state functions.

As a simple application of the continuum wave functions we consider the density of electrons near the nucleus. A quantity of this sort appears in the beta-decay transition probability. Then, since we are interested in small r, the confluent hypergeometric functions in (5.76) can be set equal to unity. The factor of interest in f^2 or g^2 or both is

$$\xi \equiv e^{\pi y}|\Gamma(\gamma + iy)|^2$$

and we consider this factor ξ for small momentum. Then, since y is large, we use Stirling's approximation[5] and

$$\xi \cong 2\pi e^{\pi y}(\gamma^2 + y^2)^{\gamma - \frac{1}{2}} e^{-2\gamma}(\gamma + iy)^{iy}(\gamma - iy)^{-iy}$$

The product of the last two factors is

$$\begin{aligned}\left(\frac{\gamma + iy}{\gamma - iy}\right)^{iy} &= e^{-2y \arctan y/\gamma} \\ &= e^{-2y(\frac{1}{2}\pi - \gamma/y + \cdots)}\end{aligned}$$

Hence

$$\xi = 2\pi(\gamma^2 + y^2)^{\gamma - \frac{1}{2}}$$

This result applies for electrons. For positrons $|\Gamma(\gamma + iy)|$ is unchanged, but the factor $\exp(\pi y)$ becomes $\exp(-\pi y)$ and we find

$$\xi_{\text{pos}} = e^{-2\pi y}\xi_{\text{el}}$$

Consequently, as $p \to 0$, the number of positrons near the nucleus is very strongly suppressed in comparison with the number of slow electrons. This is evidently an influence of the Coulomb repulsion acting on the former.

If non-relativistic wave functions are used, the value of $\psi^2(0)$, when $\psi^2(\infty)| = 1$, is known to be

$$\frac{2\pi y}{1 - e^{-2\pi y}}$$

for electrons and

$$\frac{2\pi y}{e^{2\pi y} - 1}$$

for positrons ($y = \alpha Z/p$). Again, for $y \to \infty$, the ratio of $|\psi(0)|^2_{\text{pos}}/|\psi(0)|^2_{\text{el}}$ is $\exp(-2\pi y)$, as would be expected.

33. SCATTERING THEORY

The relativistic treatment of the scattering problem was first given by Mott[19] in a famous paper in which he also showed that the electrons are polarized in the process of scattering. The physical origin of this polarization is connected with the spin dependence of the interaction (as evidenced by spin-orbit coupling) which is built into the theory. The analysis of the polarization may then be made by a second scattering, whereupon an azimuthal asymmetry in the scattered intensity appears. Since any asymmetry in a scattering process wherein the wave vector is scattered from $\mathbf{p}$ to $\mathbf{p}'$ must be a scalar of the form $\mathscr{P}\cdot\mathbf{p} \times \mathbf{p}'$, where $\mathscr{P}$ is the polarization vector, it is clear that the polarization must be at least partially transverse. As will be seen, the direction of the polarization is along the normal to the scattering plane, as could be expected on elementary principles of symmetry.

In this section we shall first develop the scattering theory for polarized electrons in a purely formal way. It will be shown then that, in contrast to the spin-independent description, there will be *two* scattering amplitudes corresponding to the two possible orientations of the electron spin. The problem of obtaining an explicit form of these scattering amplitudes will be then taken up for the case of a central field. For the first part of the discussion we shall follow the treatment of Mühlschlegel and Koppe.[20]

As a preparation for the treatment of the scattering problem we first introduce the concept of the density matrix. The present discussion will be only a very brief one; for a more comprehensive treatment the literature may be consulted.[21]

The Density Matrix

When we use a single wave function or, generally, a state vector to describe the electron, there is a tacit assumption that there exists an experiment, designed for example to measure the spin component in some direction, which will give the result $+\frac{1}{2}$ with certainty. For such a pure state the electron polarization is complete: of unit magnitude and of definite direction. Thus any linear combination of plane waves $U_{\pm} \exp(i\mathbf{p}\cdot\mathbf{r})$ not only specifies the momentum and energy uniquely but also diagonalizes $\boldsymbol{\sigma}\cdot\hat{\mathbf{n}}$ for some unit vector $\hat{\mathbf{n}}$. The precise specification of $\hat{\mathbf{n}}$ depends only on the coefficients in the pure state envisaged. However, we must recognize the existence of situations in which this characteristic of maximal information does not apply: Suppose that an electron is emitted from a nucleus in beta decay. In general, one does not perform an experiment in which all observables are measured. For instance, the neutrino (or antineutrino) may not be observed in coincidence; the nuclear magnetic substates are averaged over because the emitter is not prepared in a definite one of the substates nor is the recoil nucleus observed in a definite substate. As a consequence, the electron polarization is less than unity and what is measured is an average value. The mathematical device for performing the average, which is carried out *incoherently*, is the density matrix. The probability for electron emission in some spin state is calculated and the average of this quantity, quadratic in the electron amplitude, is taken. Thus the electron can be thought of as being in an impure state. Alternatively, we deal with an *ensemble* of pure states, each member of the ensemble corresponding, in the example above, to emission with all other physical parameters being simultaneously measured.

The formalism of the density matrix technique is based on the following definition. Consider a pure state Ψ which is expanded into a set of basic states ψ_n:

$$\Psi = \sum_n c_n \psi_n \tag{5.79}$$

Then any observable represented by an operator Ω has the average value

$$(\Psi|\Omega|\Psi) = \sum_{nn'} \Omega_{n'n} c_{n'}^{\times} c_n$$

where $\Omega_{n'n}$ are the matrix elements of Ω in the ψ basis. Now we consider an impure state. The *ensemble* average of Ω is

$$\langle\Omega\rangle = \sum_i q_i (\Psi^{(i)}|\Omega|\Psi^{(i)})$$

where q_i is the probability, or statistical weight, that corresponds to any one of the pure states $\Psi^{(i)}$. The latter are different states of the form (5.79).

It is evident that

$$\langle\Omega\rangle = \sum_{nn'} \Omega_{n'n} \sum_i q_i c_{n'}^{(i)\times} c_n^{(i)}$$

where $c_n^{(i)}$ are the expansion coefficients of $\Psi^{(i)}$ in the ψ_n basis. If the matrix ρ is defined by

$$\rho_{nn'} = \sum_i q_i c_{n'}^{(i)\times} c_n^{(i)}$$

we may write

$$\langle\Omega\rangle = \sum_{nn'} \Omega_{n'n} \rho_{nn'} = \mathrm{Tr}\,(\Omega\rho) \tag{5.80}$$

The density matrix ρ is defined by Eq. (5.80). Obviously, it depends in a quadratic way on the amplitudes $c_n^{(i)}$ and linearly on the probability parameters q_i.

Some relevant properties of ρ are:

(i) In order that $\langle\Omega\rangle$ be real when Ω is hermitian, it is necessary that ρ be hermitian:

$$\rho_{nn'} = \rho_{n'n}^{\times} \tag{5.80a}$$

(ii) When $\Omega = 1$ we must require that $\langle\Omega\rangle = 1$. Hence

$$\mathrm{Tr}\,\rho = 1 \tag{5.80b}$$

(iii) If Ω is diagonal with $\Omega_{nn} \geqslant 0$, we must require that $\langle\Omega\rangle \geqslant 0$. Hence all diagonal elements of ρ are non-negative:

$$\rho_{nn} \geqslant 0 \tag{5.80c}$$

Suppose that

$$c_n^{(i)} = \delta_{ni}$$

corresponding to $\Psi_i = \psi_i$. Then

$$\rho_{nn'} = \delta_{nn'} q_n \tag{5.80d}$$

which says that ρ is diagonal and its elements are the probabilities for finding the system in one of the base states. Consequently, $\mathrm{Tr}\,\rho = 1$ is the usual normalization for the probability parameters.

(iv) If ρ is brought to diagonal form by a unitary transformation which does not change $\mathrm{Tr}\,\rho$, we see that $(\rho_n \equiv \rho_{nn})$:

$$\mathrm{Tr}\,\rho^2 = \sum_n \rho_n^2 \leqslant \left(\sum_n \rho_n\right)^2 = (\mathrm{Tr}\,\rho)^2 = 1 \tag{5.80e}$$

Thus $\mathrm{Tr}\,\rho^2 \leqslant 1$ and each element $\rho_{nn'}$ has a square modulus equal to or less than unity.

There is a relation between ρ and the projection operators discussed in section 19. Suppose that $\langle\Omega\rangle$ is equal to the expectation value of Ω. Then

$$\langle\Omega\rangle = \Psi^*\Omega\Psi = \sum_{\sigma\lambda} \Psi_\sigma^\times \Omega_{\sigma\lambda}\Psi_\lambda$$

where the spinor index summation is now explicitly indicated. It follows then that

$$\langle\Omega\rangle = \sum_{\sigma\lambda} \Omega_{\sigma\lambda}P_{\lambda\sigma} = \text{Tr}\ \Omega P$$

where P is the projection operator: $P_{\lambda\sigma} = \Psi_\lambda\Psi_\sigma^\times$ as before. Therefore in this case the density matrix and projection operator are the same. This case corresponds to complete polarization, $\mathscr{P} = 1$. If the average polarization vector is $\boldsymbol{\mathscr{P}}$, where $\mathscr{P} < 1$, the density matrix can be obtained from the projection operator by replacing the *unit* vector $\boldsymbol{\mathscr{P}}$ by the average polarization vector. Thus for the non-relativistic case the density matrix is

$$\rho_0(\boldsymbol{\mathscr{P}}) = \tfrac{1}{2}(1 + \boldsymbol{\mathscr{P}}\cdot\boldsymbol{\sigma}), \qquad \mathscr{P}^2 < 1 \tag{5.81}$$

This satisfies all four conditions (5.80a, b, c, e). Thus

$$\rho = \rho^*; \quad \text{Tr}\ \rho = 1; \quad \rho_{\frac{1}{2}\frac{1}{2}} = \tfrac{1}{2}(1 + \mathscr{P}_z), \quad \rho_{-\frac{1}{2}-\frac{1}{2}} = \tfrac{1}{2}(1 - \mathscr{P}_z)$$

The latter two elements of ρ are both less than unity and positive; $\text{Tr}\ \rho^2 = \text{Tr}\ \tfrac{1}{4}(1 + \mathscr{P}^2 + 2\boldsymbol{\mathscr{P}}\cdot\boldsymbol{\sigma}) = \tfrac{1}{2}(1 + \mathscr{P}^2) < 1$.

For the relativistic electron the density matrix corresponding to momentum, or wave vector, equal to $\mathbf{p}$ and polarization $\boldsymbol{\mathscr{P}}$ will be obtained in a similar way from (3.61).

$$\rho(\mathbf{p}, \boldsymbol{\mathscr{P}}) = \frac{2p_0}{p_0 + 1} P_+(\mathbf{p})\tfrac{1}{2}(1 + \beta)\rho_0(\boldsymbol{\mathscr{P}})\tfrac{1}{2}(1 + \beta)P_+(\mathbf{p}) \tag{5.82}$$

where

$$P_+(\mathbf{p}) = \frac{1}{2}\left(1 + \frac{\boldsymbol{\alpha}\cdot\mathbf{p} + \beta}{p_0}\right)$$

is the positive energy projection operator. In the same way as before, when we considered $\rho_0(\boldsymbol{\mathscr{P}})$, it may be verified that the four fundamental properties are indeed satisfied.†

Formal Theory of Scattering of Polarized Electrons

We consider an elastic scattering process in which $\mathbf{p}$ and $\boldsymbol{\mathscr{P}}$ describe the initial state and $\mathbf{p}'$ and $\boldsymbol{\mathscr{P}}'$ describe the final state. The cross section per unit solid angle for this process will be denoted by $\sigma(\mathbf{p}', \mathbf{p}, \boldsymbol{\mathscr{P}})$.

† For instance, to verify that ρ is hermitian it is sufficient to observe that $\rho_0(\boldsymbol{\mathscr{P}})$ and $\tfrac{1}{2}(1 + \beta)$ commute.

We define a transition amplitude $A(\mathbf{p}', \mathbf{p})$ by

$$\sigma(\mathbf{p}', \mathbf{p}, \mathscr{P})\, \rho_0(\mathscr{P}') = A(\mathbf{p}', \mathbf{p})\, \rho_0(\mathscr{P})\, A^*(\mathbf{p}', \mathbf{p}) \tag{5.83}$$

From this definition it appears that A is a 2 by 2 matrix. In part, the succeeding development will explain why this is the relevant transition amplitude even though the scattering of a Dirac electron would seem to involve four by four matrices. Our eventual purpose is to define A explicitly (for example, in terms of phase shifts) and to relate σ and $\mathscr{P}'$ to A.

The solution of the scattering problem leads to a wave function which has the asymptotic form†

$$\psi = a(\mathbf{p}) \exp(i\mathbf{p}\cdot\mathbf{r}) + b(\mathbf{p}') \frac{\exp ipr}{r} \tag{5.84}$$

Here a and b are four-component spinors. We define $T(\mathbf{p}', \mathbf{p})$ by

$$b(\mathbf{p}') = T(\mathbf{p}', \mathbf{p})\, a(\mathbf{p}) \tag{5.85}$$

so that T transforms the incident amplitude to the amplitude of the outgoing wave. The cross section in (5.83) is

$$\sigma = b^*b \tag{5.86}$$

The density matrix for the incident beam is $\rho(\mathbf{p}, \mathscr{P})$ as given in (5.82). It is constructed from the incident wave amplitudes $a(\mathbf{p})$ as shown in section 19. Thus

$$\rho_{\sigma\lambda}(\mathbf{p}, \mathscr{P}) = a_\sigma a_\lambda^\times \tag{5.87a}$$

Although the notation does not explicitly indicate it, the fact is that a must also depend on the direction of $\mathscr{P}$. For the final state density matrix we must use $\rho(\mathbf{p}', \mathscr{P}')$, and this is constructed in a similar way from the b amplitudes. We write

$$\rho_{\sigma\lambda}(\mathbf{p}', \mathscr{P}') = \mathscr{N} b_\sigma b_\lambda^\times \tag{5.87b}$$

where $\mathscr{N}$ is a normalization factor chosen to make $\operatorname{Tr} \rho = 1$. From (5.85),

$$\begin{aligned} \mathscr{N}^{-1} \rho_{\sigma\lambda}(\mathbf{p}', \mathscr{P}') &= [T(\mathbf{p}', \mathbf{p})\, a(\mathbf{p})]_\sigma [T(\mathbf{p}', \mathbf{p})\, a(\mathbf{p})]_\lambda^\times \\ &= [T\rho(\mathbf{p}, \mathscr{P})T^*]_{\sigma\lambda} \end{aligned} \tag{5.87c}$$

Hence

$$\sigma = b^*b = b_\lambda b_\lambda^\times = \mathscr{N}^{-1} \operatorname{Tr} \rho$$

Therefore

$$\mathscr{N}^{-1} = \sigma(\mathbf{p}', \mathbf{p}, \mathscr{P})$$

and (5.87b) reads

$$\sigma(\mathbf{p}', \mathbf{p}, \mathscr{P})\, \rho(\mathbf{p}', \mathscr{P}') = b \times b^* = T(\mathbf{p}', \mathbf{p})\, \rho(\mathbf{p}, \mathscr{P})\, T^*(\mathbf{p}', \mathbf{p})$$

† There is no loss of generality in omitting the *explicit* appearance of a possible logarithmic term in the phase of incident or scattered wave.

Making use of the identity

$$P_+(\mathbf{p}')\,\rho(\mathbf{p}',\mathscr{P}')\,P_+(\mathbf{p}') = \rho(\mathbf{p}',\mathscr{P}')$$

we find that

$$\sigma(\mathbf{p}',\mathbf{p},\mathscr{P})\,\rho(\mathbf{p}',\mathscr{P}') = P_+(\mathbf{p}')\,T(\mathbf{p}',\mathbf{p})\,\rho(\mathbf{p},\mathscr{P})\,T^*(\mathbf{p}',\mathbf{p})\,P_+(\mathbf{p}') \quad (5.88)$$

Substituting (5.82) into (5.88) and writing $\rho(\mathbf{p}',\mathscr{P}')$ in the form (5.82) with primed variables ($p_0' = p_0$), we obtain

$$\begin{aligned}P_+(\mathbf{p}')\,T(\mathbf{p}',\mathbf{p})\,P_+(\mathbf{p})(1+\beta)\,\rho_0(\mathscr{P})(1+\beta)\,P_+(\mathbf{p})\,T^*(\mathbf{p}',\mathbf{p})\,P_+(\mathbf{p}')\\ = \sigma(\mathbf{p}',\mathbf{p},\mathscr{P})\,P_+(\mathbf{p}')(1+\beta)\,\rho_0(\mathscr{P}')(1+\beta)\,P_+(\mathbf{p}') \quad (5.89)\end{aligned}$$

We now multiply (5.83) on the left by $P_+(\mathbf{p}')(1+\beta)$ and on the right by $(1+\beta)P_+(\mathbf{p}')$ to obtain

$$\begin{aligned}\sigma(\mathbf{p}',\mathbf{p},\mathscr{P})\,P_+(\mathbf{p}')(1+\beta)\,\rho_0(\mathscr{P}')(1+\beta)\,P_+(\mathbf{p}')\\ = P_+(\mathbf{p}')(1+\beta)A\,\rho_0(\mathscr{P})A^*(1+\beta)\,P_+(\mathbf{p}') \quad (5.90)\end{aligned}$$

The right side of (5.89) and the left side of (5.90) are identical. Therefore we equate the remaining members to get a relation between A and T. This relation has the form

$$A = \tfrac{1}{4}|\eta(p_0)|^2(1+\beta)\,P_+(\mathbf{p}')\,T(\mathbf{p}',\mathbf{p})\,P_+(\mathbf{p})(1+\beta) \quad (5.91)$$

where the constant $|\eta|^2$ is to be fixed. Then we obtain a result

$$\begin{aligned}P_+(\mathbf{p}')T(\mathbf{p}',\mathbf{p})\,P_+(\mathbf{p})(1+\beta)\,\rho_0(\mathscr{P})(1+\beta)P_+(\mathbf{p})\,T^*(\mathbf{p}',\mathbf{p})P_+(\mathbf{p}')\\ = \tfrac{1}{4}|\eta|^4 P_+(\mathbf{p}')(1+\beta)P_+(\mathbf{p}')\,T(\mathbf{p}',\mathbf{p})P_+(\mathbf{p})(1+\beta)\,\rho_0(\mathscr{P})(1+\beta)\\ \times P_+(\mathbf{p})\,T^*(\mathbf{p}',\mathbf{p})P_+(\mathbf{p}')(1+\beta)P_+(\mathbf{p}') \quad (5.92)\end{aligned}$$

This is simplified by use of the identity

$$\frac{1}{2}\,P_+(\mathbf{p}')(1+\beta)\,P_+(\mathbf{p}') = \frac{p_0+1}{2p_0}\,P_+(\mathbf{p}') \quad (5.92')$$

Then the two sides of (5.92) are equal if

$$|\eta|^2 = \frac{2p_0}{p_0+1}$$

Substituting this in (5.91) fixes A in terms of T. To obtain the interpretation of A we see that

$$b = Ta = P_+(\mathbf{p}')b = P_+(\mathbf{p}')Ta$$

since b is a positive energy amplitude for which $P_+(\mathbf{p}')$ has the eigenvalue 1. From this it follows that

$$\tfrac{1}{2}(1 + \beta)b = \tfrac{1}{2}(1 + \beta)\, P_+(\mathbf{p}')Ta$$

But

$$a = P_+(\mathbf{p})a = \frac{2p_0}{p_0 + 1}\, P_+(\mathbf{p})[\tfrac{1}{2}(1 + \beta)]^2 a$$

where the last equality follows by use of the identity (5.92′) wherein $\mathbf{p}$ is substituted for $\mathbf{p}'$. As a consequence of this last result we may write

$$\tfrac{1}{2}(1 + \beta)b = \left[\frac{2p_0}{p_0 + 1}\,\frac{1}{2}(1 + \beta)\, P_+(\mathbf{p}')\, T(\mathbf{p}', \mathbf{p})\, P_+(\mathbf{p})\,\frac{1}{2}(1 + \beta)\right]\tfrac{1}{2}(1 + \beta)a$$

The quantity in the square brackets is A. Hence

$$\tfrac{1}{2}(1 + \beta)b = A\tfrac{1}{2}(1 + \beta)a \tag{5.93}$$

This means that A transforms the *large* components of the incident wave amplitude into the *large* components of the outgoing wave amplitude. It follows that the scattering is completely described by the manner in which the large components are influenced by the scattering field. When this part of the incident and outgoing waves is specified, the small components are automatically correctly adjusted. This is a consequence of the fact that in the asymptotic wave function the amplitudes are those corresponding to essentially plane waves for which the small components are determined in a specified and simple way from the large ones.

From (5.83) it follows that

$$\sigma(\mathbf{p}', \mathbf{p}, \mathscr{P}) = \mathrm{Tr}\, A\, \rho_0(\mathscr{P})A^* \tag{5.94}$$

and

$$\mathscr{P}' = \frac{\mathrm{Tr}\, \boldsymbol{\sigma} A\, \rho_0(\mathscr{P})A^*}{\mathrm{Tr}\, A\, \rho_0(\mathscr{P})A^*} \tag{5.95}$$

Both σ and $\mathscr{P}'$ are therefore fixed from a knowledge of A which is forthcoming from a detailed analysis of the scattering process. However, it is clear that A, a 2 by 2 matrix, must have the form $F + G\hat{\mathbf{n}}\cdot\boldsymbol{\sigma}$, where $\hat{\mathbf{n}}$ is conveniently taken to be a unit vector. From a symmetry consideration $\hat{\mathbf{n}}$ must lie in the direction of the normal to the scattering plane because, as will be evident, for an initially unpolarized beam $\mathscr{P}'$ is parallel to $\hat{\mathbf{n}}$ and no other direction is uniquely defined. We take

$$\hat{\mathbf{n}} = \frac{\mathbf{p} \times \mathbf{p}'}{|\mathbf{p} \times \mathbf{p}'|}$$

In Fig. 5.8, $\hat{\mathbf{n}}$ points into the plane of the paper for the first scattering and out of this plane for the second scattering if the scattered particle proceeds along the vector there labeled **p**.

From (5.94) we find for the cross section

$$\sigma(\mathbf{p}', \mathbf{p}, \mathscr{P}) = |F|^2 + |G|^2 + (F^\times G + G^\times F)\mathscr{P}\cdot\hat{\mathbf{n}} \tag{5.96}$$

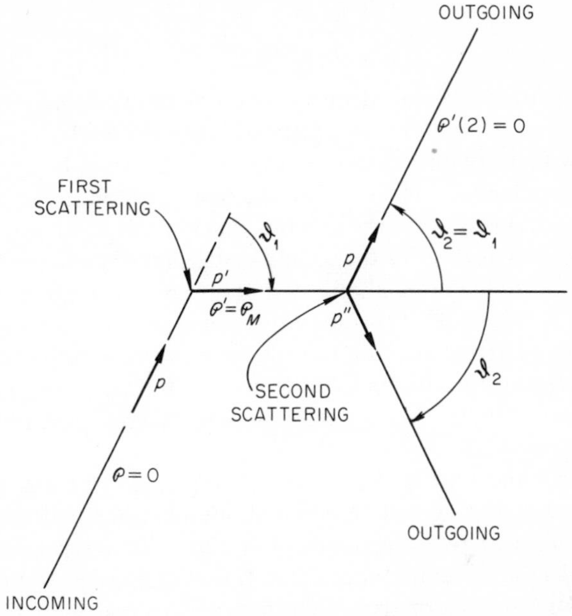

Figure 5.8 Schematic diagram illustrating double scattering. The outgoing momentum **p** is parallel to the incoming momentum **p**. The outgoing momentum **p**$''$ makes the same angle with **p**$'$ as does the outgoing momentum **p**.

The scattered intensity is therefore dependent on the initial polarization if this does not lie in the scattering plane. For the polarization after scattering a somewhat lengthier but simple calculation gives

$$\sigma(\mathbf{p}', \mathbf{p}, \mathscr{P})\mathscr{P}' = \hat{\mathbf{n}}(FG^\times + GF^\times + 2\mathscr{P}\cdot\hat{\mathbf{n}}|G|^2) + \mathscr{P}(|F|^2 - |G|^2) + i\mathscr{P} \times \hat{\mathbf{n}}(FG^\times - GF^\times) \tag{5.97}$$

If the initial beam is unpolarized, $\mathscr{P} = 0$ and then after the scattering the polarization is

$$\mathscr{P}' = \mathscr{P}_M = \frac{FG^\times + GF^\times}{|F|^2 + |G|^2}\hat{\mathbf{n}} \tag{5.97a}$$

This is the Mott polarization.[22] It is along $\hat{\mathbf{n}}$ as stated above.

There are some convenient relations which can be derived from (5.79a). For instance,

$$1 - \mathscr{P}'^2 = \frac{(1 - \mathscr{P}_M^2)(1 - \mathscr{P}^2)}{(1 + \mathscr{P}_M\cdot\mathscr{P})^2} \tag{5.97b}$$

may be verified by direct substitution. Also

$$\hat{\mathbf{n}}\cdot\mathscr{P}' = \frac{\hat{\mathbf{n}}\cdot(\mathscr{P} + \mathscr{P}_M)}{1 + \mathscr{P}_M\cdot\mathscr{P}} \tag{5.97c}$$

From these equations we can deduce some interesting consequences. If $\mathscr{P} = -\mathscr{P}_M$, then $\mathscr{P}' = 0$, or the scattered beam is unpolarized. Figure 5.8 shows how this situation could be realized. The beam before the first scattering is unpolarized, and so after the first scattering it is polarized with $\mathscr{P} = \mathscr{P}_M$. This $\mathscr{P}_M$ points into the plane of the paper and depends on the scattering angle ϑ_1. For the second scattering, wherein the outgoing particle is parallel to the original direction of motion, the original polarization is $-\mathscr{P}_M(2)$, where $\mathscr{P}_M(2)$ is the Mott polarization that would ensue if an initially unpolarized electron were scattered from $\mathbf{p}'$ to $\mathbf{p}$ for which $\hat{\mathbf{n}}$ has the *opposite* direction to the $\hat{\mathbf{n}}$ of the first scattering. Hence, after the two scatterings, both the wave vector and the (zero) polarization are unchanged.

On the other hand, in Fig. 5.8, the scattering *intensity* along $\mathbf{p}$ and $\mathbf{p}''$ after the second scattering will be different, although the scattering angle is the same for these two directions. For this it is not necessary that $\vartheta_1 = \vartheta_2$. We denote the amplitudes F and G at $\vartheta = \vartheta_i$ by F_i and G_i. Also $\hat{\mathbf{n}}_1$ and $\hat{\mathbf{n}}_2$ are the unit normals for the first and second scattering. For instance, if $\mathbf{p}_0$ is the initial wave vector,

$$\hat{\mathbf{n}}_1 = \frac{\mathbf{p}_0 \times \mathbf{p}'}{|\mathbf{p}_0 \times \mathbf{p}'|}$$

while

$$\hat{\mathbf{n}}_2 = \frac{\mathbf{p}' \times \mathbf{p}}{|\mathbf{p}' \times \mathbf{p}|}$$

for scattering into the direction $\mathbf{p}$ and

$$\hat{\mathbf{n}}_2 = \frac{\mathbf{p}' \times \mathbf{p}''}{|\mathbf{p}' \times \mathbf{p}''|}$$

for scattering into $\mathbf{p}''$. Thus $\hat{\mathbf{n}}_1\cdot\hat{\mathbf{n}}_2$ is -1 in the first case and $+1$ in the second. Then after two scatterings we find, from (5.96) and (5.97a),

$$\sigma = |F_2|^2 + |G_2|^2 \pm \frac{(F_2G_2^\times + F_2^\times G_2)(F_1G_1^\times + F_1^\times G_1)}{|F_1|^2 + |G_1|^2} \tag{5.98}$$

where $\pm$ is the value of $\hat{\mathbf{n}}_1 \cdot \hat{\mathbf{n}}_2$. This is the well-known analysis of polarization by double scattering.[22] Of course, it is now known that it is unnecessary to scatter electrons in order to polarize them. Electrons emitted in beta decay are polarized, and it is important to measure this polarization. If an analysis of the polarization of beta particles is to be made, it can be done in single scattering by comparing the intensity along two directions with the same scattering angle. Thus, in the notation of Fig. 5.8, the relative difference of intensity along $\mathbf{p}$ and $\mathbf{p}''$ is

$$\frac{\sigma(\mathbf{p}'') - \sigma(\mathbf{p})}{\sigma(\mathbf{p}'') + \sigma(\mathbf{p})} = \frac{FG^\times + F^\times G}{|F|^2 + |G|^2}\, \mathscr{P} \cdot \hat{\mathbf{n}} \tag{5.99}$$

where $\mathscr{P}$ is the polarization in the incident beam and

$$\hat{\mathbf{n}} = \frac{\mathbf{p}_{\text{inc}} \times \mathbf{p}''}{|\mathbf{p}_{\text{inc}} \times \mathbf{p}''|}$$

This measures only the polarization component along $\hat{\mathbf{n}}$, but this direction may obviously be varied at will.

From (5.97b) we see that a completely polarized beam remains completely polarized after scattering although the direction of the polarization may change. If conditions are chosen so that

$$\mathscr{P}_M \cdot \mathscr{P} \geqslant -[1 - (1 - \mathscr{P}_M^2)]^{1/2}$$

or

$$\mathscr{P} \cdot \hat{\mathbf{n}} \geqslant -\frac{1 - (1 - \mathscr{P}_M^2)^{1/2}}{\mathscr{P}_M}$$

then the polarization after scattering is at least as great as the incident polarization but, of course, $\mathscr{P}' \leqslant 1$ always. Finally, we notice that the incident and final polarization are parallel (or antiparallel) only if the initial polarization is completely transverse, that is, $\mathscr{P} \times \hat{\mathbf{n}} = 0$.

The Scattering Amplitudes

The formal solution of the scattering problem is complete when the scattering amplitudes F and G are expressed in calculable form. We do this for an arbitrary central field. The starting point is the expansion of the plane wave into spherical waves carried out in section 27, Eqs. (5.13) and (5.14). In this expansion we shall make the following changes: First, since there should be no confusion between positive and negative energy states, we shall write $p_0 = W$ throughout. Second, we shall consider a superposition of the two basic plane wave states. This means that we must replace χ^m in the plane wave by

$$\sum_m c_m \chi^m$$

where $c_{1/2}$ and $c_{-1/2}$ are arbitrary constants. Third, for convenience we change the normalization of ψ_κ^μ as defined by (5.12) so that the amplitudes at $r \to \infty$ are the same as those given for the Coulomb field in (5.78). That is, we normalize the free particle spherical wave solutions in the energy scale. These renormalized solutions are denoted by $\psi_\kappa^\mu(0)$, to emphasize that they are free particle solutions, and

$$\psi_\kappa^\mu(0) = \left[\frac{p(W+1)}{\pi}\right]^{1/2} \begin{pmatrix} j_l \chi_\kappa^\mu \\ \dfrac{ip}{W+1} S_\kappa j_{\bar{l}} \chi_{-\kappa}^\mu \end{pmatrix} \tag{5.100}$$

The asymptotic behavior may be checked by noting that

$$x j_l(x) \to \cos\left(x - \frac{l+1}{2}\pi\right)$$

$$x j_{\bar{l}}(x) \to -S_\kappa \sin\left(x - \frac{l+1}{2}\pi\right)$$

Thus, for $Z = 0$, the phase $\delta = \delta_\kappa(0)$ is

$$\delta_\kappa(0) = -\frac{l+1}{2}\pi$$

and a definite choice of phase has already been made in (5.12). Since the Coulomb phase shift must reduce to this for $Z = 0$ we observe, with

$$\cos 2\eta = -\frac{\kappa\gamma + y^2/W}{\gamma^2 + y^2}$$

$$\sin 2\eta = \frac{y(\kappa + y/W)}{\gamma^2 + y^2}$$

that η is in the third quadrant for $\kappa > 0$ and in the first quadrant for $\kappa < 0$.

With these changes the expansion of the plane wave is

$$\psi_{pl} = 4\pi\left(\frac{\pi}{2Wp}\right)^{1/2} \sum_{\kappa\mu}\sum_{m} c_m i^l\, C(l\tfrac{1}{2}j;\mu - m, m)\, Y_l^{\mu-m\,\times}(\hat{\mathbf{p}})\, \psi_\kappa^\mu(0) \tag{5.101}$$

For the Coulomb field we require a solution which has the asymptotic behavior†

$$\psi \to \psi_{pl} + \frac{b}{r} e^{i(pr + y\log 2pr)}$$

so that it is asymptotically a plane wave plus *outgoing* waves.

† For fields falling faster than the Coulomb field the logarithmic term is omitted.

For ψ we write

$$\psi = 4\pi\left(\frac{\pi}{2Wp}\right)^{1/2} \sum_{\kappa\mu}\sum_{m} s_\kappa c_m i^l\, C(l\tfrac{1}{2}j;\mu - m,m)\; Y_l^{\mu-m\,*}(\hat{\mathbf{p}})\; \psi_\kappa^\mu \qquad (5.102)$$

where ψ_κ^μ is defined by (5.3) with f and g given by the Coulomb radial functions (5.76) and (5.77). The argument of $\chi_{\pm\kappa}^\mu$ in ψ_κ^μ is the unit vector $\hat{\mathbf{r}}$ which is in the direction of observation: that is, $\hat{\mathbf{r}} = \hat{\mathbf{p}}'$, the unit vector in the direction of scattering. The constants s_κ are fixed so that the required asymptotic behavior is obtained. Using (5.78), we find that

$$s_\kappa = e^{i\delta'_\kappa} \qquad (5.102')$$

where

$$\delta'_\kappa = \eta - \tfrac{1}{2}\pi\gamma - \arg\Gamma(\gamma + iy) + \tfrac{1}{2}(l + 1)\pi \qquad (5.103)$$

That is, δ'_κ is the difference between the Coulomb phase shift exclusive of the logarithmic term and the $Z = 0$ phase shift $\delta_\kappa(0)$. It is therefore the additional phase due to the Coulomb field. For a different central field the phase δ'_κ has a similar definition but a different value, of course. It is only in these phase shifts that the detailed structure of the central field enters. With this value of s_κ the amplitude of the outgoing wave is obtained immediately. Writing only the relevant large components, we find

$$\begin{aligned}
\tfrac{1}{2}(1 + \beta)b &= -\frac{2\pi i}{p}\left(\frac{W + 1}{2W}\right)^{1/2} \sum_{\kappa\mu}\sum_{m} c_m(e^{2i\delta'_\kappa} - 1)\, C(l\tfrac{1}{2}j;\mu - m,m) \\
&\quad \times Y_l^{\mu-m\,*}(\hat{\mathbf{p}})\, \chi_\kappa^\mu(\hat{\mathbf{p}}') \\
&= -\frac{2\pi i}{p}\left(\frac{W + 1}{2W}\right)^{1/2} \sum_{\kappa\mu}\sum_{m\tau} c_m(e^{2i\delta'_\kappa} - 1)\, C(l\tfrac{1}{2}j;\mu - m,m) \\
&\quad \times C(l\tfrac{1}{2}j;\mu - \tau,\tau)\, Y_l^{\mu-m\,*}(\hat{\mathbf{p}})\, Y_l^{\mu-\tau}(\hat{\mathbf{p}}')\chi^\tau
\end{aligned} \qquad (5.104)$$

wherein $i^l e^{i\delta_\kappa(0)} = -i$ has been used. We may simplify this result by choosing the z-axis along the direction of the incident beam. Then, since

$$Y_l^{\mu-m\,*}(\hat{\mathbf{p}}) \to \left(\frac{2l + 1}{4\pi}\right)^{1/2} \delta_{\mu m}$$

we can write

$$\tfrac{1}{2}(1 + \beta)b = \left(\frac{W + 1}{2W}\right)^{1/2} \sum_{m\tau} c_m B_\tau^m \chi^\tau \qquad (5.105)$$

where

$$B_\tau^m = -\frac{i\pi^{1/2}}{p} \sum_\kappa (e^{2i\delta'_\kappa} - 1)(2l + 1)^{1/2}\, C(l\tfrac{1}{2}j;0m)\, C(l\tfrac{1}{2}j;m - \tau,\tau)\, Y_l^{m-\tau}(\hat{\mathbf{p}}') \qquad (5.106)$$

The transition amplitude A of the previous section is then obtained from

$$\sum_{m\tau} c_m B^m_\tau \chi^\tau = A \sum_m c_m \chi^m$$

Therefore

$$A = \begin{pmatrix} B^{1/2}_{1/2} & B^{-1/2}_{1/2} \\ B^{1/2}_{-1/2} & B^{-1/2}_{-1/2} \end{pmatrix} = F + G\boldsymbol{\sigma}\cdot\hat{\mathbf{n}}'$$

where $\hat{\mathbf{n}}'$ is to be determined. We write

$$\mathbf{G} = G\hat{\mathbf{n}}'$$

and

$$A = \begin{pmatrix} F + G_z & G_- \\ G_+ & F - G_z \end{pmatrix}$$

where $G_\pm = G_x \pm iG_y$. Consequently,

$$F = \tfrac{1}{2}(B^{1/2}_{1/2} + B^{-1/2}_{-1/2})$$

$$G_z = \tfrac{1}{2}(B^{1/2}_{1/2} - B^{-1/2}_{-1/2})$$

$$G_+ = B^{1/2}_{-1/2}, \qquad G_- = B^{-1/2}_{1/2}$$

For $\hat{\mathbf{p}} = \hat{\mathbf{e}}_z$, a unit vector along the z-axis, and

$$\hat{\mathbf{p}}' = \hat{\mathbf{e}}_x \sin\vartheta \cos\varphi + \hat{\mathbf{e}}_y \sin\vartheta \sin\varphi + \hat{\mathbf{e}}_z \cos\vartheta$$

we find

$$\hat{\mathbf{p}} \times \hat{\mathbf{p}}' = \hat{\mathbf{e}}_y \sin\vartheta \cos\varphi - \hat{\mathbf{e}}_x \sin\vartheta \sin\varphi$$

With

$$\hat{\mathbf{n}} = \frac{\hat{\mathbf{p}} \times \hat{\mathbf{p}}'}{|\hat{\mathbf{p}} \times \hat{\mathbf{p}}'|}$$

we see that

$$\hat{n}_z = 0, \qquad \hat{n}_x = -\sin\varphi, \qquad \hat{n}_y = \cos\varphi$$

Therefore

$$\hat{n}_\pm = \pm i e^{\pm i\varphi}$$

We can now determine the direction of $\hat{\mathbf{n}}'$ relative to $\hat{\mathbf{n}}$. First the component G_z is evaluated. This gives a sum of two terms:

$$\{[C(l\tfrac{1}{2}j; 0,\tfrac{1}{2})]^2 - C(l\tfrac{1}{2}j; 0,-\tfrac{1}{2})]^2\}\, Y^0_l(\hat{\mathbf{p}}')$$

Using the relation

$$C(l\tfrac{1}{2}j; m_1,m_2) = (-)^{l+1/2-j}\, C(l\tfrac{1}{2}j; -m_1,-m_2)$$

we see that $G_z = 0$. Next we evaluate

$$\frac{\hat{n}'_+}{\hat{n}'_-} = \frac{G_+}{G_-} = \frac{B^{1/2}_{-1/2}}{B^{-1/2}_{1/2}} = \frac{\sum_\kappa \cdots C(l\tfrac{1}{2}j; 0,\tfrac{1}{2})\, C(l\tfrac{1}{2}j; 1,-\tfrac{1}{2})\, Y^1_l(\hat{\mathbf{p}}')}{\sum_\kappa \cdots C(l\tfrac{1}{2}j; 0,-\tfrac{1}{2})\, C(l\tfrac{1}{2}j; -1,\tfrac{1}{2})\, Y_l^{-1}(\hat{\mathbf{p}}')}$$

Here the dots indicate factors, depending only on κ, which are the same in numerator and denominator. Using the relation between C-coefficients just given above, we see that the product of these coefficients is the same in numerator and denominator. From the definition (1.48) of the spherical harmonics,

$$Y_l^m = \left[\frac{2l+1}{4\pi}\frac{(l-m)!}{(l+m)!}\right]^{1/2}(-)^m e^{im\varphi}\, P_l^m(\cos\vartheta)$$

where P_l^m is the associated Legendre function. From $Y_l^{m\times} = (-)^m Y_l^{-m}$ we deduce that

$$Y_l^1 = -e^{2i\varphi}Y_l^{-1}$$

and hence

$$\frac{\hat{n}'_+}{\hat{n}'_-} = -e^{2i\varphi} = \frac{\hat{n}_+}{\hat{n}_-}$$

This demonstrates that $\hat{\mathbf{n}}$ and $\hat{\mathbf{n}}'$ are either parallel ($\hat{\mathbf{n}}' = \hat{\mathbf{n}}$) or antiparallel ($\hat{\mathbf{n}}' = -\hat{\mathbf{n}}$). As a matter of definition we can take $\hat{\mathbf{n}}' = \hat{\mathbf{n}}$, since $G\hat{\mathbf{n}}'$ is unaffected by the choice we make.

For the scattering amplitudes we obtain

$$F = -\frac{i}{4p}\sum_\kappa (e^{2i\delta'_\kappa} - 1)(2l+1)\, P_l(\cos\vartheta) \sum_\tau [C(l\tfrac{1}{2}j;\, 0\tau)]^2$$

$$= -\frac{i}{4p}\sum_\kappa (e^{2i\delta'_\kappa} - 1)(2l+1)\, P_l(\cos\vartheta) \tag{5.107}$$

by (1.57). For G we find, from $G = -ie^{-i\varphi}G_+$,

$$G = -ie^{-i\varphi}B^{1/2}_{-1/2}$$

$$= -\frac{e^{-i\varphi}}{p}\pi^{1/2}\sum_\kappa (e^{2i\delta'_\kappa} - 1)(2l+1)^{1/2}\, C(l\tfrac{1}{2}j;\, 0\tfrac{1}{2})\, C(l\tfrac{1}{2}j;\, 1, -\tfrac{1}{2})\, Y_l^1(\hat{\mathbf{p}}')$$

From (1.59),

$$C(l\tfrac{1}{2}j;\, 0\tfrac{1}{2})\, C(l\tfrac{1}{2}j;\, 1, -\tfrac{1}{2}) = -S_\kappa \frac{[l(l+1)]^{1/2}}{2l+1}$$

Using this and

$$Y_l^1(\hat{\mathbf{p}}') = -\left[\frac{2l+1}{4\pi}\frac{1}{l(l+1)}\right]^{1/2} e^{i\varphi}\, P_l^1(\cos\vartheta)$$

the result for G becomes

$$G = -\frac{1}{2p}\sum_\kappa S_\kappa (e^{2i\delta'_\kappa} - 1)\, P_l^1(\cos\vartheta) \tag{5.108}$$

Equations (5.107) and (5.108) [with (5.103) for the Coulomb field] complete the formal solution of the scattering problem. In order to obtain specific results, numerical procedures are necessary in general. Without attempting an exhaustive survey of the literature, mention may be made of the calculations of Bartlett and Watson[23] for Hg and of Bartlett and Welton,[24] also for Hg, in which screening is taken into account by straightforward numerical calculation and by using various approximation methods. More recently Sherman[25] has given numerical results for Hg, Cd, and Al for the unscreened field. Additional numerical values for cross sections have been given by Doggett and Spencer[26] for $Z = 6$, 13,

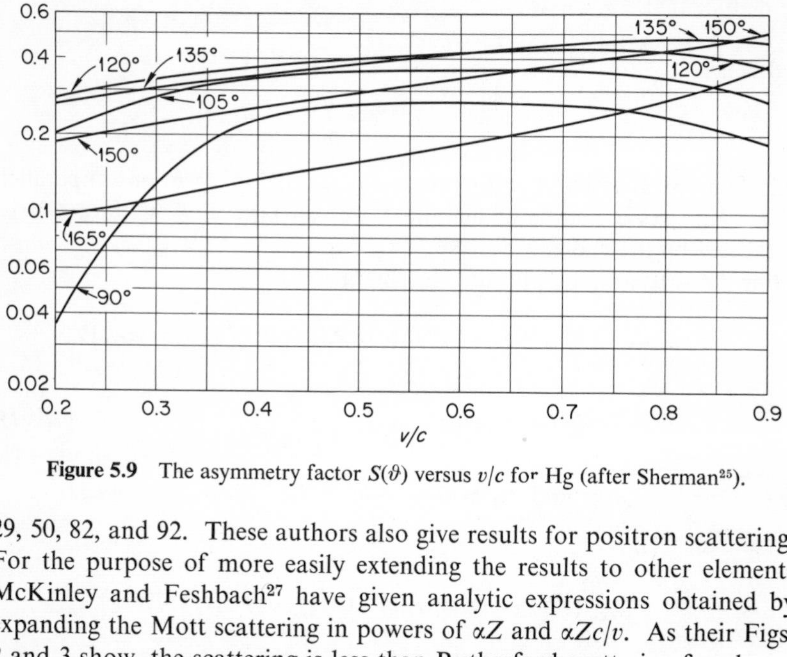

Figure 5.9 The asymmetry factor $S(\vartheta)$ versus v/c for Hg (after Sherman[25]).

29, 50, 82, and 92. These authors also give results for positron scattering. For the purpose of more easily extending the results to other elements McKinley and Feshbach[27] have given analytic expressions obtained by expanding the Mott scattering in powers of αZ and $\alpha Zc/v$. As their Figs. 2 and 3 show, the scattering is less than Rutherford scattering for almost all Z at large scattering angles but exceeds Rutherford scattering for heavy elements and scattering angles in the intermediate range. Sherman's calculation of the amplitudes F and G has been used[25] to calculate the scattering asymmetry when the incident beam is polarized. This asymmetry factor $S(\vartheta)$ is defined so that the double scattering cross section is [cf. Eq. (5.98)]

$$\sigma(\vartheta_1, \vartheta_2, \phi_2) \sim \sigma(\vartheta_1)\, \sigma(\vartheta_2)[1 + S(\vartheta_1)\, S(\vartheta_2) \cos \phi_2]$$

where $\sigma(\vartheta_1)$ and $\sigma(\vartheta_2)$ are the single scattering cross sections and ϕ_2 is the azimuthal angle of the second scattering about the direction of the beam after the first scattering. As an illustration of the results, Sherman's values of $S(\vartheta)$ for Hg have been plotted in Fig. 5.9. It is clear from (5.99) that a measurement of the azimuthal asymmetry in the single scattering of polarized electrons together with a knowledge of S determines the polarization of the incident beam.

34. TIME-DEPENDENT PERTURBATIONS

A development similar to that employed in obtaining the scattered wave in the preceding section is necessary when one wishes to answer questions concerning the angular distribution or polarization, or both, of electrons emitted in electromagnetic or weak interaction processes. Here we need to know the solutions of the Dirac equation in a Coulomb field which behave like *outgoing* waves at large distances and, as in the scattering problem, correspond to a definite direction of motion. In developing the necessary formalism we follow the work of Rose, Biedenharn, and Arfken.[28]

Consider a time-dependent perturbation $H'e^{-i\omega t} + H'^*e^{i\omega t}$. In a process wherein energy is absorbed by the electron in going from an initial state to a final state, only the first term contributes. Therefore we write the equation of motion as

$$(H + H'e^{-i\omega t})\Psi(\mathbf{r}, t) = i\partial\Psi(\mathbf{r}, t)/\partial t \tag{5.109}$$

Here H is the Hamiltonian in the Coulomb field. If we introduce the Fourier transform $\psi(W, \mathbf{r})$ according to

$$\Psi(\mathbf{r}, t) = \int \psi(W, \mathbf{r})e^{-iWt}\, dW \tag{5.110}$$

which corresponds to writing $\Psi(\mathbf{r}, t)$ as a superposition of stationary states, we obtain from (5.109)

$$(H - W)\psi(W, \mathbf{r}) = -H'\psi(W - \omega, \mathbf{r}) \tag{5.111}$$

Under the conservation of energy, $W - \omega$ is the initial energy. Moreover, in a perturbation treatment in which H' is considered only to first order, ψ on the right side of (5.111) should be replaced by the initial stationary state wave function ψ_i. Therefore we obtain an inhomogeneous equation to solve:

$$(H - W)\psi = -H'\psi_i \tag{5.112}$$

In order to solve (5.112) it is necessary to obtain the Green's function of the operator $H - W$. This means that we are required to solve

$$(\boldsymbol{\alpha}\cdot\vec{\mathbf{p}} + \beta + V - W)\, G(\mathbf{r}, \mathbf{r}') = \delta(\mathbf{r} - \mathbf{r}')I \tag{5.113}$$

where on the right side we have emphasized that there is a 4 by 4 unit matrix (I). We recognize that G is actually a 4 by 4 matrix.

The solution of the Green's function problem is more easily obtained by first considering the free particle case. Then we have

$$(\boldsymbol{\alpha}\cdot\vec{\mathbf{p}} + \beta - W)\, G_0(\mathbf{r}, \mathbf{r}') = \delta(\mathbf{r} - \mathbf{r}')I \tag{5.114}$$

and we see that

$$G_0(\mathbf{r}, \mathbf{r}') = (W + \beta + \boldsymbol{\alpha}\cdot\vec{\mathbf{p}})\,\frac{e^{ipR}}{4\pi R}\, I \tag{5.115}$$

where $\mathbf{R} = \mathbf{r} - \mathbf{r}'$. This result follows since

$$(\nabla^2 + p^2)\,\frac{e^{ipR}}{R} = -4\pi\delta(\mathbf{r} - \mathbf{r}')$$

We now introduce the well-known expansion

$$\frac{e^{ipR}}{4\pi R} = ip \sum_{lm} h_l(pr_>)\, j_l(pr_<)\; Y_l^m(\hat{\mathbf{r}})\; Y_l^{m\,\times}(\mathbf{r}') \tag{5.115'}$$

where h_l is the spherical Hankel function of the first kind:

$$h_l(x) = \left(\frac{\pi}{2x}\right)^{1/2} H^{(1)}_{l+1/2}(x)$$

To carry out the evaluation of G_0 as expressed in (5.115) we observe that

$$[\psi_\kappa^\mu]_{\text{out}} = \left[\frac{p(W + 1)}{\pi}\right]^{1/2} \begin{pmatrix} h_l\chi_\kappa^\mu \\ \dfrac{ip}{W + 1}\, S_\kappa h_{\bar{l}}\chi_{-\kappa}^\mu \end{pmatrix} \tag{5.116}$$

is a solution of the free particle Dirac equation. We consider $r > r'$ and construct the matrix

$$\mathscr{G}_{\sigma\rho} = \sum_{\kappa\mu} \{[\psi_\kappa^\mu(\mathbf{r})]_{\text{out}}\}_\sigma \{\psi_\kappa^\mu(\mathbf{r}')\}_\rho^\times$$

where ψ_κ^μ is the standing wave solutions with h_l in (5.116) replaced by j_l. We write this matrix as

$$\mathscr{G} = \begin{pmatrix} \mathscr{G}_{11} & \mathscr{G}_{12} \\ \mathscr{G}_{21} & \mathscr{G}_{22} \end{pmatrix}$$

where each of $\mathscr{G}_{11}$, etc., is a 2 by 2 matrix. Then, for example,

$$\mathscr{G}_{11} = \frac{p(W + 1)}{\pi} \sum_{\kappa\mu} h_l(r) j_l(r') \chi_\kappa^\mu(\hat{\mathbf{r}}) \chi_\kappa^{\mu\times}(\hat{\mathbf{r}}')$$

and

$$\mathscr{G}_{22} = \frac{W - 1}{W + 1}\, \mathscr{G}_{11}$$

since replacing κ by $-\kappa$ in the summand does not change the value of the sum over κ. But

$$\sum_{j\mu} \chi_\kappa^\mu(\hat{\mathbf{r}})\, \chi_\kappa^{\mu\times}(\hat{\mathbf{r}}') = \sum_{\tau\tau'} \sum_{j\mu} C(l\tfrac{1}{2}j;\mu-\tau,\tau)\, C(l\tfrac{1}{2}j;\mu-\tau',\tau')$$

$$\times\, \chi^\tau \chi^{\tau'\times}\, Y_l^{\mu-\tau}(\hat{\mathbf{r}})\, Y_l^{\mu-\tau'\times}(\hat{\mathbf{r}}')$$

where the sum over j is carried out with l fixed. The sum over j of the two C-coefficients gives $\delta_{\tau\tau'}$ from Eq. (1.58). Then we observe that

$$\sum_\tau \chi^\tau \chi^{\tau\times} = \begin{pmatrix} 1 & 0 \\ 0 & 1 \end{pmatrix} \equiv I_2$$

In the sum over μ and τ which remains, we set $\mu - \tau = m$ and sum over m and τ. Then

$$\sum_{j\mu} \chi_\kappa^\mu(\hat{\mathbf{r}})\, \chi_\kappa^{\mu\times}(\hat{\mathbf{r}}') = \sum_m Y_l^m(\hat{\mathbf{r}})\, Y_l^{m\times}(\hat{\mathbf{r}}') I_2$$

Hence

$$\mathscr{G}_{11} = \frac{p(W+1)}{\pi} \sum_{lm} h_l(pr)\, j_l(pr')\, Y_l^m(\hat{\mathbf{r}})\, Y_l^{m\times}(\hat{\mathbf{r}}') I_2$$

Comparing this with (5.113), we see that

$$(G_0)_{11} = \frac{W+1}{W-1} (G_0)_{22}$$

$$= ip(W+1) \sum_{\kappa\mu} h_l(pr)\, j_l(pr')\, \chi_\kappa^\mu(\hat{\mathbf{r}})\, \chi_\kappa^{\mu\times}(\hat{\mathbf{r}}')$$

and, in a similar way,

$$(G_0)_{12} = -(G_0)_{21} = -p^2 \sum_{\kappa\mu} S_\kappa h_{\bar{l}}(pr)\, j_l(pr')\, \chi_{-\kappa}^\mu(\hat{\mathbf{r}})\, \chi_\kappa^{\mu\times}(\hat{\mathbf{r}}')$$

Consequently, for $r > r'$,

$$G_0 = i\pi \sum_{\kappa\mu} [\psi_\kappa^\mu(\mathbf{r})]_{\text{out}}\, \psi_\kappa^{\mu\times}(\mathbf{r}') \tag{5.117}$$

For $r < r'$ we need only interchange $\mathbf{r}$ and $\mathbf{r}'$, since G_0 is symmetric in its arguments. This result is strongly reminiscent of the completeness relation, but it should be stressed that the ψ_κ^μ do not form a complete set of states.

To obtain the Green's function for the Coulomb field we need only replace the radial functions by the Coulomb functions, since the particular form of the radial functions which appear in the free particle solutions played no essential role in the development above. The desired wave function is then

$$\psi(\mathbf{r}) = -\int d^3r'\, G(\mathbf{r}, \mathbf{r}')\, H'(\mathbf{r}')\, \psi_i(\mathbf{r}') \tag{5.118}$$

and from (5.113) it is evident that (5.112) is satisfied. For the asymptotic behavior of ψ, which is all that is needed to calculate the outgoing current, we have

$$\psi_{\text{as}}(\mathbf{r}) = -\pi i \lim_{r\to\infty} \sum_{\kappa\mu} [\psi_\kappa^\mu(\mathbf{r})]_{\text{out}}(\psi_\kappa^\mu|H'|\psi_i) \tag{5.119}$$

where the quantity in brackets is the matrix element of the time-independent perturbation H'. For $(\psi_\kappa^\mu)_{\text{out}}$ we must choose radial functions which have the asymptotic behavior

$$r[f_\kappa(r)]_{\text{out}} \to i\left(\frac{W-1}{\pi p}\right)^{1/2} e^{i(pr+\delta)}$$

$$r[g_\kappa(r)]_{\text{out}} \to \left(\frac{W+1}{\pi p}\right)^{1/2} e^{i(pr+\delta)}$$

since the phase must reduce to that of the Hankel functions in the $Z = 0$ limit. Consequently,

$$\psi_{\text{as}} = -i\left(\frac{\pi}{p}\right)^{1/2} \frac{e^{ipr}}{r} \sum_{\kappa\mu} e^{i\delta_\kappa}(\psi_\kappa^\mu|H'|\psi_i)\begin{pmatrix} (W+1)^{1/2}\chi_\kappa^\mu(\hat{\mathbf{p}}) \\ -(W-1)^{1/2}\chi_{-\kappa}^\mu(\hat{\mathbf{p}})\end{pmatrix} \tag{5.120}$$

where $\hat{\mathbf{p}}$ is in the direction of the outgoing electron. The spinor in (5.120) is an eigenfunction of $\boldsymbol{\alpha}\cdot\mathbf{p} + \beta$ with eigenvalue W, so that ψ_{as} is indeed a plane wave with momentum $\mathbf{p}$.

As applications of (5.120) we may mention two. First, if we consider internal conversion,[29] ψ_i is the initial bound state and ψ_κ^μ are states in the continuum. The perturbation H' is $e(\boldsymbol{\alpha}\cdot\mathbf{A} - \Phi)$ where $\mathbf{A}$ and Φ are *outgoing* wave solutions of the Maxwell field.† The sum on κ and μ is restricted by selection rules arising from the matrix element in (5.120); for example, angular momentum conservation imposes the triangular condition $\Delta(j, L, j_i)$. As a second example the emission of beta particles may be considered. Then H' is the nuclear beta interaction of the form $\Psi_f^*\Omega\Psi_i\cdot\Omega(1+\gamma_5)$, where Ω is a Dirac matrix (of V or A type, say), and Ψ_f and Ψ_i are nuclear wave functions. The dot indicates a contraction over the tensor indices of Ω. Also ψ_i is now a neutrino state of negative energy, so that negative beta emission involves absorption of a negative energy neutrino or the creation of an antineutrino. To calculate the intensity of outgoing beta particles one considers $\psi_{\text{as}}^*\psi_{\text{as}}$, whereas for the polarization of the beta particles the quantity involved is $(\psi_{\text{as}}^*\mathcal{O}\psi_{\text{as}})/(\psi_{\text{as}}^*\psi_{\text{as}})$, where $\mathcal{O}$ is the operator discussed in section 15. In all cases the logarithmic

† For a nuclear transition $J_i \to J_f$, these Maxwell fields are superpositions of eigenfunctions of the electromagnetic angular moment L with $|J_i - J_f| \leqslant L \leqslant J_i + J_f$ and they are moreover eigenfunctions of parity. Hence for each L the potentials describe a multipole field.

term in δ_κ factors out of (5.120) as an irrelevant phase factor. It will be recognized that (5.120) is independent of the sign convention for η occurring in δ_κ since ψ_κ^μ also changes sign when $e^{i\eta}$ does, but, of course, the sign ambiguity in ψ_{as} persists in that ψ_i is not fixed as to sign.

If we think of (5.120) as a matrix element of the form

$$(\psi_f|H'|\psi_i)$$

where ψ_f plays the role of a "final state wave function," it is clear that the Coulomb phase enters ψ_f as $e^{-i\delta_\kappa}$. Hence ψ_f is not the scattered wave discussed in the previous section but, since changing the sign of the phase shifts converts outgoing waves into incoming waves, ψ_f has the behavior of a plane wave plus an *ingoing* spherical wave. This has been discussed by Breit and Bethe.[30]

PROBLEMS

1. What is the eigenvalue of the operator $I_s\beta$ for the wave function (5.3), I_s being the space inversion operator? How are the eigenvalues of $I_s\beta$ for ψ and ψ^c, given by Eq. (5.6), related? Is this relationship a generally valid one?

2. Calculate the perturbation energy for the L shell states in the case of an electron in a uniform electric field.

3. Using first-order perturbation theory, find the shift of the $1s_{1/2}$ and $2s_{1/2}$ energy levels due to screening when the screening function is

$$S = e^{-\lambda r}$$

and λ is chosen so that $(dS/dr)_{r=0}$ has the same value as for a Thomas-Fermi screening model.

4. Assume that the nucleus is a uniformly charged sphere of radius $R = \frac{1}{2}\alpha A^{1/3}$. Estimate the energy level shift of the $2s_{1/2}$ and $2p_{1/2}$ levels by using first-order perturbation theory. Under what circumstances, if any, would this perturbation result be an accurate representation of the energy shift?

5. Using first-order perturbation theory, calculate the shift in the $2p_{3/2}$ level under the influence of a perturbation

$$H' = -\frac{e^2Q}{2r^3}P_2(\cos\vartheta)$$

where Q is the "nuclear quadrupole moment." This type of perturbation would arise from the non-spherical shape of a nucleus. Obtain a numerical estimate for the energy shift for $Q = 10^{-24}$ cm^2 and for $Z = 63$. Show that the first-order perturbation of H' vanishes for all levels with $j = \frac{1}{2}$.

6. Apply the operators $I_s\beta$ (space reversal) and $i\sigma_2$ times complex conjugation (time reversal) to the scattered wave discussed in section 33 and compare the result with ψ_{as} given by (5.120).

7. Verify the result for $e^{2i\eta}$ as given in Eq. (5.71′) of the text.

8. Show that $\rho(\mathbf{p}, \mathscr{P})$ as defined in section 33 does have the properties of a density matrix.

9. How does one obtain the scattering cross section and polarization after scattering for a positron, given the corresponding results for an electron?

10. In the theory of beta decay, when the Coulomb field is included, the spectrum depends upon the following bilinear combinations of radial functions, evaluated at the nuclear radius:[31]

$$f_k^2 + g_{-k}^2$$
$$f_{-k}^2 + g_k^2$$
$$f_{-k}g_{-k} - f_k g_k$$

The subscripts ($k \geqslant 1$) give the value of κ. How are these quantities related in positron and electron emission?

11. The influence of the Coulomb field in allowed beta transitions is expressed in terms of the Fermi function $F(Z, W)$. This is defined by

$$F(Z, W) = \frac{1}{2p^2}(g_{-1}^2 + f_1^2)$$

evaluated at the nuclear radius. Taking only the first term in the series expansion of the confluent hypergeometric functions, obtain an expression for $F(Z, W)$. Verify that, for $Z = 0$, $F = 1$ and that, for $p \to 0$, pF has a finite limit when $Z > 0$ and F vanishes for $p \to 0$ when $Z < 0$. *Note*: For the $p = 0$ limit, Stirling's approximation for the gamma function is useful.

12. Find the bound state solutions for $j = \frac{1}{2}$ in a square well,

$$V = -V_0 < 0 \quad \text{for } r < r_0$$
$$V = 0 \quad\quad \text{for } r > r_0$$

What is the minimum depth V_0 with given r_0 for a bound state? What happens to the energy levels and wave functions as V_0 increases indefinitely?

13. Consider the emission of electric dipole radiation for which the selection rules are

$$\Delta l = \pm 1$$
$$\Delta j = 0, \pm 1$$

Discuss the spectrum to be expected in the transition between states with principal quantum numbers 2 and 3, and compare the number of lines predicted with the result that would be expected in the Schrödinger theory (no spin). What differences, if any, are to be expected in the Pauli spin theory and the Dirac theory?

14. Evaluate the scattering amplitudes F and G and the cross section $\sigma(\vartheta)$ in the limit of small αZ. What is the Mott polarization to the same order?

15. Define the irregular solutions in the continuum as those obtained by replacing γ in the regular solutions by $-\gamma$. What linear combination of regular and irregular standing waves has the asymptotic behavior of the outgoing waves designated by $[\psi_\kappa^\mu]_{\text{out}}$ in section 34?

16. Find the solutions of the radial wave equations in a Coulomb field for zero kinetic energy at infinity ($W = 1$).

17. Show that there exist radial functions in the Coulomb field for which the asymptotic behavior is

$$rf^0 \to i\left(\frac{W-1}{\pi p}\right)^{1/2} e^{i(pr+\delta)}$$

$$rg^0 \to \left(\frac{W+1}{\pi p}\right)^{1/2} e^{i(pr+\delta)}$$

Hint: If $\bar{f}$ and $\bar{g}$ are the real irregular (at $r = 0$) solutions, consider the r dependence of $r^2(f\bar{g} - \bar{f}g)$.

18. In the scattering wave (5.102) take the terms $\kappa = \pm 1$ only and evaluate ψ in the limit of small r. Note that ψ may be written as a spinor which closely resembles a plane wave. With this ψ, for small r construct a projection operator[32] with elements $P_{\alpha\beta} = \psi_\alpha \psi_\beta^\times$.

19. For free electrons of definite momentum $\mathbf{p}$ and energy p_0, show from the definition of the density matrix ρ that

$$\text{Tr}\, \rho\boldsymbol{\alpha} = \mathbf{p}/p_0, \quad \text{Tr}\, \rho\beta = 1/p_0, \quad \text{Tr}\, \rho\beta\gamma_5 = 0$$

and that the traces of $\rho\gamma_5$, $\rho\beta\boldsymbol{\sigma}$, and $\rho\beta\boldsymbol{\alpha}$ are linearly related to the Tr $\rho\boldsymbol{\sigma}$. Hence, show that

$$4\rho = 1 + (\boldsymbol{\alpha}\cdot\mathbf{p} + \beta)/p_0 + (\text{Tr}\, \rho\boldsymbol{\sigma})\cdot\boldsymbol{\sigma} - (\text{Tr}\, \rho\boldsymbol{\sigma}\cdot\mathbf{p})\mathbf{p}\cdot\beta\boldsymbol{\sigma}/p_0$$
$$+ p_0(\text{Tr}\, \rho\boldsymbol{\sigma})\cdot\beta\boldsymbol{\sigma} + i\mathbf{p} \times (\text{Tr}\, \rho\boldsymbol{\sigma})\cdot\beta\boldsymbol{\alpha} - (\text{Tr}\, \rho\boldsymbol{\sigma}\cdot\mathbf{p})\, \gamma_5/p_0$$

REFERENCES

1. M. H. L. Pryce, *Proc. Roy. Soc. (London)* **A195,** 62 (1948).
2. M. E. Rose, *Phys. Rev.* **82,** 389 (1951).
3. M. E. Rose and R. R. Newton, *Phys. Rev.* **82,** 470 (1951).
4. K. M. Case, *Phys. Rev.* **80,** 797 (1950).
5. *Higher Transcendental Functions,* Bateman Manuscript Project, McGraw-Hill Book Co., New York, 1953, Vol. I, Chapter VI.
6. W. E. Lamb and R. C. Retherford, *Phys. Rev.* **72,** 241 (1947). Also see *Phys. Rev.* **75,** 1325 (1949); **79,** 549 (1950); **81,** 222 (1951); **85,** 259 (1952); and **86,** 1014 (1952) by W. E. Lamb and co-workers.
7. R. D. Hill, E. L. Church, and J. W. Mihelich, *Rev. Sci. Instr.* **23,** 523 (1952).
8. J. R. Reitz, *Phys. Rev.* **77,** 10 (1950).
9. R. Christy and J. Keller, *Phys. Rev.* **61,** 147 (1942).
10. E. T. Whittaker and G. N. Watson, *Modern Analysis,* Cambridge University Press, American Edition (1943), Chapter XVI.
11. H. Margenau, *Phys. Rev.* **57,** 383 (1940).
12. G. Breit, *Phys. Rev.* **35,** 1447 (1930).
13. G. Racah, *Z. Physik* **71,** 431 (1931).
14. E. Fermi, *Z. Physik* **60,** 320 (1930).
15. G. Breit, *Phys. Rev.* **38,** 463 (1931).
16. G. E. Brown, *Proc. Natl. Acad. Sci. U.S.* **36,** 15 (1950).
17. See, for example, H. A. Bethe and R. F. Bacher, *Revs. Mod. Phys.* **8,** 82 (1936).
18. M. E. Rose, *Phys. Rev.* **51,** 484 (1937).

19. N. F. Mott, *Proc. Roy. Soc.* (*London*) **A124,** 438 (1929).
20. H. Mühlschlegel and H. Koppe, *Z. Physik* **150,** 474 (1958).
21. For example, U. Fano, *Revs. Mod. Phys.* **29,** 74 (1957). Also R. C. Tolman, *The Principles of Statistical Mechanics*, Oxford University Press, Oxford, 1938.
22. N. F. Mott, *Proc. Roy. Soc.* (*London*) **A135,** 438 (1932).
23. J. H. Bartlett, Jr., and R. E. Watson, *Phys. Rev.* **56,** 612 (1939).
24. J. H. Bartlett, Jr., and T. A. Welton, *Phys. Rev.* **59,** 281 (1941).
25. N. Sherman, *Phys. Rev.* **103,** 1601 (1956).
26. J. A. Doggett and V. L. Spencer, *Phys. Rev.* **103,** 1597 (1956).
27. W. A. McKinley, Jr., and H. Feshbach, *Phys. Rev.* **74,** 1759 (1948).
28. M. E. Rose, L. C. Biedenharn, and G. B. Arfken, *Phys. Rev.* **85,** 5 (1952).
29. M. E. Rose, *Multipole Fields*, John Wiley and Sons, New York, 1955.
30. G. Breit and H. A. Bethe, *Phys. Rev.* **93,** 888 (1954).
31. For example, M. Deutsch and O. Kofoed-Hansen, in E. Segrè (Ed.), *Experimental Nuclear Physics*, Vol. III, John Wiley and Sons, New York, 1959, p. 523.
32. J. D. Jackson, S. B. Treiman, and H. H. Wyld, Jr., *Z. Physik* **150,** 640 (1958).

VI.

Approximation methods

For many problems, exact solutions of the Dirac equations are not available and it is highly important to develop methods of approximation. In this chapter we discuss some of the more important methods which have been developed. Some of these are applicable to stationary state problems, others to dynamical processes, and some to both types of problems.

35. THE CLASSICAL LIMIT

The classical limit of the Dirac equations is obtained by considering that $\hbar$ is small compared to such quantities as $\langle x\vec{p}\rangle$. In this limit one should recover the relativistic Hamilton-Jacobi equations. Pauli[1] has considered this limiting case in some detail and, except for some modification of notation, we shall follow his presentation.

Restoring the constants $\hbar$, m, and c, the wave equation for a particle in a field with vector potential $\mathbf{A}$ and scalar potential $\Phi = A_0$ is

$$\left[\boldsymbol{\alpha}\cdot\left(\frac{\hbar}{i}\nabla + \frac{e}{c}\mathbf{A}\right) + \frac{\hbar}{i}\frac{\partial}{\partial x_0} - \frac{e}{c}A_0 + \beta mc\right]\psi = 0 \tag{6.1}$$

where $x_0 = ct$. The field components $\mathbf{A}$ and A_0 are taken to be real. We introduce the usual representation of ψ in terms of the action function S:

$$\psi = a\exp(iS/\hbar) \tag{6.2}$$

Then, with

$$\boldsymbol{\pi} = \nabla S + \frac{e}{c}\mathbf{A} \tag{6.3a}$$

$$\pi_0 = -\frac{\partial S}{\partial x_0} + \frac{e}{c}A_0 \tag{6.3b}$$

we find

$$\boldsymbol{\alpha}\cdot\left(\frac{\hbar}{i}\nabla + \boldsymbol{\pi}\right)a + \left(\frac{\hbar}{i}\frac{\partial}{\partial x_0} - \pi_0\right)a + \beta mca = 0 \tag{6.4}$$

The expansion in powers of $\hbar$ is made in the amplitude a:

$$a = a_0 + \frac{\hbar}{i}a_1 + \cdots$$

Then the coefficient of $\hbar^0$ is

$$(\boldsymbol{\alpha}\cdot\boldsymbol{\pi} + \beta mc - \pi_0)a_0 = 0 \tag{6.5}$$

and the coefficient of $\hbar$ gives

$$(\boldsymbol{\alpha}\cdot\boldsymbol{\pi} + \beta mc - \pi_0)a_1 = -\left(\boldsymbol{\alpha}\cdot\nabla + \frac{\partial}{\partial x_0}\right)a_0 \tag{6.6}$$

The homogeneous equations (6.5) are consistent with $a_0 \neq 0$ if

$$\boldsymbol{\pi}^2 + m^2c^2 = \pi_0^2 \tag{6.7}$$

as can be seen, for instance, by operating on the left of (6.5) with $\boldsymbol{\alpha}\cdot\boldsymbol{\pi} + \beta mc + \pi_0$. Equation (6.7) is the relativistic Hamilton-Jacobi equation.

By taking the hermitian conjugate of (6.5) we obtain

$$a_0^*(\boldsymbol{\alpha}\cdot\boldsymbol{\pi} + \beta mc - \pi_0) = 0 \tag{6.8}$$

We have used the fact that real fields imply a real S and hence real $\boldsymbol{\pi}$ and π_0. From (6.8) it follows that

$$a_0^*(\boldsymbol{\pi}\cdot\boldsymbol{\alpha} + \beta mc - \pi_0)a_n = 0$$

for any $n = 0, 1, \ldots$. Hence, from (6.6) with $n = 1$, we see that

$$a_0^*\left(\boldsymbol{\alpha}\cdot\nabla a_0 + \frac{\partial a_0}{\partial x_0}\right) = 0 \tag{6.9a}$$

The hermitian conjugate of this is

$$\nabla a_0^*\cdot\boldsymbol{\alpha}a_0 + \frac{\partial a_0^*}{\partial x_0}a_0 = 0 \tag{6.9b}$$

and, adding (6.9a) and (6.9b), we obtain the continuity equation

$$\operatorname{div}\mathbf{j} + \frac{\partial\rho}{\partial t} = 0$$

with

$$\mathbf{j} = ca_0^*\boldsymbol{\alpha}a_0$$

$$\rho = a_0^*a_0$$

The relation of this current density to the velocity of the particle is seen from the following: Eq. (6.5) is multiplied on the left by $a_0^* \boldsymbol{\alpha}$ and (6.8) is multiplied on the right by $\boldsymbol{\alpha} a_0$. Adding these, we find

$$a_0^*(\boldsymbol{\alpha}\, \boldsymbol{\alpha}\cdot\boldsymbol{\pi} + \boldsymbol{\alpha}\cdot\boldsymbol{\pi}\, \boldsymbol{\alpha})a_0 = 2\pi_0 a_0^* \boldsymbol{\alpha} a_0$$

or since

$$\boldsymbol{\alpha}\, \boldsymbol{\alpha}\cdot\boldsymbol{\pi} + \boldsymbol{\alpha}\cdot\boldsymbol{\pi}\, \boldsymbol{\alpha} = 2\boldsymbol{\pi}$$

we see that

$$\pi_0 \mathbf{j} = c\rho\boldsymbol{\pi} \tag{6.10}$$

The velocity is deduced from the canonical equations:

$$\dot{x}_k = \frac{\partial H}{\partial p_k}$$

with

$$H = -\frac{\partial S}{\partial t} = -c\frac{\partial S}{\partial x_0} = c\left(\pi_0 - e\frac{A_0}{c}\right)$$

Hence, from (6.7),

$$\dot{x}_k = \frac{c\pi_k}{(\boldsymbol{\pi}^2 + m^2c^2)^{1/2}} = \frac{c\pi_k}{\pi_0} \tag{6.11}$$

Consequently,

$$j_k = \rho \dot{x}_k \tag{6.12}$$

Here the positive root in (6.7) was chosen. For the negative root,

$$\dot{x}_k = -\frac{c\pi_k}{(\boldsymbol{\pi}^2 + m^2c^2)^{1/2}} = \frac{c\pi_k}{\pi_0}$$

so that (6.12) applies in any case. It follows that the orbit of the particle is along the direction of $\mathbf{j}$: the current is convective, as would be expected classically.

The preceding discussion is a formal one designed to exhibit the classical limit. However, as is well known, the limiting form of the theory for $\hbar \to 0$ can sometimes be used as an approximation for getting wave functions and eigenvalues in the limit of large quantum numbers. This involves, of course, the application of the Wentzel-Kramers-Brillouin (WKB) method to the Dirac equation.[2] Clearly, the application of the method is facilitated very greatly if the wave equation can be reduced to one degree of freedom although a more general treatment is obviously possible, in principle.

For the radial part of the central field problem we consider the second-order equation (5.8). The application of the WKB method to this equation has been discussed at some length by Bessey[3] and by Good.[4] If the units are restored, this equation now reads

$$u_1'' + \frac{V'}{W - V + mc^2} u_1' + (Q_0 + Q_1)u_1 = 0 \qquad (6.13)$$

where the prime means differentiation with respect to r and

$$Q_0 = \frac{(W - V)^2 - m^2c^4}{\hbar^2c^2} - \frac{\kappa^2}{r^2}$$

$$Q_1 = -\frac{\kappa}{r^2} + \frac{\kappa}{r}\frac{V'}{W - V + mc^2}$$

The terms have been grouped as shown because it is consistent to treat κ as large, and $\kappa\hbar/r$ is then of order mc. Consequently Q_1 must be treated as smaller than Q_0 by one order of magnitude. Thus the two terms in Q_1 are of order

$$1/\kappa \sim (\hbar/mcr) \quad \text{and} \quad \alpha Z/\kappa$$

times the term κ^2/r^2 in Q_0. The large value of r compared to $\hbar/mc$ can be understood in terms of a pair of turning points which delineate a classically allowed region of motion which encompasses the point at infinity as $\hbar \to 0$.

The term in u_1' in (6.13) can be eliminated by the substitution

$$u_1 = v_1(W - V + mc^2)^{1/2}$$

and this gives

$$v_1'' + (Q_0 + Q_1 + Q_2)v_1 = 0$$

where

$$Q_2 = -\frac{3}{4}\left(\frac{V'}{W - V + mc^2}\right)^2 - \frac{1}{2}\frac{V''}{W - V + mc^2}$$

Both terms in Q_2 are negligible in the classical limit. They are, in fact, of second order relative to Q_0, and they will be dropped in the following treatment. Hence the WKB solutions are of the form $(Q_0 + Q_1 > 0)$

$$u_1 \cong \left(\frac{W - V + mc^2}{Q_0^{1/2}}\right)^{1/2} \exp\left[\pm i \int_{r_1}^{r} Q_0^{1/2}\left(1 + \frac{Q_1}{2Q_0}\right) dr\right] \qquad (6.14)$$

The small component u_2 is obtained from (5.5). These solutions are for the region where $Q_0 + Q_1 > 0$. It is obvious that for $Q_0 + Q_1 < 0$ the solutions have the real exponential form and $i(Q_0 + Q_1)$ is replaced by $|Q_0 + Q_1|$. In (6.14) an expansion has been made for $Q_1 \ll Q_0$ and r_1 is a root of the integrand.

For a bound state, neglecting Q_1, it is seen that Q_0 has two real positive roots and $Q_0 > 0$ between these roots. If these roots are denoted by r_1 and r_2, with $r_2 > r_1$, the energy quantization condition is

$$\int_{r_1}^{r_2} Q_0^{1/2}\, dr = (n_r + \tfrac{1}{2})\pi \tag{6.15}$$

where n_r is the number of radial nodes. The evaluation of the integral for a Coulomb field is elementary, and it gives the result (5.36) provided that we identify $n_r + \frac{1}{2}$ with n'. This identification is not exact, but it is permissible in the limit of large n'. If the Q_1 correction is added to the integrand, the eigenvalues depend on the sign of κ, contrary to the behavior of the exact result.

An improved form of the WKB solutions has been given by Good,[4] who has applied the method to the continuum states in the calculation of the Fermi function which describes the influence of the screened Coulomb field on the energy spectrum of allowed beta transitions. For bound states this modified method gives the same energy eigenvalues as the standard WKB procedure.

36. THE BORN APPROXIMATION

Retarded Interaction between Charged Particles

One of the most important methods which has been used very extensively, especially in dynamical problems, is the Born approximation. The term Born approximation is used in two different contexts. In one it involves neglect of all interactions in zero order so that the zero-order wave functions are plane waves or free particle spherical waves. The broader meaning of the Born approximation may be illustrated by a specific example. In the treatment of the problem of beta decay the electrons are in a Coulomb field and the decay process takes place by virtue of the beta coupling. It is customary and justified to treat the latter as small and to calculate transition probabilities to lowest order in the beta coupling constant. This is a Born approximation in which the expansion parameter is expressed in terms of the coupling constant. If the Coulomb field is neglected and plane waves are used for the beta particle, this constitutes an additional approximation, a Born approximation in the sense first described above. Then the expansion parameter depends on the Coulomb field and is essentially αZ. In this case, then, a double expansion in powers of two parameters is being made. In the present application we shall be concerned with situations in which the electromagnetic coupling is the only one present. In this kind of problem the term Born approximation has the same two-fold meaning. For instance, in the electromagnetic interaction between two charged particles, electrons say, there may also be an external field which, for example, is due to the presence of the nucleus. We can take this field as fixed; essentially this means that the nucleus is treated as a classical system of charges (and currents). Then the Born approximation consists of a perturbation treatment of the two-electron interaction which is equivalent to an expansion in powers of $e^2 = \alpha$. In addition, we may use the Born approximation in the sense that the external field is neglected so that the electrons are represented by plane waves for example. The sense in which the approximations are made should be clear from the context.

The problem of interaction between charged particles will be formulated by assuming that two Dirac particles are coupled to the electromagnetic field. Then for each particle the equation of motion

$$\gamma_\mu\left(\frac{\partial}{\partial x_\mu} + \frac{ie}{\hbar c}A_\mu\right)\psi + k_0\psi = 0 \tag{6.16}$$

applies. Here A_μ, the four-potential of the electromagnetic field, is evaluated at x_1 in the equation for particle 1 and similarly at x_2 in the equation for particle 2. We shall make no distinction between t_1 and t_2, using a common time t for both particles. The field A_μ at x_1, say, is generated by particle 2 according to

$$\frac{\partial^2 A_\nu}{\partial x_\mu\, \partial x_\mu} = -\frac{4\pi}{c}s_\nu \tag{6.17}$$

where the current four-vector due to 2 is

$$s_\nu = -iec\bar{\psi}^{(2)}\gamma_{2\nu}\,\psi^{(2)} \tag{6.18}$$

If we consider a dynamical problem where particle 2 makes a transition from state $\psi_i^{(2)}$ to $\psi_f^{(2)}$, we must replace s_ν by

$$s_\nu = -iec\bar{\psi}_f^{(2)}\,\psi_{2\nu}\psi_i^{(2)} \tag{6.18'}$$

Then

$$A_\nu(\mathbf{r}_1, t) = \frac{1}{c}\int \frac{s_\nu(\mathbf{r}_2, t')}{R}\,d^3r_2 \tag{6.18''}$$

where $\mathbf{R} = \mathbf{r}_1 - \mathbf{r}_2$ and $t' = t - R/c$. Under the influence of A_ν, particle 1 is considered to make a transition from state $\psi_i^{(1)}$ to $\psi_f^{(1)}$. Then the matrix element for this is written, in correspondence principle fashion, as

$$H_{fi} = ie\int \bar{\psi}_f^{(1)}\gamma_{1\mu}\,A_\mu(\mathbf{r}_1)\,\psi_i^{(1)}\,d^3r_1 \tag{6.19}$$

where we recognize that only the space part of the potential A_μ enters in the results of the perturbation theory. In fact, $s_\mu(\mathbf{r}_2, t)$ has a time dependence given by $\exp[i(W_f - W_i)t/\hbar] = \exp(-i\omega t)$, and replacing t by $t - R/c$ gives a factor

$$e^{-i\omega t}e^{ikR}$$

where $k = \omega/c = (W_i - W_f)/\hbar c$. The A_μ in (6.19) includes everything but the time factor, $\exp(-i\omega t)$.

From (6.18′) and (6.18″) we find

$$H_{fi} = e^2 \int \bar{\psi}_f^{(2)}\, \bar{\psi}_f^{(1)} \gamma_{1\mu}\gamma_{2\mu} \frac{e^{ikR}}{R}\, \psi_i^{(2)}\, \psi_i^{(1)}\, d^3r_1\, d^3r_2 \tag{6.20}$$

This may be written in the alternative form

$$H_{fi} = e^2 \int \psi_f^{(2)*} \psi_f^{(1)*} (1 - \boldsymbol{\alpha}_1 \cdot \boldsymbol{\alpha}_2) \frac{e^{ikR}}{R}\, \psi_i^{(2)}\, \psi_i^{(1)}\, d^3r_1\, d^3r_2 \tag{6.20′}$$

This is the well-known retarded interaction between two electrons. It was first obtained by Møller[5] and has been discussed by many other authors.[6] The retardation is expressed through the scalar Green's function $(\exp ikR)/R$. The first term is recognized as the Coulomb repulsion, the second is the relativistic current-current interaction. While the operator appearing in (6.20) is a contraction of two four-vectors and is relativistically invariant, it should be emphasized that the matrix element as obtained here is correct only to first order in e^2 or α. This is brought out explicitly in a more detailed derivation given in Appendix E. There it will be seen more clearly that the Coulomb repulsion term arises from the virtual emission and absorption of longitudinally polarized quanta, while both transverse and longitudinal polarizations contribute to the $\boldsymbol{\alpha}_1 \cdot \boldsymbol{\alpha}_2$ term. The wave functions in (6.20) or (6.20′) need not be free particle wave functions. For instance, in the Auger effect $\psi^{(1)}$ and $\psi^{(2)}$ are wave functions in the field of the nucleus. For two electrons antisymmetrization in initial, final states is necessary. In internal conversion this is not needed, of course, because then one of the particles is a nucleon, the other a Dirac electron. For this problem $\boldsymbol{\alpha}$ in the nuclear space should be thought of as a current operator whose precise specification depends on questions of nuclear dynamics. The matrix element (6.20′) would also include a sum over all nucleons.

The Breit Interaction

A different approach to the problem of two electrons has been developed by Breit.[7] In this treatment of the problem the instantaneous Coulomb repulsion is included as a zero-order term in the total Hamiltonian, and an additional approximately relativistic current-current interaction B is deduced from the mutual emission and absorption of transverse quanta between the two electrons. Thus we would write the equation of motion for a stationary state in the form

$$\left(W - H_0(1) - H_0(2) - \frac{e^2}{r_{12}}\right)\Psi = B\Psi \tag{6.21}$$

Here W is the total energy of the system, $H_0(n) = \boldsymbol{\alpha}_n\cdot\vec{\boldsymbol{\pi}}_n + \beta_n + V_{\text{ext}}(\mathbf{r}_n)$ where $\vec{\boldsymbol{\pi}}_n = \vec{\mathbf{p}}_n + e\mathbf{A}_{\text{ext}}(\mathbf{r}_n)$ in general. To determine B the zero-order solutions of (6.21) with $B = 0$ are used in a second-order perturbation treatment. This gives the interaction energy

$$\Delta W = -\frac{e^2}{4\pi^2}\sum_\lambda \int \frac{d^3k'}{k'} \sum_n \left\{\frac{\langle 0|\alpha_{1\lambda} \exp(i\mathbf{k}'\cdot\mathbf{r}_1)|n\rangle\langle n|\alpha_{2\lambda} \exp(-i\mathbf{k}\cdot\mathbf{r}_2)|0\rangle}{k' + W_n - W_0} + \frac{\langle 0|\alpha_{2\lambda} \exp(i\mathbf{k}'\cdot\mathbf{r}_2)|n\rangle\langle n|\alpha_{1\lambda} \exp(-i\mathbf{k}\cdot\mathbf{r}_1)|0\rangle}{k' + W_n - W_0}\right\}$$

This result corresponds to emission of a quantum with wave number $\mathbf{k}'$, polarization λ by particle 2 and its absorption by particle 1 (first term) and (second), the same process in which particles 1 and 2 are interchanged. The numerical factor comes about from the $(2\pi)^{-3}$ coming from the density of states of wave number $\mathbf{k}'$ and a factor $2\pi/k'$ from the normalization of the radiation field.† The index n designates an intermediate state in which the energy is $k' + W_n$.

The Breit interaction results from the neglect of the energy differences $W_n - W_0$ compared to k'. This implies a neglect of retardation. The justification for this step may be made by noting that in an atom of atomic number Z the important values of k' are of order $\langle 1/r\rangle \sim \alpha Z$ while $W_n - W_0 \sim (\alpha Z)^2$. Thus we must assume $\alpha Z \ll 1$. When this is done the sum over n is carried out by the completeness relation, giving

$$\Delta W = \langle 0|B|0\rangle$$

where

$$B = -\frac{e^2}{2\pi^2}\sum_\lambda \int \frac{d^3k'}{k'^2} \exp(i\mathbf{k}'\cdot\mathbf{R})\, \alpha_{1\lambda}\alpha_{2\lambda} \tag{6.22}$$

The sum over polarization states λ is carried out for transverse degrees of polarization only. Then

$$\begin{aligned}\sum_\lambda \alpha_{1\lambda}\alpha_{2\lambda} &= (\boldsymbol{\alpha}_1 - \hat{\mathbf{k}}'\,\boldsymbol{\alpha}_1\cdot\hat{\mathbf{k}}')\cdot(\boldsymbol{\alpha}_2 - \hat{\mathbf{k}}'\,\boldsymbol{\alpha}_2\cdot\hat{\mathbf{k}}') \\ &= \boldsymbol{\alpha}_1\cdot\boldsymbol{\alpha}_2 - \boldsymbol{\alpha}_1\cdot\hat{\mathbf{k}}'\,\boldsymbol{\alpha}_2\cdot\hat{\mathbf{k}}'\end{aligned}$$

† See Appendix E.

and

$$B = -\frac{e^2}{2\pi^2}\int \frac{d^3k'}{k'^2} \exp(i\mathbf{k}'\cdot\mathbf{R})\,(\boldsymbol{\alpha}_1\cdot\boldsymbol{\alpha}_2 - \boldsymbol{\alpha}_1\cdot\hat{\mathbf{k}}'\,\alpha_2\cdot\hat{\mathbf{k}}') \tag{6.22'}$$

The integrals are evaluated by elementary means:

$$\int \frac{d^3k'}{k'^2} \exp(i\mathbf{k}'\cdot\mathbf{R}) = \frac{2\pi^2}{R}$$

$$\begin{aligned}\int \frac{d^3k'}{k'^2} \exp(i\mathbf{k}'\cdot\mathbf{R})\,(\boldsymbol{\alpha}_1\cdot\hat{\mathbf{k}}')(\boldsymbol{\alpha}_2\cdot\hat{\mathbf{k}}') &= \frac{i}{2}\,\boldsymbol{\alpha}_1\cdot\nabla_R \int d^3k' \exp(i\mathbf{k}'\cdot\mathbf{R})\,\boldsymbol{\alpha}_2\cdot\nabla_{k'}\frac{1}{k'^2} \\ &= \pi^2(\boldsymbol{\alpha}_1\cdot\nabla_R)\,\boldsymbol{\alpha}_2\cdot\hat{\mathbf{R}} \\ &= \frac{\pi^2}{R}(\boldsymbol{\alpha}_1\cdot\boldsymbol{\alpha}_2 - \boldsymbol{\alpha}_1\cdot\hat{\mathbf{R}}\,\boldsymbol{\alpha}_2\cdot\hat{\mathbf{R}})\end{aligned}$$

The integrals over k' are carried out by inserting a "convergence factor" $e^{-\alpha k'}$ and then taking the limit $\alpha \to 0$. Hence the Breit operator becomes

$$B = -\frac{e^2}{2R}(\boldsymbol{\alpha}_1\cdot\boldsymbol{\alpha}_2 + \boldsymbol{\alpha}_1\cdot\hat{\mathbf{R}}\,\boldsymbol{\alpha}_2\cdot\hat{\mathbf{R}}) \tag{6.23}$$

The complete two-electron interaction is then

$$V_{12} = \frac{e^2}{R} + B \tag{6.24}$$

in the Breit theory. In contrast to this, from (6.20′) we would take this interaction to be

$$V_{12} = e^2(1 - \boldsymbol{\alpha}_1\cdot\boldsymbol{\alpha}_2)\frac{e^{ikR}}{R} \tag{6.25}$$

in a process involving energy transfer k. The retardation does not appear in (6.24). Indeed, the two interactions should not be expected to give identical results since the Breit interaction involves the additional assumption that $v^2/c^2 \ll 1$ and is therefore not an invariant quantity under Lorentz transformations.

To compare these two results quantitatively we consider the matrix element for electron-electron scattering, using V_{12} given by (6.25) and then by (6.24). We consider a collision process in which there are no external fields and plane waves are used in zero order. The initial state is described by electron 1 ($\mathbf{p}_1$, W_1), electron 2 ($\mathbf{p}_2$, W_2) where the symbols in parentheses are the momenta and energies. After the scattering we have, for electron 1,

$(\mathbf{p}_1', W_1')$ and, for electron 2, $(\mathbf{p}_2', W_2')$. We use conservation of energy and momentum so that

$$\mathbf{q} \equiv \mathbf{p}_1 - \mathbf{p}_1' = -(\mathbf{p}_2 - \mathbf{p}_2')$$

and

$$k = W_1 - W_1' = -(W_2 - W_2')$$

The cross section per unit solid angle in units of $(\hbar/mc)^2$ is

$$\sigma = \frac{2\pi\mathfrak{S}|H_{fi}|^2 n(W_1', W_2')}{j_{\text{inc}}} \tag{6.26}$$

where $\mathfrak{S}$ is a sum over final spin orientations and an average over initial orientations, $n(W_1', W_2')$ is the density of states, and j_{inc} is the incident current density. The matrix element for the Møller interaction (6.25) is then†

$$H_{fi} = e^2 \int d^3R \, \frac{e^{ikR}}{R} \exp{(i\mathbf{q}\cdot\mathbf{R})}[U^*(\mathbf{p}_1') \, U^*(\mathbf{p}_2')(1 - \boldsymbol{\alpha}_1\cdot\boldsymbol{\alpha}_2) \, U(\mathbf{p}_1) \, U(\mathbf{p}_2)] \tag{6.27}$$

The integral in (6.27) is

$$\int d^3R \, \frac{\exp{(ikR + i\mathbf{q}\cdot\mathbf{R})}}{R} = \frac{2\pi}{iq}\int_0^\infty dR e^{ikR}(e^{iqR} - e^{-iqR})$$

This is evaluated, as usual, by inserting a convergence factor $e^{-\alpha R}$ and taking the limit $\alpha \to 0$ after integration. Then the integral is

$$\frac{2\pi}{q}\left(\frac{1}{k+q} - \frac{1}{k-q}\right) = \frac{4\pi}{q^2 - k^2}$$

and

$$H_{fi} = \frac{4\pi e^2}{q^2 - k^2}\, [U^*(\mathbf{p}_1') \, U^*(\mathbf{p}_2')(1 - \boldsymbol{\alpha}_1\cdot\boldsymbol{\alpha}_2) \, U(\mathbf{p}_1) \, U(\mathbf{p}_2)] \tag{6.28}$$

We shall not evaluate this further, although a subsequent example will illustrate the manner in which this would be done. Instead, the Breit interaction will be used to obtain a result to compare with (6.28). For this case,

$$H_{fi} = e^2 \int \frac{d^3R}{R} \exp{(i\mathbf{q}\cdot\mathbf{R})}\{U^*(\mathbf{p}_1') \, U^*(\mathbf{p}_2') \times [1 - \tfrac{1}{2}(\boldsymbol{\alpha}_1\cdot\boldsymbol{\alpha}_2 + \boldsymbol{\alpha}_1\cdot\hat{\mathbf{R}} \, \boldsymbol{\alpha}_2\cdot\hat{\mathbf{R}})] \, U(\mathbf{p}_1) \, U(\mathbf{p}_2)\}$$

† Normalizing in a box of unit volume. For our present purpose it is not necessary explicitly to consider antisymmetrization since we shall eventually compare two different *operators* which are treated in the same way.

The second part, involving B, is simply done by using (6.22′) for B rather than the form displayed here. Then B contributes

$$H_{fi}(B) = -\frac{e^2}{2\pi^2}\int d^3R \exp(i\mathbf{q}\cdot\mathbf{R})\int \frac{d^3k'}{k'^2}\exp(i\mathbf{k}'\cdot\mathbf{R})$$
$$\times\,[U^*(\mathbf{p}_1')\,U^*(\mathbf{p}_2')(\boldsymbol{\alpha}_1\cdot\boldsymbol{\alpha}_2 - \boldsymbol{\alpha}_1\cdot\hat{\mathbf{k}}'\,\boldsymbol{\alpha}_2\cdot\hat{\mathbf{k}}')\,U(\mathbf{p}_1)\,U(\mathbf{p}_2)]$$

The integration over $\mathbf{R}$ gives $(2\pi)^3\,\delta(\mathbf{q}+\mathbf{k}')$ and

$$H_{fi}(B) = -\frac{4\pi e^2}{q^2}\left(U^*(\mathbf{p}_1')\,U^*(\mathbf{p}_2')\,\middle|\,\boldsymbol{\alpha}_1\cdot\boldsymbol{\alpha}_2 - \frac{\boldsymbol{\alpha}_1\cdot\mathbf{q}\,\boldsymbol{\alpha}_2\cdot\mathbf{q}}{q^2}\,\middle|\,U(\mathbf{p}_1)\,U(\mathbf{p}_2)\right)$$

But $\mathbf{q} = \mathbf{p}_1 - \mathbf{p}_1'$. Therefore

$$\begin{aligned} U^*(\mathbf{p}_1')\,\boldsymbol{\alpha}_1\cdot\mathbf{q}\,U(\mathbf{p}_1) &= U^*(\mathbf{p}_1')\,\boldsymbol{\alpha}_1\cdot\mathbf{p}_1\,U(\mathbf{p}_1) - [\boldsymbol{\alpha}_1\cdot\mathbf{p}_1'\,U(\mathbf{p}_1')]^*\,U(\mathbf{p}_1) \\ &= U^*(\mathbf{p}_1')(W_1 - \beta_1)\,U(\mathbf{p}_1) - U^*(\mathbf{p}_1')(W_1' - \beta_1)\,U(\mathbf{p}_1) \\ &= kU^*(\mathbf{p}_1')\,U(\mathbf{p}_1) \end{aligned}$$

Similarly, $\mathbf{q} = -(\mathbf{p}_2 - \mathbf{p}_2')$ and

$$U^*(\mathbf{p}_2')\,\boldsymbol{\alpha}_2\cdot\mathbf{q}\,U(\mathbf{p}_2) = kU^*(\mathbf{p}_2)\,U(\mathbf{p}_2)$$

so

$$H_{fi}(B) = -\frac{4\pi e^2}{q^2}\left[U^*(\mathbf{p}_1')\,U^*(\mathbf{p}_2')\left(\boldsymbol{\alpha}_1\cdot\boldsymbol{\alpha}_2 - \frac{k^2}{q^2}\right)U(\mathbf{p}_1)\,U(\mathbf{p}_2)\right]$$

This is added to the matrix element of e^2/R. We use

$$e^2\int\frac{d^3R}{R}\exp(i\mathbf{q}\cdot\mathbf{R}) = \frac{4\pi e^2}{q^2}$$

and the total matrix element, from (6.24), becomes

$$H_{fi} = \frac{4\pi e^2}{q^2}\left\{U^*(\mathbf{p}_1')\,U^*(\mathbf{p}_2')\left(1 + \frac{k^2}{q^2} - \boldsymbol{\alpha}_1\cdot\boldsymbol{\alpha}_2\right)U(\mathbf{p}_1)\,U(\mathbf{p}_2)\right\} \tag{6.29}$$

for the Breit interaction. Comparing with the Møller result (6.28), we see that the two are identical only if the retardation as expressed by k is neglected. This assumption of $k = 0$ will be exact if $p_1 = p_1'$ and hence $p_2 = p_2'$. For example, if $p_2 = 0$ then $k = 0$ only for forward scattering. For small p and p', $k^2/q^2 \ll 1$ and the two results again become identical.

To obtain the cross section for electron-electron scattering we must antisymmetrize the wave functions. Results have been given by Møller.[5] These show that for small relative velocities the cross section given by the two interactions agree up to order v^2/c^2 only.

Scattering of Fast Electrons by Nuclei

As an application of the Born approximation we consider the effect of the finite extent of the nucleus in the scattering of electrons.[8] When the deBroglie wavelength of the electrons is of the order of nuclear dimensions† we may expect destructive interference from waves emanating from different parts of the nucleus. Essentially exact calculations[9] show that the Born approximation gives approximately correct results except over certain angular ranges where strong destructive interference occurs; the scattering in Born approximation is then predicted to be smaller than the true value. Our purpose here, however, is illustrative rather than one of obtaining precise numerical cross sections.

The nucleus will be considered a static charge distribution with density $Ze\rho$. The cross section (6.26) for unit solid angle is

$$\sigma = \frac{W^2}{8\pi^2} Z^2 e^4 \mathfrak{S} \left| \int d^3r\, d^3r_N \frac{\rho(\mathbf{r}_N)}{R} \psi_f^*(\mathbf{r})\, \psi_i(\mathbf{r}) \right|^2 \tag{6.30}$$

where we disregard retardation in (6.20′) since only elastic scattering is considered. We neglect the negligible current term in view of the non-relativistic treatment of the nucleus. Here $\rho(\mathbf{r}_N) = \psi_N^* \psi_N$ replaces $\psi_f^{(2)*}\psi_i^{(2)}$. The matrix element in (6.30) is

$$U^*(\mathbf{p}')\, U(\mathbf{p}) \int d^3r\, d^3r_N\, \rho(\mathbf{r}_N) \frac{\exp(i\mathbf{q}\cdot\mathbf{r})}{R}$$

where $\mathbf{q} = \mathbf{p} - \mathbf{p}'$ is the momentum transfer and $\mathbf{R} = \mathbf{r} - \mathbf{r}_N$. The integral is

$$\int d^3r_N\, \rho(\mathbf{r}_N) \exp(i\mathbf{q}\cdot\mathbf{r}_N) \int \frac{\exp(i\mathbf{q}\cdot\mathbf{R})}{R}\, d^3R$$

$$= \frac{2\pi}{iq} \int d^3r_N \rho(\mathbf{r}_N) \exp(i\mathbf{q}\cdot\mathbf{r}_N) \int_0^\infty (e^{iqR} - e^{-iqR})\, dR$$

$$= \frac{4\pi}{q^2} \int d^3r_N \rho(\mathbf{r}_N) \exp(i\mathbf{q}\cdot\mathbf{r}_N)$$

where use of the convergence factor is again made. Since we assume a spherically symmetric charge distribution $\rho(\mathbf{r}_N)$, the integration over the directions of $\mathbf{r}_N$ may be made to give for the integral

$$\frac{(4\pi)^2}{q^2} \int_0^\infty r_N^2 \rho(r_N) \frac{\sin qr_N}{qr_N}\, dr_N$$

† More exactly, the nuclear radius times the momentum transfer is of order unity.

The sum over spin orientations is done by standard means:

$$\begin{aligned}\mathfrak{S}|U^*(\mathbf{p}')\,U(\mathbf{p})|^2 &= \mathfrak{S}U_\tau^\times(\mathbf{p}')\,U_\xi(\mathbf{p}')\,U_\tau(\mathbf{p})\,U_\xi^\times(\mathbf{p})\\ &= \mathrm{Tr}\,P_+(\mathbf{p}')\,P_+(\mathbf{p})\\ &= 1 + \frac{1}{W^2}(1 + \mathbf{p}\cdot\mathbf{p}')\\ &= \frac{W^2 + 1 + p^2\cos\vartheta}{W^2} = \frac{2}{W^2}\left(1 + p^2\cos^2\frac{\vartheta}{2}\right)\end{aligned}$$

where ϑ is the scattering angle and we have used $p = p'$. Collecting results, we obtain for the cross section

$$\sigma = \sigma_0 F_0^2 \tag{6.31}$$

where

$$\sigma_0 = \frac{Z^2e^4[1 + p^2\cos^2(\vartheta/2)]}{4p^4\sin^4(\vartheta/2)} \tag{6.31a}$$

is the scattering per unit solid angle from a point nucleus and

$$F_0 = 4\pi\int_0^\infty \rho(\mathbf{r}_N)\,\frac{\sin qr_N}{qr_N}\,r_N^2\,dr_N \tag{6.31b}$$

is the form factor for scattering from the distribution ρ. If the nucleus has a sharp radius r_0 and a constant density $\rho = 3/4\pi r_0^3$, the form factor is

$$F_0 = \frac{3}{(qr_0)^2}\left(\frac{\sin qr_0}{qr_0} - \cos qr_0\right)$$

For $qr_N \ll 1$ for all r_N for which $\rho(\mathbf{r}_N)$ is appreciable, the form factor can be expanded to give

$$F_0 = 1 - \frac{1}{3!}q^2\langle r_N^2\rangle_{\mathrm{Av}} + \frac{1}{5!}q^4\langle r_N^4\rangle_{\mathrm{Av}} - \cdots$$

In first approximation the correction for finite size of the scatterer depends on $\langle r_N^2\rangle_{\mathrm{Av}}$. In all cases $F_0 \leqslant 1$, since ρ is normalized to unity. Noting that $q = 2p\sin\frac{1}{2}\vartheta$, it is evident that $F_0 = 1$ in the forward direction. This is expected since all waves arising from different parts of the scattering volume are then in phase.

The validity of the Born approximation in scattering has been investigated by Parzen.[10] For a central field with potential energy $V(r)$ which is not singular at $r = 0$ (finite nuclear size) and which falls at infinity faster than a Coulomb field (screening) the requirement is found to be

$$\left|\int_0^\infty V(r)\,dr\right| \ll 1$$

In contrast to the expectation following from the non-relativistic treatment, it does not follow that at sufficiently high energy the Born approximation is valid. If $V(r)$ violates the condition above, as it would for high Z, the Born approximation cannot be justified. The distinction in the two cases lies in the interpretation of the Born parameter $e^2Z/\hbar v$ which approaches zero if we superficially take $v \to \infty$ as in the non-relativistic description but approaches αZ in actuality. As a rough estimate of the above integral we can cut off the Coulomb field at $r = \frac{1}{2}\alpha A^{1/3}$ at the lower limit (which is of order of the nuclear radius) and at an upper limit equal to $(\alpha Z)^{-1/3}$ which is of the order of the atomic radius. Then

$$\left|\int V(r)\, dr\right| \cong \alpha Z \ln \frac{2(137)^2}{ZA^{1/3}}$$

which is roughly of order αZ.

37. COMPTON SCATTERING OF CIRCULARLY POLARIZED RADIATION

Strictly speaking, the discussion of processes involving emission and absorption of quanta, electromagnetic or otherwise, involves the formulation and application of a theory in which these fields are quantized. However, as we have already emphasized, the evaluation of transition probabilities and cross sections is to a large extent an application of the single particle theory developed in this book. As an illustration of this fact we consider the Compton scattering, starting with the general formulas of the perturbation theory in which the lowest-order non-vanishing contributions in a power series in $\alpha = e^2/\hbar c$ are retained. This is often an excellent approximation, and this remark applies to the Compton scattering in the range of energies (nuclear gamma-ray energies) where many practical applications are made.

The effect we shall discuss is the analysis of circularly polarized radiation, where the application in mind is to nuclear gamma rays following beta decay. As is well known, the effect of non-conservation of parity in beta decay results in a residual nuclear state which is polarized† even in allowed transitions. Then a gamma ray emitted from such a nuclear state, observed in coincidence with the beta particle, is circularly polarized. To analyze the circular polarization Compton scattering by polarized electrons constitutes the most practical procedure.[11]

† In a representation in which the density matrix is diagonal the nuclear substates with magnetic quantum number M can be described by a population distribution (following allowed transitions) of the form of a linear function of M.

The influence of the Coulomb field in the Compton scattering is negligible, and the electron can be represented by plane waves. Hence the present consideration represents an example of the Born approximation in both senses in which this term is employed. The present section constitutes an application of not only the Born approximation but also of several other considerations which have been discussed in previous chapters.

The electron is initially at rest but in a specified spin state. The photon has initial momentum $\mathbf{k}_0$, and after scattering its momentum is $\mathbf{k}$. The electron therefore acquires momentum $\mathbf{p}$ given by†

$$\mathbf{p} = \mathbf{k}_0 - \mathbf{k} \tag{6.32}$$

Then the final state is reached from the initial state via either of two intermediate states:

(i) The initial photon is absorbed and the electron acquires momentum

$$\mathbf{p}' = \mathbf{k}_0 \tag{6.33a}$$

and energy

$$W' = \pm(p^2 + 1)^{1/2} \tag{6.33b}$$

The electron of this energy will exist in either of two possible spin states, and so in summing over intermediate states all four states of the given momentum must be counted.

(ii) The final photon is emitted first, so that in this intermediate state there are two photons, with momentum $\mathbf{k}_0$ and $\mathbf{k}$, and an electron with momentum

$$\mathbf{p}'' = -\mathbf{k} \tag{6.33c}$$

and energy

$$W'' = \pm(p''^2 + 1)^{1/2} \tag{6.33d}$$

Again both spin states and hence four intermediate states are to be included.

The final state is reached from (i) by emission of $\mathbf{k}$ and from (ii) by absorption of $\mathbf{k}_0$. In all cases it will be assumed that no observation of the final polarization of electron or photon is made. This, again, corresponds to the situation most often realized in practice.

The transition probability in units with $\hbar = m = c = 1$ is

$$2\pi\rho_f \sum_{\tau'} \left| \sum_i \frac{H_{fi}^{\times}(\mathbf{k}, \tau')\, H_{i0}(\mathbf{k}_0, \tau)}{E_0 - E_i} + \sum_{ii} \frac{H_{fi}(\mathbf{k}_0, \tau)\, H_{i0}^{\times}(\mathbf{k}, \tau')}{E_0 - E_{ii}} \right|^2 \tag{6.34}$$

† Linear momentum conservation is a consequence of the non-vanishing of the matrix elements; see below.

In (6.34) ρ_f is the density of final states per unit range of $E_f = W + k$, where

$$W = (p^2 + 1)^{1/2} > 1$$

is the final electron energy. Also in (6.34) the matrix elements $H_{fi}(\mathbf{k}, \tau')$ and so on are the plane wave matrix elements for emission (with the complex conjugation) and absorption (without complex conjugation). The arguments indicate the momentum of the photon emitted or absorbed and the polarization of that photon. We normalize the radiation field so that the energy in unit volume is k or k_0. Then the coupling energy with the field is

$$e\left(\frac{2\pi}{k_0}\right)^{1/2} \boldsymbol{\alpha}\cdot\mathbf{a}_\tau \exp(i\mathbf{k}_0\cdot\mathbf{r}) = e\boldsymbol{\alpha}\cdot\mathbf{A} \tag{6.35}$$

for the photon with energy k_0, momentum $\mathbf{k}_0$. Here $\mathbf{a}_\tau$ is a unit (complex) polarization vector:

$$\mathbf{a}_\tau = 2^{-1/2}(\hat{\mathbf{e}}_1 + i\tau\hat{\mathbf{e}}_2) \tag{6.35$'$}$$

where $\hat{\mathbf{e}}_1$, $\hat{\mathbf{e}}_2$, and $\hat{\mathbf{e}}_3 = \hat{\mathbf{k}}_0$ form a right-handed system and $\tau = \pm 1$. For $\tau = +1$ the radiation is right circularly polarized (by definition), and $\tau = -1$ corresponds to left circular polarization. Also, $\mathbf{a}_{\tau'}$ is expressed in a similar way in terms of two directions which with $\hat{\mathbf{k}}$ form a right-handed coordinate system. The superscript $^{(\times)}$ on the matrix elements means that only the vector potential $\mathbf{A}$ in (6.35) is conjugated. Since the space-dependent exponential factors cancel out by linear momentum conservation, this means that only $\mathbf{a}_{\tau'}$ will be conjugated. The sum over τ' implies that even this operation is actually unessential ($\mathbf{a}_{\tau'}^{\times} = \mathbf{a}_{-\tau'}$). A sum over final spin states is implied in (6.34). Finally, the energy denominators in (6.34) are

$$E_0 = 1 + k_0 \tag{6.36a}$$

$$E_i = W' \tag{6.36b}$$

$$E_{ii} = k + k_0 + W'' \tag{6.36c}$$

The density of final states is

$$\rho_f = \frac{dk}{dE_f}\frac{k^2\,d\Omega}{(2\pi)^3} \tag{6.37}$$

where the volume of the box, in which the entire system is enclosed, has been set equal to unity. In (6.37), $d\Omega$ is the element of solid angle for the outgoing photon. From

$$W = (k_0^2 + k^2 - 2\mathbf{k}_0\cdot\mathbf{k} + 1)^{1/2}$$

we find

$$\rho_f = \frac{Wk}{k_0}\frac{k^2\,d\Omega}{(2\pi)^3} \tag{6.37$'$}$$

The cross section per unit solid angle is obtained from (6.34) by dividing by $c = 1$ and hence, in units of $(\hbar/mc)^2$,

$$\sigma = e^4 W \frac{k^2}{k_0^2} \sum_{r'} \left| \sum_i \frac{(\mathbf{p}|\boldsymbol{\alpha}\cdot\mathbf{a}_{r'}^{\times}|\mathbf{p}')(\mathbf{p}'|\boldsymbol{\alpha}\cdot\mathbf{a}_r|0)}{1 + k_0 - W'} + \sum_{ii} \frac{(\mathbf{p}|\boldsymbol{\alpha}\cdot\mathbf{a}_r|\mathbf{p}'')(\mathbf{p}''|\boldsymbol{\alpha}\cdot\mathbf{a}_{r'}^{\times}|0)}{1 - k - W''} \right|^2 \quad (6.38)$$

This refers to one electron. In an atom of atomic number Z the electrons scatter incoherently, and the cross section would then be multiplied by Z.

In (6.38) the plane wave states have been labeled by their momentum. It is important to remember that the initial state labeled 0 is an eigenstate corresponding to a definite spin direction $\mathbf{s}$: that is, it is an eigenstate of $\mathcal{O}\cdot\mathbf{s}$, where $\mathbf{s}$ may be taken to be unit vector for the present. These states were discussed in section 19. For the remaining states the spin representation need not be specified explicitly since a sum over spin states is to be carried out.

The sums over four intermediate states in (6.38) are carried out as follows. In the first sum we multiply numerator and denominator by $1 + k_0 + W'$ so that the denominator then becomes $(1 + k_0)^2 - W'^2 = 2k_0$ and is independent of the specification of the intermediate state spin and energy sign. The factor $1 + k_0 + W'$ in the numerator can be taken into either matrix element where, multiplying the state with momentum $\mathbf{p}'$, it is replaced by $1 + k_0 + h(\mathbf{k}_0)$, where

$$h(\mathbf{k}_0) = \boldsymbol{\alpha}\cdot\mathbf{k}_0 + \beta$$

Then the first sum has the form

$$\frac{1}{2k_0} \sum_i (\mathbf{p}|Q_1|\mathbf{p}')(\mathbf{p}'|Q_2|0)$$

with

$$Q_1 = \boldsymbol{\alpha}\cdot\mathbf{a}_{r'}^{\times}[1 + k_0 + h(\mathbf{k}_0)]$$

$$Q_2 = \boldsymbol{\alpha}\cdot\mathbf{a}_r$$

Introducing spinor indices, this sum is

$$[\mathbf{p}]_\rho^{\times}(Q_1)_{\rho\lambda}[\mathbf{p}']_\lambda[\mathbf{p}']_{\rho'}^{\times}(Q_2)_{\rho'\lambda'}[0]_{\lambda'} \quad (6.39)$$

wherein the momenta in square brackets are used as symbols for the amplitudes. The only quantity involved in the sum over intermediate states is $[\mathbf{p}']_\lambda[\mathbf{p}']_{\rho'}^{\times}$ and

$$\sum_i [\mathbf{p}']_\lambda[\mathbf{p}']_{\rho'}^{\times} = \delta_{\lambda\rho'}$$

since the states labeled by $\mathbf{p}'$ form a complete set of given momentum. Hence (6.39) becomes simply

$$(\mathbf{p}|Q_1 Q_2|0)$$

In a similar way, the second sum in (6.38) is evaluated by multiplying numerator and denominator by $1 - k + W''$. The result is

$$\sigma = \frac{e^4 W}{4}\frac{k^2}{k_0^2}\sum_{\tau'}\left|\frac{(\mathbf{p}|\Omega_1|0)}{k_0} - \frac{(\mathbf{p}|\Omega_2|0)}{k}\right|^2 \tag{6.40}$$

where

$$\Omega_1 = \boldsymbol{\alpha}\cdot\mathbf{a}_{\tau'}^{\times}[1 + k_0 + h(\mathbf{k}_0)]\boldsymbol{\alpha}\cdot\mathbf{a}_\tau \tag{6.40a}$$

$$\Omega_2 = \boldsymbol{\alpha}\cdot\mathbf{a}_\tau[1 - k - h(-\mathbf{k})]\boldsymbol{\alpha}\cdot\mathbf{a}_{\tau'}^{\times} \tag{6.40b}$$

Carrying out the square operation and introducing the projection operators previously studied in section 19, we find

$$\sigma = \frac{e^4 W k^2}{4k_0^2}\sum_{\tau'}\mathrm{Tr}\,(A - B - C + D) \tag{6.41}$$

where

$$k_0^2 A = P_+\Omega_1 P(\mathbf{s})\Omega_1^*$$

$$k^2 D = P_+\Omega_2 P(\mathbf{s})\Omega_2^*$$

$$kk_0 B = P_+\Omega_1 P(\mathbf{s})\Omega_2^*$$

$$kk_0 C = P_+\Omega_2 P(\mathbf{s})\Omega_1^*$$

Here we have already carried out the spin sum for the final electron states by introducing the (positive) energy projection operator

$$P_+ = \frac{1}{2}\left(1 + \frac{\boldsymbol{\alpha}\cdot\mathbf{p} + \beta}{W}\right) \tag{6.41a}$$

Compare Eq. (3.49). We have also introduced the projection operator $P(\mathbf{s})$ for the initial electron. This is,

$$P(\mathbf{s}) = \tfrac{1}{4}(1 + \boldsymbol{\sigma}\cdot\mathbf{s})(1 + \beta) \tag{6.41b}$$

Compare Eq. (3.60a).

The evaluation of the traces in (6.41) is quite lengthy but straightforward. It is facilitated by noting relations such as

$$\mathbf{a}_\tau\cdot\mathbf{a}_\tau^{\times} = \mathbf{a}_{\tau'}\cdot\mathbf{a}_{\tau'}^{\times} = 1$$

$$i\mathbf{a}_\tau \times \mathbf{a}_{\tau'}^{\times} = \tau'\hat{\mathbf{e}}_3 = \tau'\hat{\mathbf{k}}$$

$$\sum_{\tau'}\boldsymbol{\sigma}\cdot\mathbf{a}_{\tau'}\,\boldsymbol{\sigma}\cdot\mathbf{p}\,\boldsymbol{\sigma}\cdot\mathbf{a}_{\tau'}^{\times} = -2\boldsymbol{\sigma}\cdot\hat{\mathbf{k}}\,\mathbf{p}\cdot\hat{\mathbf{k}}$$

The final result is, for a single electron,[12]

$$\sigma = \frac{1}{2}r_0^2\frac{k^2}{k_0^2}\left[\frac{k_0}{k} + \frac{k}{k_0} - \sin^2\vartheta - \tau(1 - \cos\vartheta)\,\mathbf{s}\cdot(\mathbf{k}\cos\vartheta + \mathbf{k}_0)\right] \tag{6.42}$$

where $\cos\vartheta = \hat{\mathbf{k}}\cdot\hat{\mathbf{k}}_0$ is the scattering angle of the photon and we have introduced the classical electron radius $r_0 = e^2/mc^2 = e^2$ in our units. The first three terms in (6.42) give the well-known Klein-Nishina formula for Compton scattering. The last term, dependent on τ, gives the anisotropy due to the circular polarization of the photon and the magnetization of the electron. For scattering in magnetized iron, **s** would be replaced by its average value so that the anisotropic term would be of order $2/26 \approx 0.08$.

38. SOMMERFELD-MAUE APPROXIMATION

Plane waves for the Dirac particles have been used very frequently for the calculation of a number of other effects. Among these mention may be made of bremsstrahlung,[13] external pair formation,[13] photoelectric effect,[14] and internal pair formation.[15] In most cases appreciable deviations from these Born approximation† results are seen to occur when essentially exact calculations are carried out.[16] Since the exact calculations are very laborious, an improvement on the Born approximation is desirable. This is afforded by use of the Sommerfeld-Maue wave functions.[17] These wave functions, which have been worked out for the Coulomb field, correspond very closely to the well-known solutions of the non-relativistic problem in parabolic coordinates. As such, they give an approximate solution of the Dirac equation in closed form which can be used when the direction of motion of the particle at infinity is specified. The solutions are approximate, as could be expected, since the Dirac equation for central fields, unlike its non-relativistic counterpart, is not separable in parabolic coordinates. The solutions exhibited below have been used to obtain improved values for bremsstrahlung and external pair production cross sections[18] and photoelectric cross sections.[19]

The starting point is the exact second-order wave equation (4.23) which is written in the form

$$(\nabla^2 + W^2 - 2WV - 1]\psi = \boldsymbol{\alpha}\cdot(\vec{\mathbf{p}}V)\psi - V^2\psi \tag{6.43}$$

where $\vec{\mathbf{p}}$ operates only on V, the central field potential. The terms on the right side of (6.43) are to be treated as small correction terms, and the second term with V^2 is regarded as a second-order term while the first gives a first-order correction. Hence we write

$$\psi = \psi_0 + \psi_1 + \psi_2 + \cdots$$

Then with $p^2 = W^2 - 1$ and

$$D \equiv \nabla^2 + p^2 - 2WV$$

† In the narrow sense.

we obtain the series of equations

$$D\psi_0 = 0 \tag{6.44a}$$

$$D\psi_1 = -i\boldsymbol{\alpha}\cdot(\nabla V)\psi_0 \tag{6.44b}$$

$$D\psi_2 = -i\boldsymbol{\alpha}\cdot(\nabla V)\psi_1 - V^2\psi_0 \qquad \text{etc.} \tag{6.44c}$$

Our consideration is restricted to ψ_0 and the first-order correction ψ_1, so that only (6.44a) and (6.44b) will be considered.

We recognize that the operator D is diagonal. Since for $V \to 0$ the solution ψ_0 must become the free particle solutions, we write

$$\psi_0 = U(\mathbf{p})f(\mathbf{r}) \tag{6.45}$$

where $U(\mathbf{p})$ is the usual four-component Dirac spinor which gives the plane waves in momentum space. Then for $V \to 0$ we require $f \to \exp(i\mathbf{p}\cdot\mathbf{r})$. To simplify (6.44b) we set

$$\psi_1 = -i\boldsymbol{\alpha}\cdot\boldsymbol{\varphi} \tag{6.45$'$}$$

and (6.44b) becomes

$$D\boldsymbol{\varphi} = (\nabla V)\psi_0 \tag{6.45$''$}$$

The solution of (6.44a) for the Coulomb field is exactly the same as the non-relativistic equation, except that the rest mass of the latter equation is replaced by the moving mass. This is seen by introducing pr as a variable in (6.44a); then the equation becomes identical with the non-relativistic one if the coefficient $\alpha ZW/p$ of $1/r$ in the Coulomb term is written $\alpha Z/v$. The solution[20] of the non-relativistic equation in parabolic coordinates can be taken over so that

$$f(\mathbf{r}) = \exp(i\mathbf{p}\cdot\mathbf{r})\,F(-n, 1, u) \tag{6.46}$$

where

$$u = i(pr - \mathbf{p}\cdot\mathbf{r}) \tag{6.46a}$$

and the confluent hypergeometric function can be represented by the convergent series

$$F(-n, 1, u) = 1 - nu + \frac{n(n-1)u^2}{(2!)^2} + \cdots \tag{6.46b}$$

with

$$n = -i\,\frac{\alpha ZW}{p} \tag{6.46c}$$

We verify first that f reduces to a plane wave for $Z = 0$. That (6.46) is a solution is checked by using

$$\nabla^2 f = \exp(i\mathbf{p}\cdot\mathbf{r})\{-p^2F + 2i\mathbf{p}\cdot\nabla F + \nabla^2 F\}$$

and

$$\nabla F = i(p\hat{\mathbf{r}} - \mathbf{p})F'$$

where prime means the derivative with respect to u. Also

$$\nabla^2 F = \operatorname{div} \nabla F = i[(p\hat{\mathbf{r}} - \mathbf{p})\cdot\nabla F' + pF' \operatorname{div} \hat{\mathbf{r}}]$$

$$= -2p(p - \mathbf{p}\cdot\hat{\mathbf{r}})F'' + \frac{2ip}{r} F'$$

Hence

$$Df = \frac{2ip}{r} \exp(i\mathbf{p}\cdot\mathbf{r})[uF'' + (1-u)F' + nF] = 0$$

since the square bracket, set equal to zero, is the differential equation for the hypergeometric function.[21]

The following procedure gives, in outline form, the method of obtaining $\boldsymbol{\varphi}$. Let ψ_0 and ψ_0' be the solutions of (6.44a) for energies W and W' respectively. Then, by multiplication of (6.44a) by $\psi_0'^*$ and its counterpart for $\psi_0'^*$ by ψ_0 and subtraction, the orthogonality relation

$$\int \psi_0'^*(W + W' - 2V)\psi_0 \, d^3r = 0 \tag{6.47}$$

is obtained. Here Gauss' theorem is used to remove an integral of $\operatorname{div}[\psi_0'^*\nabla\psi_0 - (\nabla\psi_0')^*\psi_0]$. In a similar manner we demonstrate that

$$\int \psi_0'^*(W + W' - 2V)\left(\boldsymbol{\varphi} - \frac{1}{2W}\nabla\psi_0\right) d^3r = 0$$

Hence $\boldsymbol{\varphi} - \nabla\psi_0/2W$ must be a solution of (6.44a) since the solutions form a complete set. Therefore

$$\boldsymbol{\varphi} = \frac{1}{2W}\nabla\psi_0 + \mathbf{X}, \qquad D\mathbf{X} = 0 \tag{6.48}$$

and $\mathbf{X}$ is determined so that, in the limit $Z \to 0$, the ratio $\boldsymbol{\varphi}/\psi_0 \to 0$. The quantity $\nabla\psi_0$ is obtained from the above:

$$\nabla\psi_0 = U(\mathbf{p})\nabla f$$

$$= iU(\mathbf{p}) \exp(i\mathbf{p}\cdot\mathbf{r})[\mathbf{p}F + (p\hat{\mathbf{r}} - \mathbf{p})F'] \tag{6.49}$$

From (6.46b) it is seen that F' is proportional to n or αZ. On the other hand, the first term in (6.49) is of the same order as ψ_0. Hence, since this term is just $i\mathbf{p}\psi_0$, we can choose $\mathbf{X}$ so that this term is cancelled. Hence the Sommerfeld-Maue wave function is

$$\psi = \exp(i\mathbf{p}\cdot\mathbf{r})\left[F + \frac{1}{2W}\boldsymbol{\alpha}\cdot(p\hat{\mathbf{r}} - \mathbf{p})F'\right] U(\mathbf{p}) \tag{6.50}$$

where F is given in (6.46b). Of course, for $Z = 0$ they reduce to the familiar plane waves. Detailed analysis of the Sommerfeld-Maue approximation for the photoelectric effect[19] and for bremsstrahlung[18] shows that the expansion parameter is of order $\alpha Z/W$, and hence these functions are very well suited for high energy processes. Sommerfeld and Maue[17] have used the wave functions to calculate the Coulomb scattering. We note that the wave function as given in (6.50) does indeed have the asymptotic form[21] of a scattering function: plane wave plus outgoing spherical wave.

As an application of the result (6.50), we consider the modification of the positive energy projection operator due to the Coulomb field. We evaluate

$$[P_+(Z)]_{\sigma\rho} = (\psi_\sigma \psi_\rho^\times)_{r=0}$$

since this is the pertinent quantity for applications to beta decay where, following standard practice, the wave functions are evaluated on the nucleus. Then with F replaced by 1 and F' by $-n$ and recalling that $n^\times = -n$, we find

$$P_+(Z) = \left[1 - \frac{n}{2W}\,\boldsymbol{\alpha}\cdot(p\hat{\mathbf{r}} - \mathbf{p})\right] P_+ \left[1 + \frac{n}{2W}\,\boldsymbol{\alpha}\cdot(p\hat{\mathbf{r}} - \mathbf{p})\right]$$

Keeping only first-order corrections in n, we obtain

$$P_+(Z) = P_+ - \frac{i\alpha Z}{2W}\,[\beta(\boldsymbol{\alpha}\cdot\hat{\mathbf{r}} - \boldsymbol{\alpha}\cdot\hat{\mathbf{p}}) + 2i\boldsymbol{\sigma}\cdot\mathbf{p}\times\hat{\mathbf{r}}] \tag{6.51}$$

To first order in n this is a unitary transformation on the $Z = 0$ projection operator P_+. For negative energy states we find

$$P_-(Z) = P_- + \frac{i\alpha Z}{2W}\,[\beta(\boldsymbol{\alpha}\cdot\hat{\mathbf{r}} - \boldsymbol{\alpha}\cdot\hat{\mathbf{p}}) + 2i\boldsymbol{\sigma}\cdot\mathbf{p}\times\hat{\mathbf{r}}] \tag{6.51$'$}$$

and $P_+(Z) + P_-(Z) = 1$; also $P_+(Z)P_-(Z) = P_-(Z)P_+(Z) = 0$, and $\mathrm{Tr}\,P_+(Z) = \mathrm{Tr}\,P_-(Z) = 2$ just as for $Z = 0$. The results (6.51) and (6.51′) apply for waves which are plane waves plus outgoing waves at infinity. For the case in which the Coulomb field produces an incoming wave at infinity the sign of the Z-dependent terms is changed.[22]

39. FINITE NUCLEAR SIZE EFFECTS

In this section we take up the question of corrections due to the finite size of the nucleus. These arise in beta decay, internal conversion, electron scattering, isotope shift, hyperfine structure, and in many other situations.

Wave Functions inside the Nucleus[23]

We develop a method by which the solution of the Dirac equations can be expressed as an infinite series of quadratures for any central field. The method is essentially exact since it can be made to yield results of any desired degree of accuracy. The only approximation enters in terminating the series with a finite number of terms.

We write (5.5) in the form

$$\frac{du_1}{dr} = -\frac{\kappa}{r}u_1 + \epsilon_{12}u_2 \tag{6.52a}$$

$$\frac{du_2}{dr} = \epsilon_{21}u_1 + \frac{\kappa}{r}u_2 \tag{6.52b}$$

with

$$\epsilon_{12} = W + 1 - V, \qquad \epsilon_{21} = -(W - 1 - V)$$

Then these equations can be put into the form of integral equations:

$$u_1 = r^{-\kappa}\left[C_1 + \int_0^r r'^{\kappa}\epsilon_{12}(r')\, u_2(r')\, dr'\right] \tag{6.53a}$$

$$u_2 = r^{\kappa}\left[C_2 + \int_0^r r'^{-\kappa}\epsilon_{21}(r')\, u_1(r')\, dr'\right] \tag{6.53b}$$

These equations can now be solved by iteration. We consider the case of $\kappa < 0$ and $\kappa > 0$ separately.

For $\kappa = -k < 0$ the condition of integrability requires that $C_2 = 0$. We write (6.53) in the form

$$u_1 = C_1 r^k + \mathscr{I}_1 u_2$$

$$u_2 = \mathscr{I}_2 u_1$$

where $\mathscr{I}_1$ and $\mathscr{I}_2$ are linear integral operators:

$$\mathscr{I}_1 y = r^k \int_0^r r'^{-k}\epsilon_{12}(r')\, y(r')\, dr' \tag{6.54a}$$

$$\mathscr{I}_2 y = r^{-k} \int_0^r r'^{k}\epsilon_{21}(r')\, y(r')\, dr' \tag{6.54b}$$

Eliminating u_2,

$$u_1 = C_1 r^k + \mathscr{I}_1\mathscr{I}_2 u_1$$

or, by iteration,

$$u_1 = C_1(1 - \mathscr{I}_1\mathscr{I}_2)^{-1} r^k = C_1 \sum_0^\infty (\mathscr{I}_1\mathscr{I}_2)^n r^k \tag{6.55}$$

$$u_2 = \mathscr{I}_2 u_1$$

For $\kappa = k > 0$ the equations (6.53) become, with $C_1 = 0$,

$$u_1 = \mathscr{J}_1 u_2$$
$$u_2 = C_2 r^k + \mathscr{J}_2 u_1$$

and $\mathscr{J}_1$ and $\mathscr{J}_2$ are linear integral operators which differ from $\mathscr{I}_1$ and $\mathscr{I}_2$ only in that the sign of k is changed. For this case

$$u_2 = C_2 \sum_0^\infty (\mathscr{J}_2 \mathscr{J}_1)^n r^k$$
$$u_1 = \mathscr{J}_1 u_2 \tag{6.56}$$

In each case the solutions contain one arbitrary (normalization) constant, C_1 or C_2, but u_1/u_2 is uniquely determined. These solutions will be of practical use for a limited range of r although, as will be seen, they converge for all r with potentials of interest. For the finite nuclear size problem the solutions (6.55) and (6.56) are joined to linear combinations of regular and irregular Coulomb solutions and the joining condition together with the normalization fixes all the constants.

We may first recognize that if $V(r)$ is a polynomial with positive powers of r, each term in (6.55) or (6.56) is a polynomial in r and the degree of each succeeding polynomial in the series increases by 2. If V is a constant over a range $r < r_0$, the terms in the polynomials can be reordered to give the series expansion of the spherical Bessel functions. It is hardly necessary to show this in detail since the Taylor expansions of u_1 and u_2 are unique. If V is bounded, as it is for a nucleus of finite size, an upper limit for each term and for the series is obtained by replacing V with its maximum positive or negative value. The resulting series is, of course, again the series of the spherical Bessel functions which converge everywhere. Hence, for bounded V, the solutions (6.55) and (6.56) converge. For a potential which is negative definite and monotonic, such as the Coulomb field with finite size modification, there is in the discrete spectrum ($W < 1$) one turning point r_1, $V(r_1) = W - 1$, such that, for $r < r_1$, $\epsilon_{21} < 0$ and, for $r > r_1$, $\epsilon_{21} > 0$. For all r, $\epsilon_{12} > 0$. Hence both series are alternating in the region $r < r_1$ and an upper limit on the error is obtained from the first term neglected. In general, for bounded V the expansion parameter is of order $[(W - V)^2 - 1]r^2$, as can be seen by replacing ϵ_{12} and ϵ_{21} in (6.54) by "average" values. It will be seen that the integrals will exist and the series will converge for all cases wherein $\lim rV = 0$ for $r \to 0$. Hence the Coulomb field, as is usual, is a special case and the method does not work for this "singular" field.

Considering the leading terms, we have for $\kappa = -k$,

$$u_1(r) \cong C_1 r^k$$

$$u_2(r) \cong \frac{C_1 r^{k+1}}{2k+1} \int_0^1 w(x)\epsilon_{12}(rx)\, dx$$

where

$$w(x) = (2k+1)x^{2k}$$

is a normalized weight function:

$$\int_0^1 w(x)\, dx = 1$$

In general, then, u_1 is determined by the centrifugal term but u_2 is strongly dependent on the potential at points between 0 and r. For very large k the weight function becomes a delta function at $x = 1$, and the value of $u_2(r)$ no longer depends on the details of the potential at points closer to the origin than r. This is readily understood in terms of the repulsion of the centrifugal terms. For $\kappa = k$ the functions u_1 and u_2 interchange their roles:

$$u_2 \cong C_2 r^k$$

$$u_1 \cong C_2 \frac{r^{k+1}}{2k+1} \int_0^1 w(x)\epsilon_{21}(rx)\, dx$$

For the constant density nucleus of radius r_0,

$$V = -\frac{\alpha Z}{2r_0}\left(3 - \frac{r^2}{r_0^2}\right)$$

The radial functions for $\kappa = k$ are

$$u_1 = \left(\frac{r}{r_0}\right)^{k+1} \sum_0^\infty a_n \left(\frac{r}{r_0}\right)^{2n} \tag{6.57a}$$

$$u_2 = \left(\frac{r}{r_0}\right)^{k} \sum_0^\infty b_n \left(\frac{r}{r_0}\right)^{2n} \tag{6.57b}$$

with

$$b_0 = \frac{(2k+1)a_0}{r_0(W+1) + 3\alpha Z/2} \tag{6.58a}$$

and the recurrence relations

$$(2k + 2n + 1)a_n = \left[r_0(W+1) + 3\frac{\alpha Z}{2}\right]b_n - \frac{\alpha Z}{2} b_{n-1} \tag{6.58b}$$

$$2(n+1)b_{n+1} = -\left[r_0(W-1) + 3\frac{\alpha Z}{2}\right]a_n + \frac{\alpha Z}{2} a_{n-1}$$

determine the remaining coefficients in terms of a_0, which is a normalization constant. For $\kappa = -k$ we interchange u_1 and u_2 and change the sign of W and Z; see section 26. These wave functions have been used in a number of problems.[24] For beta-particle energies three terms of the series usually give the wave functions for all $r < r_0$ to better than 1 percent.

Scattering Phase Shifts

Phase shifts for scattering may be obtained by joining the solutions inside the nucleus (see above) to the Coulomb solutions outside the nucleus. This procedure is sometimes laborious, and a more direct method for obtaining the phase shifts will be of interest. Generally, the method to be described is approximate. However, when the potential energy V deviates from the Coulomb value over a finite distance and the solutions inside the nucleus are known (see above) exactly, the method becomes exact.

The difference between the actual potential V and the Coulomb value is denoted by $\mathscr{V}(r)$:

$$\mathscr{V}(r) = V + \alpha Z/r \tag{6.59}$$

Then the radial equations (5.5) become

$$\frac{d}{dr}\begin{pmatrix} u_1 \\ u_2 \end{pmatrix} - M(r)\begin{pmatrix} u_1 \\ u_2 \end{pmatrix} = \begin{pmatrix} 0 & -\mathscr{V} \\ \mathscr{V} & 0 \end{pmatrix}\begin{pmatrix} u_1 \\ u_2 \end{pmatrix} \tag{6.60}$$

where the matrix M is given by

$$M = \begin{pmatrix} -\kappa/r & W + 1 + \alpha Z/r \\ -W + 1 - \alpha Z/r & \kappa/r \end{pmatrix} \tag{6.60'}$$

The real Coulomb ($\mathscr{V} = 0$) radial functions multiplied by r are denoted by v_1 and v_2 for the solution regular at the origin and by $\bar{v}_1$ and $\bar{v}_2$ for the solution irregular at the origin. Then the Wronskian

$$v_1\bar{v}_2 - v_2\bar{v}_1$$

has a constant value, as may be verified by differentiation and the use of (5.5). We normalize the Coulomb solutions so that

$$v_2\bar{v}_1 - v_1\bar{v}_2 = 1 \tag{6.61}$$

Then an integral equation equivalent to (6.60) is

$$u_i(r) = v_i(r)\left[1 - \int_r^\infty \bar{v}_j(r')\, u_j(r')\, \mathscr{V}(r')\, dr'\right] - \bar{v}_i(r)\int_0^r v_j(r')\, u_j(r')\, \mathscr{V}(r')\, dr' \tag{6.62}$$

Repeated indices are to be summed over the two values 1, 2. This expression for u_i can be written more compactly in terms of the Green function matrix of (6.60):

$$u_i = v_i - \int_0^\infty G_{ij}(r, r')\, u_j(r')\, \mathscr{V}(r')\, dr' \tag{6.63}$$

where

$$\begin{aligned} G_{ij}(r, r') &= v_i(r)\, \bar{v}_j(r'), \qquad r' > r \\ &= \bar{v}_i(r)\, v_j(r'), \qquad r > r' \end{aligned} \tag{6.63'}$$

The asymptotic behavior of v_i and $\bar{v}_i$ with the normalization (6.61) is (cf. sections 32 and 34)

$$\begin{aligned} v_1 &\to -[p/(W-1)]^{1/2} \cos(pr + \delta) \\ v_2 &\to [(W-1)/p]^{1/2} \sin(pr + \delta) \\ \bar{v}_1 &\to [p(W-1)]^{1/2} \sin(pr + \delta) \\ \bar{v}_2 &\to [(W-1)/p]^{1/2} \cos(pr + \delta) \end{aligned}$$

where δ is defined in (5.75). The subscripts κ are omitted throughout. Thus the solutions of section 32 have been multiplied by $-\pi^{1/2}$. The irregular solutions are obtained from these by the change of sign of γ. The asymptotic behavior of u_1 and u_2 will be

$$\begin{aligned} u_1 &\to -[p/(W-1)]^{1/2}[\cos(pr + \delta) - \tan\Delta \sin(pr + \delta)] \\ u_2 &\to [(W-1)/p]^{1/2}[\sin(pr + \delta) + \tan\Delta \cos(pr + \delta)] \end{aligned}$$

so that Δ is the additional phase shift produced by the deviation from the Coulomb field. Comparing with (6.63), we find

$$\tan\Delta = -\int_0^\infty v_j(r')\, u_j(r')\, \mathscr{V}(r')\, dr' \tag{6.64}$$

When $\mathscr{V} \neq 0$ for $r < r_0$ only, the integral is taken over the finite region $r < r_0$. However, this result has the disadvantage that the solutions u_j must be normalized, and the solutions for $r > r_0$ must be continued to infinity in order to do this. An alternative expression for the phase can be obtained from (6.63) and (6.64).[23,25] This is

$$-\cot\Delta = \frac{\displaystyle\int_0^\infty dr\, \mathscr{V}(r)\, u_j(r)\, u_j(r) + \int_0^\infty dr \int_0^\infty dr'\, \mathscr{V}(r)\, u_i(r)\, G_{ij}(r, r')\, u_j(r')\, \mathscr{V}(r')}{\left[\displaystyle\int_0^\infty dr\, \mathscr{V}(r)\, u_j(r)\, v_j(r)\right]^2} \tag{6.65}$$

with sums over repeated indices implied. The normalization constant in u_j now cancels out. The expression (6.65) is actually stationary[25] with respect to first-order variations in $u_j(r)$. This is not true of (6.64). When $\mathscr{V}(r) = 0$ for $r > r_0$, the solution u_j for $r < r_0$ obtained as described above can be used to evaluate $\cot \Delta$ directly.

40. THE DIRAC EQUATION AT HIGH ENERGIES

A high energy electron behaves very much like a particle with zero rest mass. In this respect at high energies the properties of electrons are related to those of the neutrinos to be studied in Chapter VII. Of course, one major distinction, compared to the neutrino case, is the fact that for an electron interactions with electromagnetic fields are possible. A second, as will be seen, is the fundamentally different polarization possible.

We consider an electron in a central field V. Instead of the $\boldsymbol{\alpha}$ and β standard representation we use[9]

$$\boldsymbol{\alpha}' = \rho_3\boldsymbol{\sigma} = \begin{pmatrix} \boldsymbol{\sigma} & 0 \\ 0 & -\boldsymbol{\sigma} \end{pmatrix}, \qquad \beta' = \rho_1 = \begin{pmatrix} 0 & 1 \\ 1 & 0 \end{pmatrix} \tag{6.66}$$

which can be obtained from the standard representation by

$$\rho_3\boldsymbol{\sigma} = S\rho_1\boldsymbol{\sigma}S^{-1}$$

where the unitary matrix S is

$$S = \frac{1}{\sqrt{2}}\begin{pmatrix} 1 & 1 \\ 1 & -1 \end{pmatrix} = \frac{1}{\sqrt{2}}(\rho_3 + \rho_1) \times I_2 \tag{6.67}$$

and each element appearing in the first form of S is a 2 by 2 matrix.

The wave equation written in terms of upper and lower components is now

$$\begin{aligned} (\boldsymbol{\sigma}\cdot\vec{\mathbf{p}} + V - W)\psi'^u &= 0 \\ (-\boldsymbol{\sigma}\cdot\vec{\mathbf{p}} + V - W)\psi'^l &= 0 \end{aligned} \tag{6.68}$$

where the transformed wave function is

$$\psi' = \begin{pmatrix} \psi'^u \\ \psi'^l \end{pmatrix}$$

and where the rest mass term is neglected. It is seen that as a consequence of the representation (6.66) the upper and lower components are now decoupled. However, we still deal with a *four*-component wave function.

For a free particle,

$$\begin{aligned} \boldsymbol{\sigma}\cdot\vec{\mathbf{p}}\ \psi'^{u} &= W\psi'^{u} \\ \boldsymbol{\sigma}\cdot\vec{\mathbf{p}}\ \psi'^{l} &= -W\psi'^{l} \end{aligned} \tag{6.69}$$

The plane wave solutions $\psi' = A' \exp(i\mathbf{p}\cdot\mathbf{r})$ or

$$\psi'^{u} = A'^{u} \exp(i\mathbf{p}\cdot\mathbf{r})$$

$$\psi'^{l} = A'^{l} \exp(i\mathbf{p}\cdot\mathbf{r})$$

are obtained with the amplitudes given by the helicity eigenvalue equations

$$\begin{aligned} \boldsymbol{\sigma}\cdot\hat{\mathbf{p}}A'^{u} &= A'^{u} \\ \boldsymbol{\sigma}\cdot\hat{\mathbf{p}}A'^{l} &= -A'^{l} \end{aligned} \tag{6.70}$$

These eigenvalue problems were solved in Chapter I, where $\boldsymbol{\sigma}\cdot\hat{\mathbf{p}}$ was diagonalized in the Pauli theory. From (1.33a) we deduce that

$$A' = \begin{pmatrix} c_1\begin{pmatrix} e^{-i\varphi/2}\cos\vartheta/2 \\ e^{i\varphi/2}\sin\vartheta/2 \end{pmatrix} \\ c_2\begin{pmatrix} -e^{-i\varphi/2}\sin\vartheta/2 \\ e^{i\varphi/2}\cos\vartheta/2 \end{pmatrix} \end{pmatrix} \tag{6.71}$$

where ϑ and φ are the polar and azimuth angles of $\hat{\mathbf{p}}$. To understand the significance of the constants c_1 and c_2 we transform the standard representation wave function ψ_{st}.

$$\psi_{\mathrm{st}} = U_m(\mathbf{p}) \exp(i\mathbf{p}\cdot\mathbf{r})$$

where, in the high energy limit,

$$U_m(\mathbf{p}) = \frac{1}{\sqrt{2}}\begin{pmatrix} \chi^m \\ \boldsymbol{\sigma}\cdot\hat{\mathbf{p}}\chi^m \end{pmatrix}$$

Then from (6.67) the transformed wave function is

$$\psi' = S\psi_{\mathrm{st}} = U'_m \exp(i\mathbf{p}\cdot\mathbf{r})$$

$$\begin{aligned} U'_m &= \frac{1}{2}\begin{pmatrix} (1 + \boldsymbol{\sigma}\cdot\mathbf{p})\,\chi^m \\ (1 - \boldsymbol{\sigma}\cdot\mathbf{p})\,\chi^m \end{pmatrix} \\ &= \begin{pmatrix} P^{+}(\hat{\mathbf{p}})\,\chi^m \\ P^{-}(\hat{\mathbf{p}})\,\chi^m \end{pmatrix} \end{aligned} \tag{6.72}$$

where $P^{\pm}(\hat{\mathbf{p}})$ are the Pauli spin projection operators.

Writing these in detail,

$$U'_{1/2} = \frac{1}{2}\begin{pmatrix} 1+\cos\vartheta \\ \sin\vartheta\, e^{i\varphi} \\ 1-\cos\vartheta \\ -\sin\vartheta\, e^{i\varphi} \end{pmatrix} = \begin{pmatrix} \cos^2\vartheta/2 \\ \sin\vartheta/2\cos\vartheta/2\, e^{i\varphi} \\ \sin^2\vartheta/2 \\ -\sin\vartheta/2\cos\vartheta/2\, e^{i\varphi} \end{pmatrix} \tag{6.73a}$$

$$U'_{-1/2} = \frac{1}{2}\begin{pmatrix} \sin\vartheta\, e^{-i\varphi} \\ 1-\cos\vartheta \\ -\sin\vartheta\, e^{-i\varphi} \\ 1+\cos\vartheta \end{pmatrix} = \begin{pmatrix} \sin\vartheta/2\cos\vartheta/2\, e^{-i\varphi} \\ \sin^2\vartheta/2 \\ -\sin\vartheta/2\cos\vartheta/2\, e^{-i\varphi} \\ \cos^2\vartheta/2 \end{pmatrix} \tag{6.73b}$$

These amplitude spinors diagonalize $\mathcal{O}_z' = S\mathcal{O}_z S^{-1}$, where $\mathcal{O}$ is the spin operator discussed in section 15. To diagonalize $\mathcal{O}'\cdot\hat{\mathbf{n}}$, where $\hat{\mathbf{n}}$ is a unit vector with polar and azimuth angles ϑ_n, φ_n, the usual procedure is followed. The amplitudes are transformed to

$$A'_+ = \cos\frac{\vartheta_n}{2}\, e^{-i\varphi_n/2}\, U'_{1/2} + \sin\frac{\vartheta_n}{2}\, e^{i\varphi_n/2}\, U'_{-1/2}$$

$$A'_- = -\sin\frac{\vartheta_n}{2}\, e^{-i\varphi_n/2}\, U'_{1/2} + \cos\frac{\vartheta_n}{2}\, e^{i\varphi_n/2}\, U'_{-1/2}$$

We now take $\hat{\mathbf{n}} = \hat{\mathbf{p}}$ so that $A'_\pm$ will be amplitudes for states of positive and negative helicity respectively. Then $\vartheta_n = \vartheta$, $\varphi_n = \varphi$, and

$$A'_+ = \begin{pmatrix} e^{-i\varphi/2}\cos\vartheta/2 \\ e^{i\varphi/2}\sin\vartheta/2 \\ 0 \\ 0 \end{pmatrix} \tag{6.74a}$$

$$A'_- = \begin{pmatrix} 0 \\ 0 \\ -e^{-i\varphi/2}\sin\vartheta/2 \\ e^{i\varphi/2}\cos\vartheta/2 \end{pmatrix} \tag{6.74b}$$

We see that the solutions for mean spin along $\pm\hat{\mathbf{p}}$ are effectively *two-component* spinors with Pauli spin functions. From (6.71) these two solutions are obtained by setting $c_1 = 1$, $c_2 = 0$ and $c_1 = 0$, $c_2 = 1$. Of course, this result would have been predicted, since the upper and lower components in (6.70) have opposite signs for the eigenvalues of $\boldsymbol{\sigma}\cdot\hat{\mathbf{p}}$, so that if this operator is diagonal one of the components must be identically zero.

It is clear that throughout this development the nomenclature "large components" and "small components" is no longer significant. The upper and lower components have the same order of magnitude.

It is useful to observe that for free particles it is possible to remove the rest mass term from the Hamiltonian in a rigorous manner.† This is done by the (unitary) Foldy-Wouthuysen transformation discussed in section 18. From

$$H\psi = W\psi$$

we transform again to ψ' by

$$\psi' = e^{i\mathfrak{U}}\psi$$

with the hermitian $\mathfrak{U}$ written exactly as in (3.32). Then

$$H'\psi' = W\psi'$$

with

$$H' = e^{i\mathfrak{U}}He^{-i\mathfrak{U}}$$

given by Eq. (3.33). However, this time we eliminate β by choosing

$$\tan p\,\varphi/m = -m/p \tag{6.75}$$

In this case

$$H' = \frac{\boldsymbol{\alpha}\cdot\mathbf{p}}{p}(p^2 + m^2)^{1/2}$$

Here $\mathbf{p}$ is everywhere an operator. If we take a plane wave solution, then $\mathbf{p}$ is replaced by the momentum eigenvalue. Consequently, with

$$\psi = A\exp(i\mathbf{p}\cdot\mathbf{r})$$

$$\psi' = A'\exp(i\mathbf{p}\cdot\mathbf{r})$$

$$A' = e^{i\mathfrak{U}}A$$

we have

$$\boldsymbol{\alpha}\cdot\hat{\mathbf{p}}A' = A'$$

The amplitude A' is to be distinguished from (6.71). If now the representation (6.66) is used, the equations (6.70) apply rigorously to the amplitude

$$A'' = \frac{1}{\sqrt{2}}\begin{pmatrix}1 & 1\\ 1 & -1\end{pmatrix}A'$$

The transformation from A to A' is made with

$$e^{i\mathfrak{U}} = \left[\frac{1}{2}\left(1 + \frac{p}{W}\right)\right]^{1/2} - \beta\boldsymbol{\alpha}\cdot\hat{\mathbf{p}}\left[\frac{1}{2}\left(1 - \frac{p}{W}\right)\right]^{1/2} \tag{6.76}$$

† See reference 17 of Chapter III.

The connection with the transformation discussed at the beginning of this section is obvious. If $W \to \infty$, the second term in (6.76) vanishes and $\exp(i\mathfrak{U}) = 1$ so that $A' = A$ and $\psi' = \psi$. Then only the transformation (6.67) is needed to go from A to A''.

It is also of interest to discuss the central field solutions in the angular momentum representation. These are obtained from (5.3) and (6.67).

$$\psi_\kappa^\mu = \frac{1}{\sqrt{2}}\begin{pmatrix} g\chi_\kappa^\mu + if\chi_{-\kappa}^\mu \\ g\chi_\kappa^\mu - if\chi_{-\kappa}^\mu \end{pmatrix} \tag{6.77}$$

The total angular momentum is diagonal, as is its z-component:

$$\mathbf{j}^2\psi_\kappa^\mu = j(j+1)\psi_\kappa^\mu$$

$$j_z\psi_\kappa^\mu = \mu\psi_\kappa^\mu$$

and βI_s has the eigenvalue $(-)^{l+1}$, where β is given by (6.66). Similarly $K = \beta(\boldsymbol{\sigma}\cdot\mathbf{l} + 1)$ has the eigenvalue $-\kappa$ with the same β.

The radial functions for the Coulomb field are obtained from (5.76) and (5.77) with

$$e^{2i\eta} = -\frac{\kappa}{\gamma + i\alpha Z}$$

y is everywhere replaced by αZ and the factors $(W \pm 1)^{1/2}$ are replaced by $W^{1/2}$. From the radial equations in the high energy limit,

$$\frac{dg_\kappa}{dr} = -\frac{\kappa+1}{r}g_\kappa + (W - V)f_\kappa$$

$$\frac{df_\kappa}{dr} = -(W - V)g_\kappa + \frac{\kappa - 1}{r}f_\kappa$$

we see that changing the sign of κ restores the equation if the replacements $f \to -g$ and $g \to f$ are made. Hence

$$f_{-\kappa} = -g_\kappa, \qquad g_{-\kappa} = f_\kappa \tag{6.78}$$

From the asymptotic behavior given in (5.78a) and (5.78b) it is then evident that

$$\delta_{-\kappa} = \delta_\kappa + \pi/2 \tag{6.79}$$

a relation which is useful in the analysis of high energy scattering.[26] From (5.75), this relation between the phases is equivalent to

$$\eta_{-\kappa} - \eta_\kappa = \pi/2$$

and the definition of $e^{2i\eta}$ given above is seen to give a verification of this result. In fact, the correction term is seen from

$$\exp\left[2i(\eta_{\kappa} - \eta_{-\kappa})\right] \cong -\left(1 - \frac{2i\alpha Z}{p\kappa}\right)$$

to be completely negligible at energies of order 50 Mev. The relative signs of $\eta_{-\kappa}$ and η_{κ} were fixed by the choice of phase made in (6.78). Obviously, for given f_{κ} and g_{κ} it would be equally valid to reverse the sign of both $f_{-\kappa}$ and $g_{-\kappa}$. The application of these central field solutions to the high energy scattering problem has been made by Yennie et al.[9]

For the extreme relativistic limit a rough approximation using the asymptotic form of the radial functions f and g will often yield useful results. This is the so-called Casimir limit.

PROBLEMS

1. Find the cross section for electron-electron scattering with the Møller interaction in the limit of small scattering angles. Take one electron to be initially at rest.

2. Show that in the Born approximation the scattering amplitudes F and G as defined in section 33 are out of phase by $\pi/2$ and hence that there is no effect on the scattering of the initial electron polarization.

3. Derive the expression (6.65) for the phase shifts.

4. Obtain the high energy solutions for a positron. Write phase in the form of wave functions for positive and negative helicity.

5. Find the transformed spin operator $\mathcal{O}$ in the representation (6.66).

6. Show that for the state described by (6.71) with $c_1 = c_2 = 1$ the mean spin along the direction of motion vanishes.

7. In beta decay the electron is emitted with polarization $-v/c$ along the direction of the momentum. What does this mean with regard to the relative amplitude of positive and negative helicity states. In what way, if any, would the answer change if one considers the limit $v \to c$.

8. Estimate the order of magnitude of the phase shifts in scattering due to the finite size of the nucleus (1) by assuming a constant proton charge density and (2) by using only the first terms of the expansion of the wave functions occurring in (6.65). Comment on the validity of this approximation at high scattering energies.

9. Inelastic scattering of electrons by atoms is obtained in the Born approximation by using the matrix element (6.20′), replacing $\boldsymbol{\alpha}$ for the atomic electrons by the operator which gives the non-relativistic current density, and summing over all bound electrons.[27] Show that if polarized electrons are inelastically scattered there is no scattering asymmetry in the Born approximation.

10. Discuss the high energy approximation in which one uses

$$S' = \frac{1}{\sqrt{2}}\begin{pmatrix} 1 & 1 \\ -1 & 1 \end{pmatrix}$$

in place of (6.67). Start with the standard representation and find the transformed wave functions which diagonalize $S'\mathcal{O}\cdot\vec{\mathbf{p}}S'^{-1}$.

REFERENCES

1. W. Pauli, *Helv. Phys. Acta* **5,** 179 (1932).
2. See, for example, L. I. Schiff, *Quantum Mechanics*, McGraw-Hill Book Co., New York, 2nd ed., 1955, section 28.
3. R. J. Bessey, Thesis, University of Michigan (1942), unpublished.
4. R. H. Good, Jr., *Phys. Rev.* **90,** 131 (1953); **94,** 931 (1954).
5. C. Møller, *Z. Physik* **70,** 786 (1931); *Ann. Physik* **14,** 531 (1932).
6. L. Rosenfeld, *Z. Physik* **73,** 253 (1931); H. A. Bethe and E. Fermi, *Z. Physik* **77,** 296 (1932); W. Heitler and L. Nordheim, *J. phys.* **5,** 449 (1934).
7. G. Breit, *Phys. Rev.* **34,** 553 (1929); **36,** 383 (1930); **39,** 616 (1932). See also J. R. Oppenheimer, *Phys. Rev.* **35,** 461 (1930).
8. See, for example, M. E. Rose, *Phys. Rev.* **73,** 279 (1948).
9. D. R. Yennie, D. G. Ravenhall, and R. N. Wilson, *Phys. Rev.* **95,** 500 (1954).
10. G. Parzen, *Phys. Rev.* **80,** 261 (1950).
11. H. Schopper, *Nuclear Instr.* **3,** 158 (1958); L. Grodzins, *Prog. in Nuclear Phys.* **7,** 163 (1959).
12. W. Franz, *Ann. Physik* **33,** 689 (1938); F. W. Lipps and H. A. Tolhoek, *Physica* **20,** 85, 395 (1954).
13. W. Heitler, *Quantum Theory of Radiation*, Oxford Press, 3rd ed., 1954.
14. F. Sauter, *Ann. Physik* **9,** 217 (1931); **11,** 454 (1931).
15. M. E. Rose, *Phys. Rev.* **76,** 678 (1949); **78,** 184 (1950).
16. Photoelectric effect: H. R. Hulme, J. McDougal, R. Buckingham, and R. Fowler, *Proc. Roy. Soc.* (*London*) **A149,** 131 (1935). Internal pairs: J. C. Jäger and H. R. Hulme, *Proc. Roy. Soc.* (*London*) **A148,** 708 (1935).
17. A. Sommerfeld and A. W. Maue, *Ann. Physik* **22,** 629 (1935); see also W. Furry, *Phys. Rev.* **46,** 391 (1934).
18. H. A. Bethe and L. Maximon, *Phys. Rev.* **93,** 768 (1954). See also H. Davies, H. A. Bethe, and L. Maximon, *Phys. Rev.* **93,** 788 (1954); H. Olsen, *Phys. Rev.* **99,** 1335 (1955).
19. H. Banerjee, *Nuovo cimento* **10,** 863 (1958). Also T. Erber, *Ann. Phys.* **8,** 435 (1959).
20. G. Temple, *Proc. Roy. Soc.* (*London*) **A121,** 673 (1928); A. Sommerfeld, *Ann. Physik* **11,** 257 (1931).
21. *Higher Transcendental Functions*, Bateman Manuscript Project, McGraw-Hill Book Co., New York, 1953, Vol. I, Chapter VI.
22. J. D. Jackson, S. B. Treiman, and H. W. Wyld, Jr., *Z. Physik* **150,** 640 (1958).
23. M. E. Rose, *Phys. Rev.* **82,** 389 (1951).
24. L. K. Acheson, Jr., *Phys. Rev.* **82,** 488 (1951); T. A. Green and M. E. Rose, *Phys. Rev.* **110,** 105 (1958); M. E. Rose and D. K. Holmes, *Phys. Rev.* **83,** 190 (1951).
25. J. M. Blatt and J. D. Jackson, *Phys. Rev.* **76,** 18 (1949).
26. H. Feshbach, *Phys. Rev.* **84,** 1206 (1951).
27. H. A. Bethe, *Handbuch der Physik*, XXIV/1, Julius Springer, Berlin, p. 495.

VII.

NEUTRINO THEORY

41. FOUR-COMPONENT FORMULATION

Mass of the Neutrino

The unique position of the neutrino arises from the null character of many of its physical attributes. That it has no charge is obvious. The neutrino magnetic moment is either zero or so extremely small as to preclude any likelihood of its observation. In fact, since the only interaction known to exist for this particle is the very small coupling leading to decay processes, there seems to be no mechanism for providing the neutrino with an appreciable magnetic moment. Finally, the neutrino mass is extremely small (in units of m) and the experiments are consistent with this mass m_ν being zero.

The most reliable value for the mass of the neutrino comes from the observation of the shape of the nuclear beta spectrum near the maximum electron energy where, if there were a non-zero neutrino rest mass, its effect would be noticeable when the corresponding rest energy is of the order of the neutrino kinetic energy. In order that this portion of the spectrum constitute a non-negligible portion of the total spectrum an emitter with a small energy release is studied. The best source for this purpose is H^3.

The effect of the possible non-zero neutrino rest mass is observed in the alteration of the statistical factor

$$p^2\,dp \int q^2\,dq\;\delta(W_0 - W - W_\nu) = dW\,pW(W_0 - W)[(W_0 - W)^2 - m_\nu^2]^{1/2} \quad (7.1)$$

Here q is the magnitude of the neutrino momentum and W_ν is its total energy. Besides this statistical factor, the spectrum for emission of electrons is proportional to

$$\mathrm{Tr}\left(1 + \frac{\boldsymbol{\alpha}\cdot\mathbf{p} + \beta}{W}\right)\Omega(1 + \gamma_5)\left(1 + \frac{\boldsymbol{\alpha}\cdot\mathbf{q} \mp \beta m_\nu}{W_\nu}\right)\Omega^*(1 + \gamma_5) \quad (7.2)$$

where

$$\Omega = M(1) - \lambda\boldsymbol{\sigma}\cdot M(\sigma)$$

contains the nuclear matrix elements. The upper sign above corresponds to e^- emission accompanied by the emission of an antineutrino (charge conjugate of a positive energy state) and the lower sign implies emission of a positive energy neutrino. At this stage the distinction is purely a formal one. The only contribution to (7.2) arising from m_ν is

$$\mp \frac{m_\nu}{WW_\nu} \mathrm{Tr}\, \beta\Omega(1 + \gamma_5)\, \beta\Omega^*(1 + \gamma_5)$$

However, Ω as well as Ω^* commutes with $1 + \gamma_5$ while

$$\beta(1 + \gamma_5) = (1 - \gamma_5)\beta$$

Hence we obtain the trace of a matrix containing $(1 + \gamma_5)(1 - \gamma_5)$ as a factor, and this product is identically zero. If the $(1 + \gamma_5)$ factors in (7.2) are replaced by $1 + \epsilon\gamma_5$, the result of (2) gives a term in m_ν proportional to $1 - \epsilon^2$ and experimentally $1 - \epsilon^2 \ll 1$. Consequently, the altered form of the statistical weight is the only effect which needs to be considered. The experimental result[1] is $m_\nu < 10^{-3}$.

Since this mass is so small and may well be zero, we shall take $m_\nu = 0$ in what follows. In this connection it should be realized that all measurable quantities are continuous in the limit $m_\nu = 0$, and so far as experiments are concerned there seems to be no prospect of distinguishing between theories with zero and non-zero but very small rest mass of the neutrino.

Neutrino Helicity

With $m_\nu = 0$ the theory developed in section 40 for high energy electrons holds rigorously for the neutrino. Using the notation $\mathbf{q}$ for momentum and $q > 0$ for the energy, we write

$$\boldsymbol{\alpha}\cdot\nabla\psi = -\frac{\partial\psi}{\partial t} \quad (7.3)$$

and with the plane wave solutions

$$\psi = A \exp\left[i(\mathbf{q}\cdot\mathbf{r} - qt)\right] \quad (7.4)$$

we find

$$\boldsymbol{\alpha}\cdot\hat{\mathbf{q}}\, A = A \quad (7.5)$$

where the unit vector $\hat{\mathbf{q}}$ is

$$\hat{\mathbf{q}} = \mathbf{q}/q$$

In the representation (6.66) wherein

$$\boldsymbol{\alpha} = \begin{pmatrix} \boldsymbol{\sigma} & 0 \\ 0 & -\boldsymbol{\sigma} \end{pmatrix}$$

we obtain, as before, the general solution for positive energies,

$$A = \begin{pmatrix} c_1 A_+ \\ c_2 A_- \end{pmatrix} \tag{7.6}$$

where

$$A_+ = \begin{pmatrix} e^{-i\varphi/2} \cos \vartheta/2 \\ e^{i\varphi/2} \sin \vartheta/2 \end{pmatrix} \tag{7.7a}$$

$$A_- = \begin{pmatrix} -e^{-i\varphi/2} \sin \vartheta/2 \\ e^{i\varphi/2} \cos \vartheta/2 \end{pmatrix} \tag{7.7b}$$

and ϑ, φ are the polar and azimuth angles of $\hat{\mathbf{q}}$. In (7.6), c_1 and c_2 are constants which may be subject to the normalizing condition

$$|c_1|^2 + |c_2|^2 = 1$$

and A_+, A_- are positive and negative helicity solutions:

$$\boldsymbol{\sigma}\cdot\hat{\mathbf{q}}\, A_\pm = \pm A_\pm \tag{7.8}$$

We now introduce two projection operators which have the property of selecting one or the other of the two eigenstates of the so-called chirality† operator γ_5. These projection operators are

$$\omega_\pm = \tfrac{1}{2}(1 \pm \gamma_5) \tag{7.9}$$

where, clearly,

$$\omega_+ + \omega_- = 1$$
$$\omega_\pm^2 = \omega_\pm$$
$$\omega_+\omega_- = \omega_-\omega_+ = 0$$

The states $\omega_\pm \psi$ will be denoted by $\phi_\mp$ where the reason for the inversion of indices ($\pm$) will be clear presently; thus

$$\phi_\mp = \omega_\pm \psi$$
$$= B_\mp \exp\,[i(\mathbf{q}\cdot\mathbf{r} - qt)]$$

$$B_\mp = \omega_\pm A \tag{7.10}$$

† The chirality transform of ψ is $\gamma_5\psi$.[2]

Then, from (7.5),

$$\begin{aligned}\boldsymbol{\sigma}\cdot\hat{\mathbf{q}}\, B_{\mp} &= \tfrac{1}{2}(\boldsymbol{\sigma}\cdot\hat{\mathbf{q}} \mp \boldsymbol{\alpha}\cdot\hat{\mathbf{q}})A \\ &= \tfrac{1}{2}(\mp 1 - \gamma_5)\boldsymbol{\alpha}\cdot\hat{\mathbf{q}}\, A \\ &= \mp\tfrac{1}{2}(1 \pm \gamma_5)A \\ &= \mp B_{\mp} \end{aligned} \tag{7.11}$$

Hence B_+, B_- are the amplitudes of the positive, negative helicity states respectively and $\frac{1}{2}(1 \pm \gamma_5)$ may be regarded as helicity projection operators: positive helicity (ω_-) and negative helicity (ω_+).

In detail, we see that in the representation (6.66) used here

$$\gamma_5 = S\begin{pmatrix} 0 & -1 \\ -1 & 0 \end{pmatrix}S^{-1}$$

where $S = S^{-1}$ is given by (6.67). Thus

$$\gamma_5 = \begin{pmatrix} -1 & 0 \\ 0 & 1 \end{pmatrix}$$

and

$$\omega_+ = \begin{pmatrix} 0 & 0 \\ 0 & 1 \end{pmatrix}, \qquad \omega_- = \begin{pmatrix} 1 & 0 \\ 0 & 0 \end{pmatrix} \tag{7.12}$$

Hence, choosing c_1 and c_2 in (7.6) to obtain normalized functions,

$$B_+ = \begin{pmatrix} A_+ \\ 0 \end{pmatrix}, \qquad B_- = \begin{pmatrix} 0 \\ A_- \end{pmatrix} \tag{7.12'}$$

as was expected.

Charge Conjugate States

The charge conjugate state to ψ is

$$\psi^c = C^{\times}\psi^{\times}$$

where the charge conjugation matrix C is most easily obtained from (4.83) with $C_0 = i\beta\alpha_2$ in the standard representation. Then

$$C = S^{\times}C_0S^{-1} = i\begin{pmatrix} 0 & -\sigma_2 \\ \sigma_2 & 0 \end{pmatrix} = -C_0 \tag{7.13}$$

The charge conjugate solution is then

$$\psi^c = A^c \exp\left[-i(\mathbf{q}\cdot\mathbf{r} - qt)\right]$$

where

$$A^c = C^\times A^\times$$

Since C is real, we find from (7.5) that

$$C\boldsymbol{\alpha}^\times\cdot\hat{\mathbf{q}}\, C^{-1}A^c = A^c$$

or since $C^{-1} = C$ and

$$\sigma_2\,\boldsymbol{\sigma}^\times\sigma_2 = -\boldsymbol{\sigma} \tag{7.14}$$

the eigenvalue equation for A^c becomes

$$\boldsymbol{\alpha}\cdot\hat{\mathbf{q}}\, A^c = A^c \tag{7.15}$$

just as in (7.5). In fact, direct application of (7.13) to (7.6) gives

$$A^c = -\begin{pmatrix} c_2^\times A_+ \\ c_1^\times A_- \end{pmatrix}$$

which differs from A given by (7.6) in only a trivial way. For ψ^c it is apparent that

$$\boldsymbol{\alpha}\cdot\nabla\psi^c = -\frac{\partial\psi^c}{\partial t}$$

which should be compared with (7.3). It should be emphasized that the charge conjugate solutions are not connected to a reversal of sign of electromagnetic couplings, which, of course, are absent, but rather to the existence of negative energy state solutions. As before, the antiparticle represented by ψ^c is to be interpreted, according to the hole theory, as a vacancy in the otherwise filled negative energy states.

From the fact that (7.15) and (7.5) have the same form, it appears that $\omega_\pm A^c$ are eigenfunctions of $\boldsymbol{\sigma}\cdot\hat{\mathbf{q}}$ with eigenvalue $+1$ (for $\omega_- A^c$) and -1 (for $\omega_+ A^c$). However, the charge conjugate of the positive and negative helicity states have amplitudes B_+^c and B_-^c respectively. Thus

$$\begin{aligned} B_+^c &= \tfrac{1}{2}(1 - \gamma_5^c)A^c \\ &= \tfrac{1}{2}(1 + \gamma_5)A^c = \omega_+ A^c = -c_1^\times B_- \end{aligned}$$

which is a negative helicity state. Similarly,

$$\begin{aligned} B_-^c &= \tfrac{1}{2}(1 + \gamma_5^c)A^c \\ &= \tfrac{1}{2}(1 - \gamma_5)A^c = \omega_- A^c = -c_2^\times B_+ \end{aligned}$$

which is a positive helicity state. In fact, we verify from (7.12) that

$$\begin{aligned} B_+^c &= -B_- \\ B_-^c &= -B_+ \end{aligned} \tag{7.16}$$

This illustrates a general rule which has already been seen in operation in the discussion of the spin operator in section 17: the particle and antiparticle states which are charge conjugate to each other have the opposite sign of the helicity. For example, if by some mechanism a particle is emitted into a mixture of states such that the average longitudinal polarization (or helicity) is positive, then in the process where the charge conjugate particles are emitted the corresponding antiparticle is longitudinally polarized with the opposite sign relative to its direction of motion. A case in point is $e^{\pm}$ emission in beta decay where e^{-} is accompanied by emission into one type of neutrino state, e^{+} by neutrinos in the charge conjugate states. By definition, the latter are called neutrinos (ν) and the former are the charge-conjugate antineutrinos ($\bar{\nu}$).

In the description of processes, such as beta decay, in terms of a four-component theory of the neutrino it is to be expected *a priori* that the neutrino polarization will not be complete in general. The four states have the interpretation given in preceding discussions. Even if e^{-} emission is accompanied by $\bar{\nu}$ only, both spin (helicity) states are available for $\bar{\nu}$ and the polarization of $\bar{\nu}$ depends on the relative number of decays into the two helicity eigenstates. It is primarily in just this respect that the two-component theory of the neutrino, to be described in the next section, introduces something new.

42. THE TWO-COMPONENT THEORY

The Weyl Equation

Shortly after the introduction by Dirac of the relativistic theory of the electron, a two-component theory was proposed by Weyl[3] for the massless particle. The case of zero mass and no couplings with external fields is described in the Dirac theory by the wave equation (7.3). Since here there are only three anticommuting matrices, there is the possibility of identifying the $\boldsymbol{\alpha}$ in (7.3) with the three Pauli spin matrices. This identification leaves a sign ambiguous: $\boldsymbol{\alpha} \rightarrow \pm\boldsymbol{\sigma}$. The wave equation would therefore be equivalent to two equations, and the wave function, which is designated by ϕ, is a two-component spinor. Thus we write

$$i\boldsymbol{\sigma}\cdot\nabla\phi = i\,\frac{\partial\phi}{\partial t} \tag{7.17}$$

Originally, this Weyl form of the theory was discarded on the grounds that it did not give a space-reflection invariant equation. Under the impetus of the discovery of parity non-conservation in weak interactions the two-component theory was revived,[4–6] because it was then evident that the former objection was not actually cogent. At this juncture, it should be emphasized that the properties of weak interactions and the decay processes induced by them are not consequences of the properties of the free neutrino but are instead consequences of the nature of the weak interaction itself. This becomes evident when it is recalled that a four-component conventional Dirac neutrino does not preclude asymmetries of the type attributed to violation of parity conservation. The validity of a two-component neutrino theory must be decided on grounds independent of the *existence* of non-conservation of parity in beta decay. Of course, as already emphasized, the predicted magnitude of the asymmetries depends on whether or not the two-component theory is valid.

It is clear that the two equations (7.16) are not enough because from four components we can obtain two components by a projection, for instance with $\frac{1}{2}(1 - \gamma_5)$. The complementary projection $\frac{1}{2}(1 + \gamma_5)$ yields another two-component spinor.† Thus, if we take the complex conjugate of (7.16) and introduce

$$\phi^c = c^\times \phi^\times$$

we see that

$$c^\times \boldsymbol{\sigma}^\times c^{-1\times} \cdot \nabla \phi^c = \frac{\partial \phi^c}{\partial t}$$

If the two-component matrix fulfills $c^\times = \pm c$, as we shall assume, and if

$$c \boldsymbol{\sigma}^\times c^{-1} = -\boldsymbol{\sigma} \tag{7.18}$$

as will be required, then we obtain

$$-i\boldsymbol{\sigma} \cdot \nabla \phi^c = i \frac{\partial \phi^c}{\partial t} \tag{7.19}$$

The two functions ϕ and ϕ^c, each of which is a two-component spinor, replace the four-component solutions previously studied.

In order to interpret this result we introduce plane waves

$$\phi = a \exp\left[i(\mathbf{q} \cdot \mathbf{r} - qt)\right]$$

where $|\mathbf{q}| = q$ and then (7.16) gives

$$\boldsymbol{\sigma} \cdot \hat{\mathbf{q}}\, a = -a \tag{7.20}$$

and, from (7.18),

$$\boldsymbol{\sigma} \cdot \hat{\mathbf{q}}\, a^c = a^c \tag{7.21}$$

The implication of these results follows. The plane wave state ϕ has only one possible spin state, and this corresponds to negative helicity, that is,

† Of course, these are four-component functions with either the upper or lower components zero. However, these are equivalent to a two-component wave function.

momentum and spin antiparallel. For ϕ^c there is similarly only one spin state, and this corresponds to parallel spin and momentum or positive helicity. Thus one of ϕ and ϕ^c arises from the negative energy states and the other from the positive energy states. According to our identification, which is a matter of convention only, ϕ corresponds to the neutrino in a positive energy state; ϕ^c to the antineutrino. This convention is in accord with the practice of calling the light neutral particle in e^- emission the antineutrino, because according to this rule ν is left-handed ($\boldsymbol{\sigma}\cdot\hat{\mathbf{q}}$ has eigenvalue -1) and $\bar{\nu}$ is right-handed ($\boldsymbol{\sigma}\cdot\hat{\mathbf{q}}$ has eigenvalue $+1$). Thus the reduction of the number of independent states of given momentum from four to two is a reflection of the fact that for each type of state only one and not two spin states arise. The neutrino polarization on this theory is then always complete, either ± 1 along $\hat{\mathbf{q}}$. Note that the relation between spin and momentum (and therefore the helicity) is the same for a negative energy state particle as for the "hole" in these states.

Relation to the Majorana Theory[7]

We now show that the two-component theory is a projection of the Dirac theory with the additional condition that†

$$\psi = \psi^c \tag{7.22}$$

This condition that ψ be self charge conjugate leads to a theory originally proposed by Majorana. What is discussed here is the unquantized or c-number form of the Majorana theory. The relation between the Majorana and two-component theories has been discussed by Serpe,[8] McLennan,[9] and Case.[10]

In the representation (6.66) the charge conjugation matrix is given in (7.13). Hence with

$$\psi = \begin{pmatrix} \psi_1 \\ \psi_2 \\ \psi_3 \\ \psi_4 \end{pmatrix} \equiv \begin{pmatrix} \varphi' \\ \varphi \end{pmatrix}$$

we see that (7.22) requires

$$i\begin{pmatrix} -\sigma_2\varphi^{\times} \\ \sigma_2\varphi'^{\times} \end{pmatrix} = \begin{pmatrix} \varphi' \\ \varphi \end{pmatrix}$$

† It is important to distinguish between the condition of self charge conjugate solutions as applied to ψ where it is pertinent and as applied to a projected wave function of the form $\begin{pmatrix} \varphi \\ 0 \end{pmatrix}$ or $\begin{pmatrix} 0 \\ \varphi \end{pmatrix}$ where it is not pertinent.

or

$$\psi_1 = -\psi_4^\times, \qquad \psi_2 = \psi_3^\times$$

Consequently,

$$\varphi' = \begin{pmatrix} \psi_1 \\ \psi_2 \end{pmatrix} = \begin{pmatrix} -\psi_4^\times \\ \psi_3^\times \end{pmatrix} = -i\sigma_2\varphi^\times$$

This, it will be seen, has the form

$$\varphi' = c^\times \varphi^\times$$

where $c = -i\sigma_2$ has the property†

$$c\boldsymbol{\sigma}^\times c^{-1} = -\boldsymbol{\sigma}$$

$$c^\times = c = -\tilde{c} = -c^{-1} = -c^* \tag{7.18$'$}$$

Hence the self charge conjugate ψ is

$$\psi = \begin{pmatrix} -i\sigma_2\varphi^\times \\ \varphi \end{pmatrix} = \begin{pmatrix} \varphi^c \\ \varphi \end{pmatrix} \tag{7.23}$$

The wave equation (7.3) now becomes

$$\boldsymbol{\sigma}\cdot\nabla\varphi = \frac{\partial\varphi}{\partial t} \tag{7.17$'$}$$

and

$$\boldsymbol{\sigma}\cdot\nabla\varphi^c = -\frac{\partial\varphi^c}{\partial t} \tag{7.19$'$}$$

in agreement with (7.17) and (7.19) when we identify φ with ϕ. Since (7.19′) follows from (7.17′) by taking the complex conjugate, it is clear that the four Dirac equations are equivalent to *two* equations.

If the projections with the helicity operators are now constructed, we find that

$$\psi_- = \tfrac{1}{2}(1 + \gamma_5)\psi = \begin{pmatrix} 0 \\ \varphi \end{pmatrix} \tag{7.24}$$

and

$$\psi_+ = \tfrac{1}{2}(1 - \gamma_5)\psi = \begin{pmatrix} \varphi^c \\ 0 \end{pmatrix} \tag{7.24$'$}$$

are two-component neutrino functions for which the following auxiliary conditions obviously hold:

$$\gamma_5\psi_- = \psi_- \tag{7.25}$$

$$\gamma_5\psi_+ = -\psi_+ \tag{7.26}$$

† The replacement of c by c^{-1} in (7.18) is irrelevant since by any choice of phase $c = \pm c^{-1}$.

Here $\gamma_5^2 = 1$ is used. It is of interest to note that the conditions (7.25) and (7.26) are consistent only with zero neutrino rest mass. Thus, from

$$\gamma_\mu \frac{\partial \psi}{\partial x_\mu} + k_\nu \psi = 0$$

where k_ν is the reciprocal Compton wavelength of the neutrino, we have, by multiplication on the left by γ_5,

$$-\gamma_\mu \gamma_5 \frac{\partial \psi}{\partial x_\mu} + k_\nu \gamma_5 \psi = 0$$

since γ_μ and γ_5 anticommute. From (7.25) or (7.26) this equation can be consistent only if $k_\nu = 0$ or the neutrino mass must vanish.[11] The converse, that $m_\nu = 0$ implies (7.25) or (7.26), is not a valid conclusion.

It will be recognized that the conditions (7.25) and (7.26) applied to a four-component wave function as described by (7.3) lead to the two-component description as given, for example, by (7.17) or (7.19). This is another way of saying that the two-component theory is a projection of the usual four-component formalism.

For the plane wave solutions the explicit form of the amplitudes has already been given. For the positive helicity solution ψ_+ this amplitude is B_+ defined by (7.12′) and (7.7a). For ψ_- we use B_- defined in (7.12′) and (7.7b).

The complete set of projection operators for the two-component neutrino is two in number and not four, since there are only two states of given momentum. The new projection operators are then

$$P^{\mp} = \omega_\pm P \omega_\pm^*$$

where P, on the right side, refers to the four-component solutions with zero rest mass. We see that

$$P^{\pm} = \tfrac{1}{2}(1 \pm \boldsymbol{\sigma}\cdot\hat{\mathbf{q}})\omega_\mp$$

as was to be expected.

Covariance of the Theory

We now turn to the question of the Lorentz covariance of the theory. For the most part it is sufficient to consider only the negative helicity solution, since the corresponding results for the positive helicity state is obtained by conjugation. Then we can discuss the properties of either ψ_- or φ. In the former case $\boldsymbol{\sigma}$ would be the set of 4 by 4 matrices which are the direct products of unity in Dirac space and the Pauli $\boldsymbol{\sigma}$. In the latter case $\boldsymbol{\sigma}$ is the set of 2 by 2 matrices. We discuss the equations first in two-component form. Then (7.17) is written

$$\sigma_\mu \frac{\partial \varphi}{\partial x_\mu} = 0 \tag{7.27}$$

where

$$\sigma_4 = -i$$

The hermitian conjugate of (7.27) reads

$$\frac{\partial \varphi^*}{\partial x_\mu} \sigma_\mu = 0 \tag{7.27'}$$

since $x_4 = it$ is pure imaginary and $\sigma_4^* = -\sigma_4$. Then, in the usual manner, we multiply (7.27) by φ^* on the left and (7.27′) by φ on the right, and, after adding,

$$\frac{\partial}{\partial x_\mu} \varphi^* \sigma_\mu \varphi = 0 \tag{7.28}$$

Thus we obtain a continuity equation. That

$$j_\mu = -\varphi^* \sigma_\mu \varphi \tag{7.29}$$

is a four-vector will be justified below. The space and time parts are

$$\mathbf{j} = -\varphi^* \boldsymbol{\sigma} \varphi \tag{7.29a}$$

$$ij_4 = \rho = \varphi^* \varphi \tag{7.29b}$$

In terms of ψ_- the current density would be $-\psi_-^* \boldsymbol{\sigma} \psi_-$ and, recalling (7.25), this is the same as $\psi_-^* \boldsymbol{\alpha} \psi_-$. The positive definite ρ defines a normalization according to

$$\int \rho \, d^3x = 1$$

and, if j_μ is a four-vector, this integral is a relativistic invariant according to arguments previously adduced.

For the Lorentz transformations we first consider the proper rotations

$$x'_\mu = a_{\mu\nu} x_\nu$$

Then

$$\sigma_\mu \frac{\partial}{\partial x'_\mu} \varphi'(x') = 0$$

becomes

$$a_{\mu\nu} \sigma_\mu \frac{\partial}{\partial x_\nu} \varphi'(x') = 0$$

Setting

$$\varphi'(x') = \Lambda\varphi(x) \tag{7.30}$$

we obtain a covariant result if

$$a_{\mu\nu}\sigma_\nu = \Lambda^*\sigma_\mu\Lambda \tag{7.30'}$$

This differs from the defining equation (2.60b). Nevertheless we can see that the Λ obtained from (7.30′) is the same as the matrix for the continuous transformations discussed in Chapter II, section 14. To see this, consider a rotation around a direction $\hat{\mathbf{n}}$ through an angle θ. Let the vector $\theta\hat{\mathbf{n}}$ be denoted by $\mathbf{n}$. Then take[12]

$$\Lambda = \exp\,(i\mathbf{n}\cdot\boldsymbol{\sigma}/2) \tag{7.31}$$

as in section 14. To verify the correctness of this, we calculate the right side of (7.30′) first for a space rotation: $a_{i4} = a_{4i} = 0$, $a_{44} = 1$.

$$\begin{aligned}\Lambda^*\sigma_i\Lambda &= (\cos\tfrac{1}{2}\theta - i\hat{\mathbf{n}}\cdot\boldsymbol{\sigma}\sin\tfrac{1}{2}\theta)\,\sigma_i(\cos\tfrac{1}{2}\theta + i\hat{\mathbf{n}}\cdot\boldsymbol{\sigma}\sin\tfrac{1}{2}\theta)\\ &= \sigma_i\cos^2\tfrac{1}{2}\theta + \hat{\mathbf{n}}\cdot\boldsymbol{\sigma}\,\sigma_i\hat{\mathbf{n}}\cdot\boldsymbol{\sigma}\sin^2\tfrac{1}{2}\theta + i\cos\tfrac{1}{2}\theta\sin\tfrac{1}{2}\theta\,(\sigma_i\hat{\mathbf{n}}\cdot\boldsymbol{\sigma} - \hat{\mathbf{n}}\cdot\boldsymbol{\sigma}\,\sigma_i)\end{aligned}$$

The last factor in parentheses is

$$\begin{aligned}\sigma_i\,\hat{\mathbf{n}}\cdot\boldsymbol{\sigma} - \hat{\mathbf{n}}\cdot\sigma\,\sigma_i &= 2i\boldsymbol{\sigma}\cdot(\hat{\mathbf{e}}_i \times \hat{\mathbf{n}}) = 2i\epsilon_{klm}\,\delta_{il}\hat{n}_m\sigma_k\\ &= 2i\epsilon_{kim}\hat{n}_m\sigma_k\end{aligned}$$

where $\hat{\mathbf{e}}_i$ is a unit vector in the direction of the ith coordinate axis and ϵ_{klm} is the antisymmetric unit tensor of third rank. Also

$$\begin{aligned}\hat{\mathbf{n}}\cdot\boldsymbol{\sigma}\,\sigma_i\hat{\mathbf{n}}\cdot\boldsymbol{\sigma} &= [\hat{\mathbf{n}}_i + i\boldsymbol{\sigma}\cdot(\hat{\mathbf{n}} \times \hat{\mathbf{e}}_i)]\hat{\mathbf{n}}\cdot\boldsymbol{\sigma}\\ &= \hat{n}_i\hat{\mathbf{n}}\cdot\boldsymbol{\sigma} - \boldsymbol{\sigma}\cdot(\hat{\mathbf{n}} \times \hat{\mathbf{e}}_i) \times \hat{\mathbf{n}}\\ &= 2\hat{n}_i\hat{\mathbf{n}}\cdot\boldsymbol{\sigma} - \sigma_i\end{aligned}$$

Hence (7.30′) becomes

$$a_{ij}\sigma_j = \sigma_i + \hat{n}_i\hat{\mathbf{n}}\cdot\boldsymbol{\sigma}(1 - \cos\theta) + \epsilon_{ikm}\hat{n}_m\sigma_k\sin\theta$$

If we multiply this by σ_l and evaluate the trace of the resulting equation, we obtain

$$a_{il} = \delta_{il}\cos\theta + \hat{n}_i\hat{n}_l(1 - \cos\theta) + \epsilon_{ilm}\hat{n}_m\sin\theta \tag{7.32}$$

That this gives just the expected result can be verified easily. For example, if $\hat{\mathbf{n}}$ is along the z-axis we find

$$a = \begin{pmatrix} \cos\theta & \sin\theta & 0 & 0\\ -\sin\theta & \cos\theta & 0 & 0\\ 0 & 0 & 1 & 0\\ 0 & 0 & 0 & 1\end{pmatrix}$$

Since there is nothing special about the z-axis, this constitutes a sufficient proof that (7.32) describes a three-dimensional rotation.

For a translation in the direction $\hat{\mathbf{v}}$ with uniform velocity v the vector $\mathbf{n}$ becomes

$$\mathbf{n} = i\hat{\mathbf{v}} \operatorname{arctanh} v/c$$

and that this leads to the appropriate Lorentz matrix a may be left as an exercise for the reader.

It is of interest to examine the properties of $\mathbf{n}$ under three-space rotations. If the rotation is described by the Lorentz matrix a whose elements are a_{ij}, then

$$a_{ij}\,\sigma_j = \overline{\Lambda}^*\sigma_i\overline{\Lambda}$$

where, under the rotation, $\psi(x) \to \bar{\psi}(x) = \overline{\Lambda}\psi(x)$. Then

$$\psi'(x') = \exp\,(i\mathbf{n}\cdot\boldsymbol{\sigma}/2)\psi(x) = \Lambda\psi(x)$$

and

$$\bar{\psi}'(x') = \overline{\Lambda}\psi'(x')$$

Consequently,

$$\begin{aligned}\bar{\psi}'(x') &= \overline{\Lambda}\Lambda\psi(x)\\ &= \overline{\Lambda}\Lambda\overline{\Lambda}^{-1}\bar{\psi}(x)\\ &\equiv \exp\,(i\bar{\mathbf{n}}\cdot\boldsymbol{\sigma}/2)\;\bar{\psi}(x)\end{aligned}$$

In the case of the rotation considered here $\overline{\Lambda}^{-1} = \overline{\Lambda}^*$; that is, $\overline{\Lambda}$ is unitary. Hence

$$\begin{aligned}\exp\,(i\bar{\mathbf{n}}\cdot\boldsymbol{\sigma}/2) &= \overline{\Lambda}\exp\,(i\mathbf{n}\cdot\boldsymbol{\sigma}/2)\overline{\Lambda}^*\\ &= \exp\left(\frac{i}{2}\,\overline{\Lambda}\mathbf{n}\cdot\boldsymbol{\sigma}\overline{\Lambda}^*\right)\end{aligned}$$

Since

$$\Lambda\sigma_k\Lambda^* = \sigma_i a_{ik}$$

we find

$$\bar{n}_i = a_{ik}n_k$$

Thus $\mathbf{n}$ behaves like any three-space vector under rotations. The transformation law (7.30′) is supplemented by

$$\varphi^{*\prime}(x') = \varphi^*(x)\Lambda^*$$

Then we readily see that

$$\begin{aligned}j'_\mu(x') &= -\varphi^*(x)\Lambda^*\sigma_\mu\Lambda\;\varphi(x)\\ &= a_{\mu\nu}j_\nu(x)\end{aligned}$$

justifying the statement that the j_μ are the components of a four-vector.

Turning to the improper Lorentz transformations, we see that under either

$$x_i' = -x_i, \qquad x_4' = x_4$$

or

$$x_i' = x_i, \qquad x_4' = -x_4$$

that is, space or time reflections, the wave equation (7.27) would acquire a relative sign change between the space and time derivative terms. Starting with

$$\sigma_\mu \frac{\partial \varphi'}{\partial x_\mu'}(x') = 0$$

a linear transformation of the type

$$\varphi'(x') = \Lambda\varphi(x)$$

would require that

$$\Lambda^{-1}\boldsymbol{\sigma}\Lambda = -\boldsymbol{\sigma}$$

which is impossible, since there is no 2 by 2 matrix which anticommutes with all three σ_i. Therefore we consider the antilinear transformation and set

$$\varphi'(x') = [\Lambda\varphi(x)]^\times \tag{7.33}$$

Then we find

$$\Lambda^{-1}\sigma_k^\times\Lambda = -\sigma_k$$

From this we can conclude that Λ is equal to σ_2, within a phase. We write

$$\varphi'(x') = \epsilon(i\sigma_2\varphi(x))^\times \tag{7.34}$$

where $i\sigma_2$ is real but ϵ may not be; however, $|\epsilon| = 1$.

Two-Component Neutrino in Beta Decay

We can discuss the problem of covariants by considering the important question of beta decay. The interaction density may be tentatively written

$$H_\beta' = \sum_i g_i(\psi_p^*, \Omega_i\psi_n)(\psi_e^*, \Omega_i\psi_-) \tag{7.35}$$

for negative electron emission. The positron emission would arise from $H_\beta'^*$. Here the annihilated neutrino is represented by ψ_-. In (7.35) the g_i are the coupling constants and i runs over the five possible interaction types; see section 14. The Ω_i are the corresponding operators formed from products of the Dirac γ's, and a contraction between nucleon and lepton bilinear covariant quantities is tacitly assumed in (7.35) and in the following variants of the interaction. All this follows standard procedure.

We shall consider the behavior of H'_β under space reflection. Then, for the ψ_p, ψ_n, and ψ_e we can write (see section 25)

$$\psi'_\lambda(x') = \eta_\lambda \beta \psi_\lambda(x)$$

where λ stands for p, n, or e and η_λ is a phase: $|\eta_\lambda| = 1$. For ψ_- we must use

$$\psi'_-(x') = \begin{pmatrix} 0 \\ \varphi'(x') \end{pmatrix}$$

From (7.24) and (7.34), the transform of ψ_- under space reflection is

$$\psi'_-(x') = \begin{pmatrix} 0 \\ \epsilon i\sigma_2 \varphi^\times(x) \end{pmatrix} \equiv \epsilon \psi_\nu(x)$$

Consequently, under space reflection H'_β transforms into the right side of (7.36):

$$\begin{aligned} H'_\beta &\to \sum_i g_i \eta_p^\times \eta_n \eta_e^\times \epsilon(\psi_p^*, \beta\Omega_i \beta\psi_n)(\psi_e^*, \beta\Omega_i \psi_\nu) \\ &= \sum_i g_i \eta_p^\times \eta_n \eta_e^\times \epsilon(\psi_p, \Omega_i \psi_n)(\psi_e^*, \Omega_i \beta\psi_\nu) \end{aligned} \tag{7.36}$$

since Ω_i and β either commute or anticommute: $\beta\Omega_i\beta = \pm\Omega_i$ and this operation has been carried out twice in (7.36). It is clear that there is no choice of phases which will make the right side of (7.36) the same as H'_β.

Alternatively, we can consider the interaction

$$H''_\beta = \sum_i g_i \eta_p^\times \eta_n \eta_e^\times \epsilon(\psi_p^*, \Omega_i \psi_n)(\psi_e^*, \Omega_i \beta\psi_\nu) \tag{7.37}$$

so that under space reflection $H'_\beta \to H''_\beta$. To complete our consideration of transformation we examine the form of H''_β under the space reflection. Then

$$\psi'_\nu(x') = \begin{pmatrix} 0 \\ i\sigma_2 \varphi'^\times(x') \end{pmatrix} = \epsilon^\times \begin{pmatrix} 0 \\ (i\sigma_2)^2 \varphi(x) \end{pmatrix} = -\epsilon^\times \psi_-(x)$$

and

$$H''_\beta \to -\sum_i g_i (\eta_p^\times \eta_n \eta_e^\times)^2 \epsilon^\times \epsilon(\psi_p^*, \Omega_i \psi_n)(\psi_e^*, \Omega_i \psi_-)$$

This is the same as H'_β if we choose $-\epsilon^\times\epsilon(\eta_p^\times \eta_n \eta_e^\times)^2 = 1$, which is always possible. Consequently,

$$H_\beta = H'_\beta + H''_\beta$$

is invariant under the space reflection transformation. Either H'_β or H''_β alone is not. Experiment requires that the coefficients of H'_β and H''_β in H_β cannot be equal. In fact, if the present experimental data are interpreted as a demonstration of maximum parity breakdown, then H_β is identical with H'_β or with H''_β. The choice of $H_\beta = H'_\beta$ depends on the measurement of the neutrino helicity.[13] Thus we write

$$H_\beta = H'_\beta = \tfrac{1}{2} \sum_i g_i(\psi_p^*, \Omega_i \psi_n)(\psi_e^*, \Omega_i(1 + \gamma_5)\psi)$$

where ψ is the four-component neutrino state. Since

$$\beta\psi_\nu = \psi_+$$

where β is given by (6.66), it follows that under space reflection H_β changes into a form corresponding to the opposite helicity assignment for the neutrino.

In a linear combination of H'_β and H''_β we would find that the neutrino wave function enters as

$$\tfrac{1}{2}[g_i(1 + \gamma_5) + g'_i(1 - \gamma_5)]\psi \equiv \omega\psi$$

where g_i and g'_i are the coupling coefficients in H'_β and H''_β respectively. Comparing with the notation of section 21,

$$g_i + g'_i = 2gC_i$$

$$g_i - g'_i = 2gC'_i$$

It is evident that we are now describing the neutrino as a superposition of negative helicity and positive helicity states. If we take $\omega\psi$ as above, for example, the amplitude of the negative helicity state is g_i and for the positive helicity state it is g'_i. Hence the average neutrino polarization for a particular interaction of type i would be

$$\mathscr{P}_\nu = \frac{|C_i - C'_i|^2 - |C_i + C'_i|^2}{|C_i - C'_i|^2 + |C_i + C_i|^2}$$

$$= -\frac{2ReC_iC_i'^{\times}}{|C_i|^2 + |C'_i|^2} \qquad (7.38)$$

For $C_i = C'_i$ this would give complete polarization antiparallel to the momentum, and the beta interaction would contain the factor $1 + \gamma_5$ operating on the four-component neutrino, as compared to the parity-conserving interaction where the corresponding factor is 1. This, as we have already mentioned, is the formulation of the interaction according to the two-component neutrino theory and, as is evident, this form of the theory of the weak interactions implies maximum polarizations of the emitted particles. As can be seen without great difficulty, it also implies maximum anisotropy in angular distributions where such anisotropies arise from parity violation of H_β; see section 21.

We note that the condition $C_i = C_i'$ appropriate to the two-component neutrino theory is equivalent to $f = 1$ in the discussion of section 21. This was seen to correspond to maximum breakdown of parity conservation in the beta interaction, as the foregoing remarks would imply.

Angular Momentum Representation

The wave equations (7.17′) and (7.19′) are readily solved in the angular momentum representation. Considering the latter equation, we write for a stationary state

$$\boldsymbol{\sigma}\cdot\nabla\, \varphi^c = iq\varphi^c \tag{7.39}$$

Since $\mathbf{j}^2$ and j_z still commute with $\boldsymbol{\sigma}\cdot\nabla$ while $\mathbf{l}^2$ does not, the solutions will still contain $\chi^\mu_{\pm\kappa}$. However, $\boldsymbol{\sigma}\cdot\mathbf{l}$ does not commute with $\boldsymbol{\sigma}\cdot\nabla$, as the results of section 12 demonstrate. Nor does the operation of space inversion multiplied by any 2 by 2 matrix commute with $\boldsymbol{\sigma}\cdot\nabla$. That is,

$$\tau I_s \boldsymbol{\sigma}\cdot\nabla = -\tau\boldsymbol{\sigma}\cdot\nabla I_s$$

and there is no 2 by 2 matrix τ which anticommutes with $\boldsymbol{\sigma}$. Hence the solutions will not have a definite parity and will be linear combinations of $\chi^\mu_{\pm\kappa}$. This means that K no longer represents a constant of the motion, as is evident from the fact that $(K, \boldsymbol{\sigma}\cdot\nabla) \neq 0$. This again shows the intimate connection between the K operator and parity.

Set

$$(\varphi^c)^\mu_\kappa = g\chi^\mu_\kappa + if\chi^\mu_{-\kappa} \tag{7.40}$$

Compare Eq. (6.77). Then, since

$$\boldsymbol{\sigma}\cdot\nabla = \sigma_r\left(\frac{\partial}{\partial r} - \frac{1}{r}\boldsymbol{\sigma}\cdot\mathbf{l}\right)$$

and

$$\boldsymbol{\sigma}\cdot\mathbf{l}\,\chi^\mu_\kappa = -(\kappa+1)\chi^\mu_\kappa$$

$$\sigma_r\,\chi^\mu_\kappa = -\chi^\mu_{-\kappa}$$

we find the following differential equations for the radial functions:

$$\begin{aligned} \frac{dg}{dr} &= qf - \frac{\kappa+1}{r}g \\ \frac{df}{dr} &= \frac{\kappa-1}{r}f - qg \end{aligned} \tag{7.41}$$

These are exactly the same as (5.4) with $V = 0$ and the rest mass term (there represented by ± 1 added to $W - V$) set equal to zero. Of course,

$W = q$ in our present notation. The solution, regular at $r = 0$, as comparison with (5.12) shows, is

$$\begin{aligned} g &= j_l(qr) \\ f &= S_\kappa j_{\bar{l}}(qr) \end{aligned} \tag{7.42}$$

The results for φ are obtained by charge conjugation in exactly the same way as in section 26.

We observe that the wave functions for $\kappa = k$ and $\kappa = -k$ are not linearly independent. Instead,

$$(\varphi^c)^\mu_{-k} = i(\varphi^c)^\mu_k$$

Hence, as compared to a four-component description, there are half as many states in the present theory. This corresponds to the reduction of the number of plane wave states by one-half which, as we have seen, is a consequence of the unique helicity of the two-component neutrino.

It is seen that the solution (7.40) is obtained from the four-component solution ψ^μ_κ, as given for instance by (5.3), by application of $\sqrt{2}\omega_- S$, where S in turn is given by (6.67). The remaining projection is

$$\varphi^\mu_\kappa = \sqrt{2}\omega_+ S\psi^\mu_\kappa = g\chi^\mu_\kappa - if\chi^\mu_{-\kappa} \tag{7.43}$$

and the linearly independent solutions (7.40), (7.43) may be compared with (6.77). Two-component plane waves expanded as a superposition of these spherical waves can be written down at once by applying the operators $\omega_\pm S$ to each member of the four-component expansion given in section 27.

PROBLEMS

1. Assume that for the massless neutrino there may be a magnetic moment different from zero. If the interaction of this moment with an electromagnetic field is written as Pauli has suggested, the wave equation is

$$\left(\gamma_\mu \frac{\partial}{\partial x_\mu} + \lambda \gamma_\mu \gamma_\nu F_{\mu\nu}\right)\psi = 0$$

where λ is proportional to the magnetic moment and $F_{\mu\nu}$ is the electromagnetic field tensor as defined in Eq. (4.5). Show that in the two-component theory $\lambda = 0$ is a necessary condition, so that the neutrino cannot have a magnetic moment if this theory is accepted.

2. Investigate the effect of replacing each wave function, in the beta interaction terms H'_β and H''_β as defined in (7.35) and (7.37), by the charge conjugate functions. Is either H'_β or H''_β invariant under such an operation? What linear combinations of H'_β and H''_β are invariant?

3. In what sense does the Weyl equation (7.17) come in conflict with covariance under improper Lorentz transformations?

4. What is the effect of making the space reflection transformation and replacing φ with φ^c in the Weyl equation?

5. What meaning, if any, can be given to the following statement? A particle observed in a mirror is equivalent to the corresponding antiparticle.

6. Co^{60} decays with negative electrons which are observed to be preferentially emitted antiparallel to an externally applied magnetic field. If the same type of observation is made with Co^{58} which emits positrons, what should be the observed direction of preferential emission?

7. If the electrons emitted in beta decay are described with a $V - \lambda A$ interaction, implying that $C_A = -\lambda C_V$, what sign should the polarization of these emitted electrons have? Answer the same question for positron emission.

8. In the decay of a μ meson an electron and two neutrinos are emitted. One may attempt to describe this process by the tensor coupling

$$H_{\text{decay}} \sim (\psi_e^* \gamma_4 \gamma_\alpha \gamma_\beta \psi_\nu)(\psi_\nu^* \gamma_4 \gamma_\alpha \gamma_\beta \psi_\mu)$$

where $\psi_\nu = \pm\gamma_5\psi_\nu$ is the two-component neutrino wave function. Show that this H_{decay} vanishes identically. If $\gamma_\alpha\gamma_\beta$ is replaced by γ_α and then, in an alternative form for H_{decay}, by $\gamma_\alpha\gamma_5$, show that the latter two alternative forms of H_{decay} are identical and do not necessarily vanish.

9. If the μ meson decay referred to in problem 8 is described by

$$H_{\text{decay}} \sim (\psi_e^* \gamma_4 \Omega \psi_\mu)(\psi_\nu^* \gamma_4 \Omega \psi_\nu)$$

what are the properties of H_{decay} for $\Omega = \gamma_\alpha\gamma_\beta$? Compare the results for $\Omega = \gamma_\alpha$ and $\Omega = \gamma_\alpha\gamma_\beta$. In all cases assume a two component neutrino theory.

10. The process of double beta (β^-) decay is the transformation of a nucleus with Z protons and N neutrons to one with $Z + 2$ protons and $N - 2$ neutrons with the emission of two electrons. Alternative descriptions of this process are (1) no neutrinos:

$$n_1 + n_2 \rightarrow p_1 + p_2 + e_1^- + e_2^-$$

(2) (anti) neutrinos emitted:

$$n_1 + n_2 \rightarrow p_1 + p_2 + e_1^- + e_2^- + \bar{\nu}_1 + \bar{\nu}_2$$

Show that in a two-component description of the neutrinos process (1) is impossible.

11. In the classical beta interaction one can replace each field ψ by the projection $\omega_+\psi$. The beta interaction for fermions a, b, c, d is then

$$H_\beta = \sum_X C_X \left[(\omega_+\psi^a)^* \gamma_4 \Omega_X \omega_+ \psi^b\right]\left[(\omega_+\psi^c)^* \gamma_4 \Omega_X \omega_+ \psi^d\right] + \text{h.c.}$$

where $\Omega_X = 1,\ \gamma_\mu,\ \gamma_\mu\gamma_\nu\ (\mu \neq \nu),\ \gamma_\mu\gamma_5,\ \gamma_5$ for $X = S,\ V,\ T,\ A,\ P$ respectively. Show that only the V and A interactions actually occur in H_β and that the others will vanish identically.

12. Show by direct application of the charge conjugation operation that the two-component neutrino wave functions given in (7.40) and (7.43) are charge conjugates of each other.

REFERENCES

1. D. R. Hamilton, W. P. Alford, and L. Gross, *Phys. Rev.* **92,** 1521 (1953).
2. See S. Watanabe, *Phys. Rev.* **106,** 1306 (1957); E. C. G. Sudarshan and R. E. Marshak, *Phys. Rev.* **109,** 1860 (1958).
3. H. Weyl, *Z. Physik* **56,** 330 (1929).
4. L. Landau, *Nuclear Phys.* **3,** 127 (1957).
5. A. Salam, *Nuovo cimento* **5,** 299 (1957).
6. T. D. Lee and C. N. Yang, *Phys. Rev.* **105,** 1671 (1957).
7. E. Majorana, *Nuovo cimento* **14,** 171 (1937).
8. J. Serpe, *Physica* **18,** 295 (1952).
9. J. A. McLennan, Jr., *Phys. Rev.* **106,** 821 (1957).
10. K. M. Case, *Phys. Rev.* **107,** 307 (1957).
11. Cf. W. Pauli, *Nuovo cimento* **6,** 204 (1957).
12. C. L. Hammer and R. H. Good, Jr., *Phys. Rev.* **108,** 882 (1957).
13. M. Goldhaber, L. Grodzins, and A. W. Sunyar, *Phys. Rev.* **109,** 1015 (1958).

APPENDIX A.

NOTATION

In the chapters of this book certain notations have been introduced. Although these are generally explained at the point of introduction, they are summarized here for convenience. Much of the notation used here is fairly standard and, as a rule, wherever a commonly accepted set of symbols occurs in the literature it has been adopted here. However, it is certainly fair to say that in many cases there does not exist a notation which is common to more than two or three authors. While the following remarks are not intended as a glossary of symbols used in the text, they are intended as an explanation of some general characteristics of the notation used.

In the first chapter a notation for a unit vector is introduced and this is followed throughout the book. This consists of a (circumflex accent) mark placed above the vector symbol. Boldface symbols as used here refer to three-component vectors, either operators or vectors with components which are numbers. Generally, a boldface symbol appearing as a square is a scalar: for instance, $\mathbf{j}^2 = j_x^2 + j_y^2 + j_z^2$ is an operator which is to be distinguished from j^2, which is a number related to the eigenvalue [that is, $j(j+1)$] of $\mathbf{j}^2$. Where it is convenient to use the same symbol for an operator as for its eigenvalue, the two are usually distinguished by the use of an arrow written above the operator. In general, the direction of the arrow indicates the direction in which the operator acts. The only exception to this rule occurs where no confusion is occasioned by the omission of the arrow.

In connection with matrices and wave functions (spinors) with more than one component the following notations are used:

(*) hermitian conjugate: transpose and complex conjugate
($^\times$) complex conjugate
($\sim$) transpose
(-1) inverse

In the case of conjugation and inverse operations the symbol, here placed in parentheses, appears as usual as a superscript to the right. Of course, complex conjugation and the inverse occur in connection with ordinary numbers (1 by 1 quantities) and operators which are 1 by 1 in their matrix structure. An additional symbol, appearing as a superscript, is c, which connotes charge conjugation.

Spinor indices generally appear as (Greek) subscripts. When an additional subscript is needed to distinguish between two or more matrices (for example) parentheses are used for greater clarity. Thus $a_{\mu\nu}$ is an element of a matrix a and it is associated with the μth row and νth column; similarly, the corresponding element of the matrix α_k is $(\alpha_k)_{\mu\nu}$. Indices such as k in the last example often refer to the three cartesian directions. Symbols x, y, z and indices 1, 2, 3 occur frequently and are interchangeable. That is, $\alpha_1, \alpha_2, \alpha_3$ and $\alpha_x, \alpha_y, \alpha_z$ are notations for the same set of three quantities (matrices). Similarly, x_1, x_2, x_3 is used interchangeably with x, y, z.

The sum of the diagonal elements of a matrix A is denoted by Tr A, meaning "trace of A." For a matrix element of an operator Ω between states ψ_n and ψ_m any one of the following equivalent notations is used:

$$\begin{aligned}(\psi_n, \Omega\psi_m) &= (\psi_n^*\Omega\psi_m) \\ &= (\psi_n|\Omega|\psi_m) \\ &= (n|\Omega|m)\end{aligned}$$

Of course, the parentheses in the second form of the matrix element are not really necessary when only a spinor index summation is involved. Diagonal matrix elements, or expectation values, are often designated with angular brackets:

$$(\psi_n, \Omega\psi_n) = \langle\Omega\rangle$$

Whether a matrix element involves only spinor index summation or integration over space coordinates as well should be clear from the context.

Where a labeling of a wave function (or spinor amplitude) with eigenvalues of diagonal operators occurs, these eigenvalues usually appear as subscripts or superscripts or both, but sometimes as arguments wherever a simplification of notation is thereby effected. When the angular momentum representation occurs, the general practice is to write the total angular momentum as a subscript and the eigenvalue of the z-projection of angular momentum as a superscript. The only exceptions are: the pure spin Pauli eigenfunctions always refer to angular momentum $\frac{1}{2}$ and therefore this subscript is omitted; the spin-angular functions in a central field carry a subscript κ which gives the total angular momentum j and the parity as well.

In many parts of the book it is cumbersome to carry along constants

m, c, $\hbar$ as well as e. It is customary in the description of the relativistic electron to use units such that $m = c = \hbar = 1$, and for definiteness m is the electron mass. Then $e^2 = \alpha \approx 1/137$. When two particles of different masses are involved in the same discussion, as in the decay of the meson, one can either set $\mu = 1$ and then the electron mass is $m/\mu \approx 1/207$ or one can take $m = 1$ and the mu meson mass is $\mu/m \approx 207$. If m is the unit mass, the units of some other quantities of interest are

energy W:	mc^2
momentum p:	mc
length r:	$\hbar/mc$
time t:	$\hbar/mc^2$
wave number k:	$mc/\hbar$

After each quantity there appears a symbol which is frequently used for it. To convert any result expressed in these *rational relativistic units* to ordinary units the energy symbol W should be replaced by W/mc^2, p by p/mc, and so forth. Then the symbols $W, p, \ldots$ are the energy, momentum, ... in ordinary units. It is obvious that this process automatically introduces an appropriate combination of m, c, and $\hbar$ so that correct dimensions appear in each equation. For instance, a cross section will be replaced by $\sigma/(\hbar/mc)^2$ and a transition probability $w = 1/\tau$ will be replaced by $w\hbar/mc^2$. To introduce ordinary units in a wave function it is only necessary to specify the normalization. For example, if ψ is a bound state so that

$$\int d^3x\psi^*\psi = 1$$

then ψ in rational relativistic units is replaced by $(mc/\hbar)^{-3/2}\psi$ in ordinary units. Conversion to atomic units is easily carried out by noting that in the latter system $m = \hbar = e = 1$, so that $c = 1/\alpha$. For example, the unit of energy in this system is $\alpha^2 mc^2$, which is devoid of c as it should be.

In the discussion of Lorentz transformations the four space-time coordinates are generally denoted by x_μ with Greek indices always having the range 1 to 4. Here $x_4 = ict$. Latin letters range from 1 to 3 and refer to the space part of four-vectors, for example. The dummy index rule involving summation over repeated indices is used rather frequently, although where greater clarity is achieved by explicit use of the summation sign this additional symbol appears.

The finite number of characters available in the alphabets which are more or less common knowledge† has unavoidably led to duplication wherein a single letter is used in more than one context. An attempt has been made to avoid such duplication in a single chapter, and there seems to be no reason why confusion should result.

† And readily available from the printer.

APPENDIX B.

LORENTZ TRANSFORMATIONS

For convenience the relevant facts concerning Lorentz transformations are summarized in this appendix. As indicated in Appendix A, $x_1, x_2, x_3; x_4 = x, y, z; ict = it$. Then one considers all the transformations which leave $dx_\mu \, dx_\mu$ invariant. These can be written in the form

$$x'_\mu = a_{\mu\nu} x_\nu + b'_\mu \tag{B.1}$$

where b'_μ is a constant four-vector corresponding to a space-time displacement. The transformations indicated in (B.1) constitute the inhomogeneous Lorentz group. We shall be primarily interested in the homogeneous subgroup, $b'_\mu = 0$. Then

$$x'_\mu = a_{\mu\nu} x_\nu \tag{B.1'}$$

The requirement that

$$dx'_\mu \, dx'_\mu = dx_\mu \, dx_\mu$$

implies that the 4 by 4 matrix a is orthogonal:

$$a_{\mu\nu} a_{\mu\rho} = \delta_{\nu\rho}$$

$$a_{\mu\nu} a_{\lambda\nu} = \delta_{\mu\lambda} \tag{B.2}$$

and hence $\tilde{a} = a^{-1}$. Therefore

$$\det a = \pm 1 \tag{B.3}$$

The transformations with $\det a = +1$ constitute the subgroup of the proper Lorentz transformations. Those with $\det a = -1$ are the improper transformations. The latter include

(a) space reflection $a_{ik} = -\delta_{ik}, \quad a_{44} = 1, \quad a_{j4} = a_{4j} = 0$

(b) time reflection $a_{ik} = \delta_{ik}, \quad a_{44} = -1, \quad a_{j4} = a_{4j} = 0$

and any product of a proper transformation with space or time reflection. Combined space-time reflection gives $a = -1$ and is a proper Lorentz transformation. But, since it is not obtained in a continuous way from the identity $a = 1$, it is properly considered in a separate category. The proper Lorentz transformations with $a_{44} > 0$ constitute a subgroup of transformations continuous with the identity. They are four-space rotations. This subgroup is composed of three-space rotations in which $a_{44} = 1$, $a_{4j} = a_{j4} = 0$ and of translations with uniform velocity along some direction as well as products of these two.

For a uniform translation with velocity v along the x_1-axis,

$$a(\hat{\mathbf{e}}_1 v) = \begin{pmatrix} \xi & 0 & 0 & i\xi v/c \\ 0 & 1 & 0 & 0 \\ 0 & 0 & 1 & 0 \\ -i\xi v/c & 0 & 0 & \xi \end{pmatrix} \tag{B.4}$$

$$\xi = (1 - v^2/c^2)^{-1/2} = (1 - v^2)^{-1/2}$$

so that the components of the four-vector x_μ perpendicular to $\mathbf{v}$ do not change. In (B.4) $\hat{\mathbf{e}}_1$ is a unit vector along the x_1-axis. This is easily generalized to a transformation with arbitrary but uniform velocity $\mathbf{v}$. We have

$$\mathbf{r} = \mathbf{r}\cdot\hat{\mathbf{v}}\,\hat{\mathbf{v}} + \hat{\mathbf{v}} \times (\mathbf{r} \times \hat{\mathbf{v}}) \tag{B.5}$$

where the first term is parallel to $\mathbf{v}$ and the second is perpendicular to $\mathbf{v}$. Similarly,

$$\begin{aligned} \mathbf{r}' &= \mathbf{r}'\cdot\hat{\mathbf{v}}\,\hat{\mathbf{v}} + \hat{\mathbf{v}} \times (\mathbf{r} \times \hat{\mathbf{v}}) \\ &= \xi(\mathbf{r} + ic^{-1}\mathbf{v}x_4)\cdot\hat{\mathbf{v}}\,\hat{\mathbf{v}} + \hat{\mathbf{v}} \times (\mathbf{r} \times \hat{\mathbf{v}}) \end{aligned}$$

where the first term is transformed according to (B.4). Using (B.5) again, this becomes

$$\mathbf{r}' = \mathbf{r} + (\xi - 1)\mathbf{r}\cdot\hat{\mathbf{v}}\,\hat{\mathbf{v}} + ic^{-1}\xi\mathbf{v}x_4 \tag{B.6}$$

and, by an obvious generalization of (B.4),

$$x_4' = \xi(-ic^{-1}\mathbf{v}\cdot\mathbf{r} + x_4) \tag{B.7}$$

Therefore the elements of $a(\mathbf{v})$ are

$$\begin{aligned} a_{ik} &= \delta_{ik} + (\xi - 1)\hat{v}_i\hat{v}_k \\ a_{k4} &= -a_{4k} = i\xi v_k/c \\ a_{44} &= \xi \end{aligned} \tag{B.7'}$$

In the discussion of spin-orbit coupling (section 7) it was necessary to consider two Lorentz transformations: $a(-\mathbf{v})$ followed by $a(\mathbf{v} + \mathbf{u})$, where $\mathbf{u} = \mathbf{a}\,dt$ was an infinitesimal velocity. From (B.7′) it follows that, to first order in $\mathbf{u}$,

$$a(\mathbf{v} + \mathbf{u}) = a(\mathbf{v}) + b(\mathbf{u})$$

where

$$b_{ik} = \frac{\xi - 1}{v^2}\left[\left(\frac{\xi^3}{\xi - 1} - \frac{2c^2}{v^2}\right)\frac{\mathbf{v}\cdot\mathbf{u}}{c^2}\, v_i v_k + u_i v_k + v_i u_k\right]$$

$$b_{k4} = -b_{4k} = \frac{i}{c}\,\xi\left(\xi^2\,\frac{\mathbf{u}\cdot\mathbf{v}}{c^2}\, v_k + u_k\right) \tag{B.8}$$

$$b_{44} = \xi^3\,\frac{\mathbf{u}\cdot\mathbf{v}}{c^2}$$

Thus

$$a(\mathbf{v} + \mathbf{u})\, a(-\mathbf{v}) = 1 + b(\mathbf{u})\, a(-\mathbf{v}) = 1 + a'$$

and

$$a'_{ik} = \frac{\xi - 1}{v^2}\,(u_k v_i - u_i v_k)$$

$$a'_{k4} = -a'_{4k} = ic^{-1}\xi[u_k + (\xi - 1)\hat{v}_k\hat{\mathbf{v}}\cdot\mathbf{u}] \tag{B.9}$$

$$a'_{44} = 0$$

Thus $1 + a'$ is the Lorentz matrix for two infinitesimal transformations, which obviously commute, and these are an infinitesimal translation with a velocity given by

$$\xi[\mathbf{u} + (\xi - 1)\hat{\mathbf{v}}\cdot\mathbf{u}\hat{\mathbf{v}}] \tag{B.10}$$

and an infinitesimal rotation with the rotation axis and angle given by

$$\frac{\xi - 1}{v^2}\,(\mathbf{v} \times \mathbf{u}) \tag{B.11}$$

The angular velocity of the precession arising from (B.11), with $\mathbf{u} = \mathbf{a}\,dt$, is

$$\boldsymbol{\omega} = \frac{\xi - 1}{v^2}\,(\mathbf{v} \times \mathbf{a}) \simeq \frac{1}{2c^2}\,(\mathbf{v} \times \mathbf{a})$$

where the last expression applies as an approximation for $v^2/c^2 \ll 1$.

APPENDIX C.

TIME-DEPENDENT OPERATORS

For any operator $\Omega(0)$ in the time-independent (Schrödinger) representation used throughout most of this book, a time-dependent operator $\Omega(t)$ (Heisenberg representation) can be defined by

$$\int \psi^*(t)\Omega(0)\,\psi'(t)\,d^3x = \int \psi^*(0)\,\Omega(t)\,\psi'(0)\,d^3x \tag{C.1}$$

where the prime is used to distinguish two wave functions, belonging to different energies for example.

Since

$$\psi(t) = e^{-iHt/\hbar}\psi(0)$$

$$\psi'(t) = e^{-iHt/\hbar}\psi'(0)$$

it is seen that

$$\Omega(t) = e^{iHt/\hbar}\Omega(0)e^{-iHt/\hbar} \tag{C.2}$$

From (C.2) it follows that ($\partial\Omega/\partial t = 0$):

$$\frac{d\Omega}{dt} = \frac{i}{\hbar}(H\Omega - \Omega H) \tag{C.3}$$

where, on the right, $\Omega(t)$ is meant. Hence, for any operator Ω commuting with H, $d\Omega/dt = 0$. This is always applicable when $\Omega = H$. For Dirac plane waves $\Omega = \vec{\mathbf{p}}$ is time-independent.

As an example we consider the operator for the velocity. This is

$$\dot{\mathbf{x}} = \frac{i}{\hbar}(H\mathbf{x} - \mathbf{x}H) = c\boldsymbol{\alpha} \tag{C.4}$$

for the Dirac particle. Equation (C.4) is also applicable in the presence of interactions which are not momentum-dependent. For the acceleration, assuming free particles,

$$\frac{1}{c}\ddot{\mathbf{x}} = \dot{\boldsymbol{\alpha}} = \frac{i}{\hbar}(H\boldsymbol{\alpha} - \boldsymbol{\alpha}H) = \frac{2i}{\hbar}(c\vec{\mathbf{p}} - \boldsymbol{\alpha}H)$$

$$= \frac{2i}{\hbar}(H\boldsymbol{\alpha} - c\vec{\mathbf{p}})$$

The last equation can be integrated since H and $\vec{\mathbf{p}}$ are constants in time. Thus

$$\boldsymbol{\alpha}(t) = \boldsymbol{\alpha}_0 H^{-1} e^{2iHt/\hbar} + cH^{-1}\vec{\mathbf{p}} \tag{C.5}$$

where $\boldsymbol{\alpha}_0$ is a time-independent operator. Hence the velocity operator is composed of two parts. One, the first term in (C.5), is an oscillatory term with frequency $2mc^2/\hbar$, and the second is the usual constant term with eigenvalue $c^2\mathbf{p}/p_0$. The physical interpretation of the oscillatory part is given in section 18. From (C.5) another integration gives $\mathbf{x}(t)$, which will clearly have three terms: an oscillatory term with frequency $2mc^2/\hbar$, a term increasing linearly with t, viz., $c^2\mathbf{p}t/p_0$, and a constant term.

APPENDIX D.

AN ALTERNATIVE APPROACH TO THE DIRAC MATRICES†

In the discussion of the Lorentz covariance of the equation

$$\left(\gamma_\mu \frac{\partial}{\partial x_\mu} + k_0\right)\psi(x) = 0 \tag{D.1}$$

given in section 14 the γ_μ are recognized to be a given set of matrices introduced as a device for writing four equations in one. Therefore they do not change under the Lorentz transformation:

$$x'_\mu = a_{\mu\nu} x_\nu \tag{D.2}$$

Nevertheless, with each Lorentz transformation there is associated a linear transformation of the γ_μ which was written in Eq. (2.60b) in the form

$$\gamma'_\mu = \Lambda^{-1}\gamma_\mu\Lambda = a_{\mu\nu}\gamma_\nu \tag{D.3}$$

This can be regarded as a linear (vector) transformation law. With it is associated a transformation law of the other Dirac matrices. For instance, since $\sigma_3 = -i\gamma_1\gamma_2$,

$$\begin{aligned}\sigma'_3 &= -i\gamma'_1\gamma'_2 = -i\Lambda^{-1}\gamma_1\Lambda\Lambda^{-1}\gamma_2\Lambda \\ &= -ia_{1\mu}a_{2\nu}\gamma_\mu\gamma_\nu\end{aligned}$$

For a space rotation in which $a_{i4} = a_{4i} = 0$ it follows that

$$\sigma'_3 = a_{1k}a_{2l}\epsilon_{klm}\sigma_m \tag{D.4}$$

where $-i\gamma_k\gamma_l = \epsilon_{klm}\sigma_m - i\,\delta_{lk}$ has been used. Here $\epsilon_{klm} = \epsilon'_{klm}$ is the antisymmetric third-rank unit tensor introduced in section 4.

† The material in Appendix D follows the development given by H. Feshbach and F. Villars, *Revs. Mod. Phys.* **30**, 24 (1958).

The transformation (D.3) is engendered by the coordinate four-rotation (D.2). It should not be confused with a function space transformation in which

$$\psi'(x) = S\psi(x) \tag{D.5}$$

The transformation (D.5) changes (D.1) into

$$\left(S\gamma_\nu S^{-1}\frac{\partial}{\partial x_\nu} + k_0\right)\psi'(x) = 0$$

while (D.2) and (D.3) with $\psi'(x') = \Lambda\psi(x)$ changes (D.1) into

$$\left(a_{\nu\mu}\gamma'_\mu\frac{\partial}{\partial x'_\nu} + k_0\right)\psi'(x') = 0$$

Returning to (D.4), it is clear that if we introduce an antisymmetric tensor $\mathscr{S}_{\mu\nu}$ whose space part is

$$\mathscr{S}_{ik} = \epsilon_{ikl}\sigma_l \tag{D.6a}$$

then

$$\mathscr{S}'_{ik} = a_{il}a_{km}\mathscr{S}_{lm} \tag{D.6b}$$

Equation (D.6a) introduces a three-vector whose components are

$$\mathscr{S}_{23} = \sigma_1, \qquad \mathscr{S}_{31} = \sigma_2, \qquad \mathscr{S}_{12} = \sigma_3$$

and (D.6b) is the generalization of (D.4) to which it reduces when $i = 1$, $k = 2$.

The approach of Feshbach and Villars is to start with the particle in the rest frame where the Pauli theory applies. Here the spin matrices are just the σ_i and the commutation rules are

$$\sigma_j\sigma_k = i\epsilon_{jkl}\sigma_l \qquad (j \neq k) \tag{D.7a}$$

or

$$\sigma_j = i\epsilon_{jkl}\sigma_l\sigma_k \tag{D.7b}$$

In addition,

$$\sigma_i^2 = 1 \quad \text{for all } i \tag{D.7c}$$

The relativistic description is now obtained by making a Lorentz transformation to the system in which the velocity is given by $v/c = p/mc\xi = cp/p_0$ where in ordinary units the total energy $p_0 = mc^2\xi = mc^2(1 + p^2/m^2c^2)^{1/2}$. To do this we recognize that $\mathscr{S}_{ik}$ is the space-space part of an antisymmetric four-tensor $\mathscr{S}_{\mu\nu}$. The space-time part will be denoted by $\boldsymbol{\alpha}$. That is,

$$\mathscr{S}_{i4} = \alpha_i, \qquad \mathscr{S}_{44} = \mathscr{S}_{ii} = 0$$

Although we show that these α_i have all the properties of the Dirac α_i, the similarity of notation should not be taken as an implication that this has been proved. We must regard the α_i as unknown for the moment. Under the Lorentz transformation $\mathscr{S}_{\mu\nu} \to \mathscr{S}'_{\mu\nu}$, where

$$\mathscr{S}'_{\mu\nu} = a_{\mu\lambda} a_{\nu\rho} \mathscr{S}_{\lambda\rho}$$

For instance, a Lorentz transformation in the x_1–x_4 plane, see Eq. (B.4) of Appendix B, gives

$$\begin{aligned} \sigma_1' &= \sigma_1 \\ \sigma_2' &= \xi\left(\sigma_2 + i\frac{v}{c}\alpha_3\right) \\ \sigma_3' &= \xi\left(\sigma_3 - i\frac{v}{c}\alpha_2\right) \end{aligned} \tag{D.8a}$$

and

$$\begin{aligned} \alpha_1' &= \alpha_1 \\ \alpha_2' &= \xi\left(\alpha_2 + i\frac{v}{c}\sigma_3\right) \\ \alpha_3' &= \xi\left(\alpha_3 - i\frac{v}{c}\sigma_2\right) \end{aligned} \tag{D.8b}$$

Similar relations follow for transformations in the x_2–x_4 and x_3–x_4 plane.

The relations (D.7) must be valid in the primed system. Hence it is concluded that

$$\sigma_i \alpha_i = \alpha_j \sigma_j \tag{D.9}$$

and

$$\sigma_j = i\epsilon_{jkl}\alpha_l\alpha_k \tag{D.10}$$

To see this evaluate $\sigma_2'\sigma_3'$ from (D.8a). This is

$$\sigma_2'\sigma_3' = \xi^2\left[\sigma_2\sigma_3 + \frac{iv}{c}(\alpha_3\sigma_3 - \sigma_2\alpha_2) + \frac{v^2}{c^2}\alpha_3\alpha_2\right]$$

Equating $\xi^{-2}\sigma_2'\sigma_3'$ to $i(1 - v^2/c^2)\sigma_1' = i\xi^{-2}\sigma_1$ and comparing coefficients of v/c gives an identity for the coefficient of $(v/c)^0$,

$$\alpha_3\sigma_3 = \sigma_2\alpha_2$$

for the coefficient of v/c, and

$$\sigma_1 = i\alpha_3\alpha_2$$

for the coefficient of v^2/c^2. Then (D.9) and (D.10) are the self-evident generalizations of these results. In a similar fashion $\sigma_2'^2 = 1$ gives

$$1 + i\frac{v}{c}(\sigma_2, \alpha_3)_+ - \frac{v^2}{c^2}\alpha_3^2 = 1 - \frac{v^2}{c^2}$$

or

$$\sigma_2\alpha_3 + \alpha_3\sigma_2 = 0$$

$$\alpha_3^2 = 1$$

These immediately generalize to

$$\sigma_i\alpha_k + \alpha_k\sigma_i = 0 \qquad (i \neq k) \tag{D.11}$$

$$\alpha_k^2 = 1 \tag{D.12}$$

It is now possible to deduce the commutation rules of the α_i which fixes them within a linear (unitary) transformation. Thus, from (D.10) and (D.7b), it follows that

$$\sigma_j\sigma_k = \epsilon_{jkl}\epsilon_{lnm}\alpha_n\alpha_m$$

for $j \neq k$. Since ϵ_{lnm} is antisymmetric in n and m and $\sigma_j\sigma_k \neq 0$, it follows that $\alpha_n\alpha_m$ must be antisymmetric in n and m also. Therefore

$$\alpha_n\alpha_m + \alpha_m\alpha_n = 0 \qquad (m \neq n)$$

and from (D.12) we conclude that

$$\alpha_n\alpha_m + \alpha_m\alpha_n = 2\delta_{nm} \tag{D.13}$$

in general. These are, of course, the commutation rules of the Dirac **α**-matrices.

The discussion is not yet complete because there are four fundamental Dirac matrices and we have obtained only three of them. To remedy this omission we define four matrices γ_μ by

$$(\gamma_\mu, \mathscr{S}_{\alpha\beta}) = \gamma_\mu\mathscr{S}_{\alpha\beta} - \mathscr{S}_{\alpha\beta}\gamma_\mu = 2i(\delta_{\mu\beta}\gamma_\alpha - \delta_{\mu\alpha}\gamma_\beta) \tag{D.14}$$

In the rest frame this becomes a well-known relation where, with indices running from 1 to 3, γ_k are the components of a vector in three-space. To obtain the properties of γ_μ we first evaluate

$$(\gamma_\mu, \mathscr{S}^2_{\mu\nu}) = \mathscr{S}_{\mu\nu}(\gamma_\mu, \mathscr{S}_{\mu\nu}) + (\gamma_\mu, \mathscr{S}_{\mu\nu})\mathscr{S}_{\mu\nu} \tag{D.15}$$

where now no sum over μ is implied. But $\mathscr{S}^2_{\mu\nu} = 1$ for all $\mu \neq \nu$ and 0 for $\mu = \nu$. Therefore the commutator in (D.15) is zero. From (D.14) we find $(\gamma_\mu, \mathscr{S}_{\mu\nu}) = -2i\gamma_\nu$ for $\mu \neq \nu$ and (D.15) becomes

$$\begin{aligned} -2i(\mathscr{S}_{\mu\nu}\gamma_\nu + \gamma_\nu\mathscr{S}_{\mu\nu}) &= 0 \\ (\gamma_\mu, \mathscr{S}_{\mu\nu})_+ &= 0 \end{aligned} \tag{D.16}$$

where again no sum on μ is implied.

For the commutator of γ_α^2 and $\mathscr{S}_{\alpha\beta}$ the identity

$$(\gamma_\alpha^2, \mathscr{S}_{\alpha\beta}) \equiv \gamma_\alpha(\gamma_\alpha, \mathscr{S}_{\alpha\beta})_+ - (\gamma_\alpha, \mathscr{S}_{\alpha\beta})_+\gamma_\alpha$$

holds. Again there is no sum on repeated indices. Using (D.16), it follows that

$$(\gamma_\alpha^2, \mathscr{S}_{\alpha\beta}) = 0 \qquad \text{(no sum on } \alpha) \tag{D.17}$$

This shows that γ_α^2 must be a scalar S_0 since it commutes with all rotations. Therefore, for all μ,

$$\gamma_\mu^2 = S_0 \tag{D.18}$$

From $(\gamma_\mu, \mathscr{S}_{\mu\nu}) = -2i\gamma_\nu$ we obtain by multiplication with γ_ν on the left

$$-2i\gamma_\mu\gamma_\nu = \gamma_\mu^2\mathscr{S}_{\mu\nu} - \gamma_\mu\mathscr{S}_{\mu\nu}\gamma_\mu \qquad \text{(no sum)}$$

and by multiplication with γ_μ on the right

$$-2i\gamma_\nu\gamma_\mu = \gamma_\mu\mathscr{S}_{\mu\nu}\gamma_\mu - \mathscr{S}_{\mu\nu}\gamma_\mu^2 \qquad \text{(no sum)}$$

Therefore, by (D.17),

$$(\gamma_\mu, \gamma_\nu)_+ = 0 \qquad \mu \neq \nu$$

so that

$$\gamma_\mu\gamma_\nu + \gamma_\nu\gamma_\mu = 2S_0\,\delta_{\mu\nu} \qquad \text{(all } \mu, \nu)$$

The final step is to show that S_0 commutes with all γ_μ. This is trivial since $S_0 = \gamma_\mu^2$ (any μ). Then

$$(S_0, \gamma_\mu) = (\gamma_\mu^2, \gamma_\mu) = 0$$

Consequently by Schur's lemma we can set S_0 equal to the unit matrix and there exist four matrices γ_μ for which

$$\gamma_\mu\gamma_\nu + \gamma_\nu\gamma_\mu = 2\delta_{\mu\nu}$$

This completes the chain of reasoning which leads, via the Lorentz transformation, from the non-relativistic Pauli representation of the spin to the relativistic Dirac representation. A wave equation can then be obtained by contracting γ_μ with the four-vector $\partial/\partial x_\mu$, and this operator acting on ψ must be a scalar times ψ. This leads to Eq. (2.24), where k_0 is identified (up to a sign) by the requirement that one obtain the Klein-Gordon equation as a second-order equation.

The agreement with the transformation properties already deduced in Chapter II is to be noted. Thus, $\bar{\psi}\gamma_\mu\psi$ is a four-vector, $\bar{\psi}\alpha_i\psi = \bar{\psi}\mathscr{S}_{i4}\psi$ is the space-time component of an antisymmetric four-tensor whose space-space components are $\bar{\psi}\mathscr{S}_{jk}\psi$. Here a minus sign is not uniquely defined because the commutation rules are unchanged if all α_i are replaced by $-\alpha_i$.

APPENDIX E.

RETARDED ELECTROMAGNETIC INTERACTION

In section 36, Eq. (6.20′), we obtained a result according to which the interaction between two electrons in a transition with energy transfer k is

$$e^2(1 - \boldsymbol{\alpha}_1\cdot\boldsymbol{\alpha}_2)\frac{e^{ikR}}{R} \tag{E.1}$$

where $\boldsymbol{\alpha}_1$ and $\boldsymbol{\alpha}_2$ are the Dirac matrices for electrons 1 and 2 and R is the distance between them. The present purpose is to clarify this result by showing in greater detail the assumptions which are at the basis of (E.1).

The problem is described in terms of two electrons which, in zero order in a perturbation theoretic sense, are completely decoupled. The overall process is one in which electron 1 is initially in the ground state of zero energy (since an additive constant to the energy is of no relevance) and electron 2 is in a state of energy W. In the final state electron 2 has zero energy and electron 1 is in a state of energy E. The question at issue is to determine the transition probability per unit time. It will not be necessary to complicate matters by taking the exclusion principle into account in an explicit way until the end of the calculation. Each electron is coupled to the electromagnetic field with a coupling energy $He^{-i\omega t} + H^*e^{-i\omega t}$, where $H = e(\boldsymbol{\alpha}\cdot\mathbf{A} - \Phi)$. The transition is to be pictured as a two-step process in which a quantum is first emitted and then absorbed so that there are two intermediate states: The first, for which the probability amplitude is a, is reached by the emission of a quantum of frequency ω, or wave vector $\mathbf{k}$ ($k = \omega$), polarization specified by an index λ, and electron 2 is in the ground state. From this intermediate state the final state (amplitude a_f) is reached by absorption of this quantum by electron 1 which goes to energy state E. The alternative path consists of an emission of a quantum specified by $\mathbf{k}$, λ with electron 1 in state E forming an intermediate state with amplitude a' and then the absorption of this quantum by electron 2 which thereby proceeds to the ground state. Figure E.1 illustrates these transitions in a schematic way. The symbols $H^{(n)}_{W_2W_1}(\omega)$ which appear in this figure have the meaning of absorption matrix elements of H for

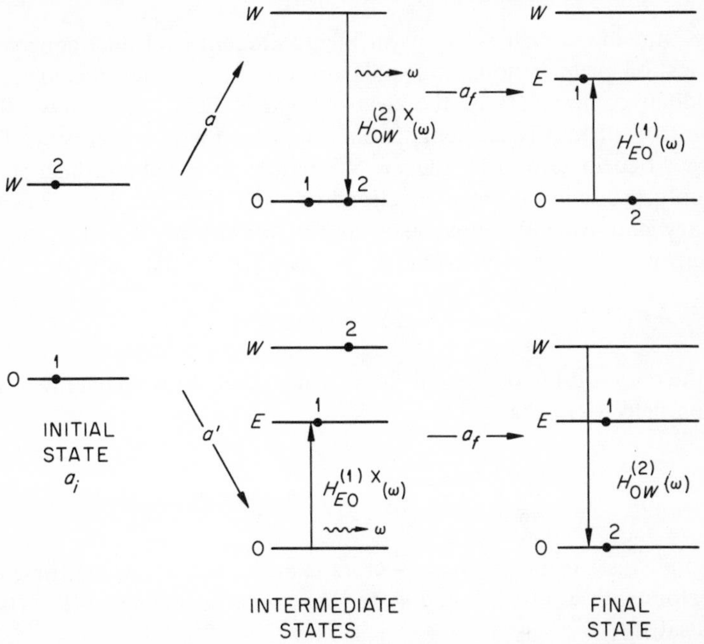

Fig. E.1. Diagram showing transitions involved in the electromagnetic interaction between two charged particles. The relevant transitions are labeled with the appropriate matrix elements which are defined in the text. The amplitudes of the various states appear as a_i, a, a', and a_f.

frequency ω by electron (n) going from energy W_1 to W_2. Of course, $H^{(n)\times}_{W_2W_1}(\omega)$ is the emission matrix element. Clearly,

$$H^{(n)\times}_{W_2W_1}(-\omega) = H^{(n)}_{W_2W_1}(\omega)$$

With a_i the initial state probability amplitude and with the expansion

$$\Psi_{\text{tot}}(t) = a_i(t)\Psi_i + a(t)\Psi + a'\Psi'(t) + a_f\Psi_f(t)$$

the equations of motion are

$$i\dot{a}_i = Wa_i + \Sigma\, H^{(2)}_{0W}a + \Sigma\, H^{(1)}_{E0}a' \tag{E.2a}$$

$$i\dot{a} = \omega a + H^{(2)\times}_{0W}a_i + \int dE\, a_f(E)\, \Sigma\, H^{(1)\times}_{E0} \tag{E.2b}$$

$$i\dot{a}' = (\omega + E + W)a' + H_{E0}^{(1)\times} a_i + \int dE\, a_f(E) \Sigma\, H_{0W}^{(2)\times} \quad \text{(E.2c)}$$

$$i\dot{a}_f = Ea_f + \Sigma\, aH_{E0}^{(1)} + \Sigma\, a'H_{0W}^{(2)} \quad \text{(E.2d)}$$

Throughout, the Σ sign is meant to include a sum over all frequencies, directions of propagation, and polarization. The latter includes the longitudinal components of the electromagnetic field; see below. The argument of all matrix elements is ω. To write these explicitly we first remember that in zero order the wave functions in initial and final states are simply products of wave functions of each particle. We write the stationary state wave functions as ψ_f and ψ_i for electron 1 and ϕ_f and ϕ_i for electron 2. For the space part of the vector potential we write

$$\mathbf{A} = (2\pi/\omega)^{1/2}\mathbf{a}_\lambda \exp(i\mathbf{k}\cdot\mathbf{r}) \quad \text{(E.3)}$$

where the constant factor $(2\pi/\omega)^{1/2}$ is chosen so that the total energy in the radiation field is ω; that is,†

$$\frac{1}{4\pi}\int d^3r(\mathscr{E}\cdot\mathscr{E}^\times + \mathscr{H}\cdot\mathscr{H}^\times) = \omega$$

The complete set of polarization vectors is $\mathbf{a}_1$, $\mathbf{a}_2$, and $\mathbf{a}_3$, where these are unit vectors with $\mathbf{a}_3$ along $\mathbf{k}$ and $\mathbf{a}_1$ and $\mathbf{a}_2$ are perpendicular to $\mathbf{k}$. These vectors satisfy‡

$$\mathbf{a}_\lambda\cdot\mathbf{a}_{\lambda'}^\times = \delta_{\lambda\lambda'} \quad \text{(E.4)}$$

For the longitudinal field $\lambda = 3$ and we note that, from the Lorentz condition $\Phi = 0$ for $\lambda = 1, 2$ and for $\lambda = 3$,

$$\Phi = a_3 \exp(i\mathbf{k}\cdot\mathbf{r}) = \exp(i\mathbf{k}\cdot\mathbf{r})$$

since the time dependence is always $\exp(-i\omega t)$. Then

$$H_{E0}^{(1)} = \left(\frac{2\pi}{\omega}\right)^{1/2} e\int d^3r_1\, \psi_f^*(\boldsymbol{\alpha}\cdot\mathbf{a}_\lambda - \delta_{\lambda 3})\exp(i\mathbf{k}\cdot\mathbf{r}_1)\,\psi_i \quad \text{(E.5a)}$$

$$H_{0W}^{(2)} = \left(\frac{2\pi}{\omega}\right)^{1/2} e\int d^3r_2 \phi_f^*(\boldsymbol{\alpha}\cdot\mathbf{a}_\lambda - \delta_{\lambda 3})\exp(i\mathbf{k}\cdot\mathbf{r}_2)\,\phi_i \quad \text{(E.5b)}$$

† Here $\mathscr{E} = -\partial\mathbf{A}/\partial t - \nabla\Phi$, $\mathscr{H} = \text{curl}\,\mathbf{A}$, where $\mathbf{A}$ and Φ are *complex* fields. The fields are normalized in a box of volume V, and then V is set equal to 1 since it cancels from final results; see M. E. Rose, *Multipole Fields*, John Wiley and Sons, New York, 1955, p. 42.

‡ For example, with $\mathbf{k}$ along the z-axis we can choose $\mathbf{a}_3 = \hat{\mathbf{e}}_z$, $\mathbf{a}_1 = 2^{-1/2}(\hat{\mathbf{e}}_x + i\hat{\mathbf{e}}_y)$, $\mathbf{a}_z = 2^{-1/2}(\mathbf{e}_x - i\mathbf{e}_y)$.

The solution of the equations of motion which gives a_f to second order in the matrix elements is

$$a_i = e^{-iWt} \tag{E.6a}$$

$$a = \frac{H_{0W}^{(2)\times}}{\omega - W}(e^{-i\omega t} - e^{-iWt}) \tag{E.6b}$$

$$a' = \frac{H_{E0}^{(1)\times}}{\omega + E} e^{-iWt}[e^{-i(\omega+E)t} - 1] \tag{E.6c}$$

$$\begin{aligned} a_f = \sum \frac{H_{E0}^{(1)}H_{0W}^{(2)\times}}{W - \omega}\left[\frac{e^{i(E-W)t} - 1}{E - W} - \frac{e^{i(E-\omega)t} - 1}{E - \omega}\right] \\ + \sum{}' \frac{H_{0W}^{(2)}H_{E0}^{(1)\times}}{\omega + E}\left[\frac{e^{i(E-W)t} - 1}{E - W} - \frac{e^{-i(W+\omega)t} - 1}{W + \omega}\right] \end{aligned} \tag{E.6d}$$

Only the first term in each square bracket in (E.6d) gives energy conservation† and a result for the total number of transitions increasing linearly with time. Retaining only these terms, the transition probability per unit time is

$$\frac{d}{dt}\int dE|a_f|^2 = 2\pi|H_{fi}|^2_{E=W}$$

where

$$H_{fi} = \sum\left[\frac{H_{E0}^{(1)}(\omega)H_{0W}^{(2)}(-\omega)}{W - \omega + i\eta} + \frac{H_{0W}^{(2)}(\omega)H_{E0}^{(1)}(-\omega)}{\omega + W - i\eta}\right] \tag{E.7}$$

We have here replaced ω by $\omega - i\eta$ since, as will be evident very soon, this prescription for performing the sum on ω gives outgoing waves.

The sum Σ is now replaced in the usual way by a sum on λ and by an integration in **k**-space. Thus

$$\begin{aligned} \sum &= (2\pi)^{-3}\int d^3k \sum_\lambda \\ &= (2\pi)^{-3}\int\int d\Omega\omega^2\, d\omega \sum_\lambda \end{aligned}$$

Then in the integration on ω the integrand of the second term in (E.7) becomes identical with the integrand of the first term if we replace ω by $-\omega$. The limits of the second term are thereby $-\infty$ to 0. Hence the two

† See, for example, L. I. Schiff, *Quantum Mechanics*, McGraw-Hill Book Co., New York, 1955, pp. 201–202.

terms combine to the integral of the first over ω from $-\infty$ to ∞. The matrix element H_{fi} is then

$$H_{fi} = \frac{e^2}{4\pi^2}\int \frac{\omega\, d\omega}{W - \omega + i\eta} \sum_\lambda \int d^3r_1 \psi_f^*(\boldsymbol{\alpha}_1\cdot\mathbf{a}_\lambda - \delta_{\lambda 3}) \exp(i\mathbf{k}\cdot\mathbf{r}_1)\,\psi_i$$
$$\times \int d^3r_2 \phi_f^*(\boldsymbol{\alpha}_2\cdot\mathbf{a}_\lambda^\times - \delta_{\lambda 3}) \exp(-i\mathbf{k}\cdot\mathbf{r}_2)\,\phi_i$$

For $\lambda = 3$ the cross-terms in the vector and scalar potential are simply evaluated by using

$$\mathbf{A} = \nabla\chi, \qquad \Phi = i\omega\chi$$

where

$$\chi = -\frac{i}{\omega}\exp(i\mathbf{k}\cdot\mathbf{r})$$

and noting that

$$\boldsymbol{\alpha}\cdot\mathbf{A} = \boldsymbol{\alpha}\cdot\nabla\chi = -i(\chi, H_0)$$

where H_0 is the zero-order Hamiltonian: $\boldsymbol{\alpha}\cdot\vec{\mathbf{p}} + \beta + V_{\text{ext}}$, where V_{ext} may include a nuclear Coulomb field for example. Then using

$$H_0^{(1)}\psi_i = H_0^{(2)}\phi_f = 0$$
$$H_0^{(1)}\psi_f = W\psi_f, \qquad H_0^{(2)}\phi_i = W\phi_i$$

we find

$$H_{fi} = \frac{e^2}{4\pi^2}\int \frac{\omega\, d\omega\, d\Omega}{W - \omega + i\eta} \sum_\lambda \iint d^3r_1\, d^3r_2 \psi_f^*\phi_f^*$$
$$\times \left[\boldsymbol{\alpha}_1\cdot\mathbf{a}_\lambda\, \boldsymbol{\alpha}_2\cdot\mathbf{a}_\lambda^\times + \left(1 - \frac{2W}{\omega}\right)\delta_{\lambda 3}\right] \exp(i\mathbf{k}\cdot\mathbf{R})\psi_i\phi_i$$

where $\mathbf{R} = \mathbf{r}_1 - \mathbf{r}_2$.

The sum over λ is evaluated with

$$\sum_\lambda \boldsymbol{\alpha}_1\cdot\mathbf{a}_\lambda\, \boldsymbol{\alpha}_2\cdot\mathbf{a}_\lambda^\times = \boldsymbol{\alpha}_1\cdot\mathbf{I}\cdot\boldsymbol{\alpha}_2 = \boldsymbol{\alpha}_1\cdot\boldsymbol{\alpha}_2$$

where

$$\mathbf{I} = \sum_\lambda \mathbf{a}_\lambda\mathbf{a}_\lambda^\times$$

is the unit dyadic. Therefore

$$H_{fi} = \frac{e^2}{4\pi^2}\int \frac{\omega\, d\omega\, d\Omega}{W - \omega + i\eta}$$
$$\times \iint d^3r_1\, d^3r_2 \psi_f^*\phi_f^*\left[\boldsymbol{\alpha}_1\cdot\boldsymbol{\alpha}_2 + 1 - \frac{2W}{\omega}\right] \exp(i\mathbf{k}\cdot\mathbf{R})\psi_i\phi_i$$

Then the integration over the directions of **k** is done by ($\omega = k$)

$$\int d\Omega \exp(i\mathbf{k}\cdot\mathbf{R}) = \frac{2\pi}{i\omega R}(e^{ikR} - e^{-ikR})$$

so that

$$H_{fi} = \frac{e^2}{2\pi i}\int \frac{d\omega}{W - \omega + i\eta}$$
$$\times \int\int d^3r_1\, d^3r_2 \psi_f^* \phi_f^* \left[\boldsymbol{\alpha}_1\cdot\boldsymbol{\alpha}_2 + 1 - \frac{2W}{\omega}\right](e^{ikR} - e^{-ikR})R^{-1}\psi_i\phi_i$$

Finally, integrating over ω, the path is closed in the upper half-plane for the term e^{ikR} so the pole at $\omega = W + i\eta$ is encircled. For the term e^{-ikR} the path must be closed in the lower half-plane and no pole is enclosed. Hence only the outgoing wave part contributes and, evaluating the residue and then taking the limit $\eta \to 0$, we obtain

$$H_{fi} = e^2 \int\int d^3r_1\, d^3r_2 \psi_f^* \phi_f^* (1 - \boldsymbol{\alpha}_1\cdot\boldsymbol{\alpha}_2)\frac{e^{iWR}}{R}\psi_i\phi_i \tag{E.8}$$

which is the desired result. To include the effect of the exclusion principle, the final and initial state wave functions are antisymmetrized. Thus $\psi_f\phi_f$ is replaced by

$$2^{-\frac{1}{2}}[\psi_f^{(1)}\,\phi_f^{(2)} - \psi_f^{(2)}\,\phi_f^{(1)}]$$

and similarly for the initial state.

The derivation given above is based on the plane wave representation of the electromagnetic field. One may use any complete set of states and obtain the same result. For an example using angular momentum waves the reference given on p. 287 may be consulted.†

† See also N. Tralli and G. Goertzel, *Phys. Rev.* **83,** 399 (1951); H. R. Hulme, *Proc. Roy. Soc.* (*London*), **A154,** 487 (1936).

General references

A. M. E. Rose, *Elementary Theory of Angular Momentum*, John Wiley and Sons, New York, 1957.

B. E. U. Condon and G. H. Shortley, *The Theory of Atomic Spectra*, Cambridge University Press, Cambridge, England, 1935.

C. H. A. Bethe and E. E. Salpeter, "Quantum Mechanics of One- and Two- Electron Systems," *Encyclopedia of Physics*, Julius Springer, Berlin, 1957, Vol. XXXV.

D. W. Pauli, "The General Principles of Quantum Mechanics," *Encyclopedia of Physics*, Julius Springer, Berlin, 1957, Vol. v/1.

E. P. A. M. Dirac, *Quantum Mechanics*, Oxford University Press, Oxford, England, fourth edition, 1958.

Author Index

Subject index